PROBLEM SOLVING
AND CHEMICAL CALCULATIONS

MILDRED D. JOHNSON

City College of San Francisco

PROBLEM SOLVING
AND CHEMICAL
CALCULATIONS

HARCOURT, BRACE & WORLD, INC.
New York / Chicago / San Francisco / Atlanta

Library of Congress Catalog Card Number: 75-87232

Printed in the United States of America

PREFACE

This book is really two books in one—a book on problem solving and a book on chemical calculations. It was written for the student who knows arithmetic operations but has difficulty setting up a problem for solution. The first half of the book deals with problem solving in this sense, the second half with chemistry problems.

Very simple problems are taken first—problems that "anyone" can do —to focus attention on the various methods and techniques. Also, a number of unusual and even absurd problems appear in the beginning so that the student is forced to examine and use the methods presented. Problems occur in increasing order of difficulty throughout the book and are set up in logical, step-by-step fashion, usually with just one new idea presented at a time. The text constantly emphasizes analysis of the problem, stresses the use of units and dimensional analysis, and encourages problem solving by analogy wherever possible. It also encourages final synthesis of the problem into a single setup incorporating the various steps in logical order. Questions, often rhetorical in nature, appear frequently to encourage the student to develop the habit of asking himself questions, a vital factor in successful problem solving. Once a student knows how to solve problems in general he usually needs just facts and patience to solve specific problems.

In the second half of the book the major categories of elementary chemistry problems are set up according to the logical methods of attack presented earlier. The mole method is used wherever appropriate throughout the chemistry section. There is also a consistent emphasis on significant figures beginning with the chapter on significant figures.

The book has a few topics that might not be expected: a chapter on conversion of word problems into symbols and equation form, a chapter on graphing that should be useful for students in experimental classes, and a chapter on physics problems that offers many opportunities to practice problem solving and contains information particularly helpful to chemistry students who have not had physics courses. Finally, because the book is intended not only for use in specific courses but also for independent study, it includes, in addition to numerous solved examples of graded difficulty, an extensive section at the end of the book giving setups and/or answers for all problems.

The author would like to thank the students who used this material in preliminary form. She would also like to express her appreciation to her colleagues who graciously used the material in their classes: Dr. Frances Connick, Miss Mayme Fung, Mr. Stanley Furuta, Mr. William Hoskins, Mrs. Isabel Hurd, Mrs. Shirley Kelly, Dr. Alfred Lee, Mr. Wayne Matthews, Dr. William McInerny, Mr. Eugene Roberts, Mrs. Anne Thacher, Mr. Kenneth Thunem, and Dr. William Tsatsos. She also thanks Dr. Clement Skrabak for permission to use this material in classes, and Drs. John Booher and Mannfred Mueller for advice and information generously given over the years.

MILDRED D. JOHNSON

CONTENTS

1

INTRODUCTION

Well-trained, intelligent students often have difficulty solving problems. Too many students are unable to understand how or why they have "solved" problems. They know—or can find out—how to do a problem once it is set up, but they have difficulty setting up the problem. *This setting up of the problem is what we mean by problem solving.*

There is an almost infinite number of ways to approach problem solving, perhaps because the human mind is such a marvelously complex thing. No one can really teach anyone else how to solve problems. The best that anyone can do is to present a series of approaches, to arrange situations so that the mind itself discovers how to solve problems.

Problem solving could be likened to diamond cutting. There is more than one way to cut a diamond, but no matter which way is chosen the cutter must have a knowledge of crystal structure. Presumably he studies the particular diamond, decides how to cut it, and cuts it. Problems, unlike diamonds, can be cut and recut over and over, but still one must know the basic techniques of problem solving and must look for the facets of a particular problem—must *analyze* the problem, in other words—in order to solve it, regardless of method.

Naturally, not all problems are solved in the same manner, nor do all people find various methods equally congenial. We hope to help you find methods that work quickly and effectively for you, but we hope especially to help you find an *understanding* of several methods that can be used. Only with understanding can the methods be applied skillfully and surely in a variety of problems. We hope to put difficulty with problems where it belongs, in the particular set of circumstances in a particular problem. We hope to leave you with just the difficulty of the subject matter of a particular problem, not with a difficulty about how to put known and understood subject matter into workable setups.

You will be presented with a number of methods that are different from one another. You will also come in contact with what might be called the "percolation" and "hit and run" approach to problem solving. In this approach simple and apparently scattered items are presented at various times to seep into the mind, to provide the mind with a particular background, to give the mind something to work on. Please remember this when we seem to be presenting almost random items in a variety of ways.

Do not be repelled by the simplicity of many of the problems. Where possible, problems that anyone could solve have been chosen so that attention can be focused on the techniques involved. We have introduced a number of unreal and occasionally even absurd problems to encourage use of the methods being presented. Such problems usually cannot be solved by memorized methods; they yield only to methods that are understood by the problem solver.

In various books there are all manner of lists of how to solve problems. They are usually not very helpful unless you already know how to solve problems. Problem solving becomes almost intuitive after a while. However, a list of things to do in solving a problem may serve as a starting point.

1. Read the problem carefully and ask yourself exactly what you are looking for.
2. Make a list of things given in the problem.
3. Where suitable, make a drawing or diagram to help the physical reality of the problem and the phenomena involved seep below the surface of your mind.
4. Look up—in textbooks, in technical dictionaries, in dictionaries— definitions, descriptions, discussions, etc., of the factors you are dealing with. You may not have the information you need. You may have excess, irrelevant information. In fact, prior to searching suitable references you may not even know that you need certain information or that certain other information is irrelevant.
5. Look for relationships between the things you are looking for and the known factors in the problem.
6. Look for the relationships between or among the factors in the problem.

7. Look for a common factor to which both the thing you are looking for and the factors presented in the problem are related.

8. Note the nature of the relationships—direct, inverse, squares, cube roots, etc.

9. Look for limits. Something you have in the problem may be related to what you are seeking, but you may not have the information in the range or area in which you are working.

10. Be sure to attach all units to all figures. If the units do not cancel out to the proper unit for the answer, you automatically know that you have made an error. Often a glance at the units in such a case will reveal where the error was made.

11. If you still cannot solve the problem, then
    a. Look for reasonable assumptions on which to base a solution. Carried to its logical extreme this would make any problem solvable, so one has to be careful about this and state precisely what the assumption is, making sure that one has a good reason for making the assumption.
    b. Reword the problem. Put it into simple, clear English. Get rid of all unnecessary words.
    c. Dismantle the problem. Make up little problems with parts of the data. This is a valid way to help your mind find or connect factors whose connection previously eluded it.
    d. Imitate. Look at solved problems involving some or all of the data involved in the problem. This is a valid tool *if* used in an attempt to understand how and why a particular problem was solved. If one merely copies a setup into which to put numbers, then it is utterly useless as a tool for learning problem solving.

If these techniques do not help, you may have a problem that cannot be solved. It is obviously very important to know that a particular problem cannot be solved, but it is often difficult to distinguish an as yet unsolved problem from one which cannot be solved. The techniques in 4, 5, 6, and 7 are often helpful in making such a distinction.

Some minds seem to discover how to solve problems almost instantly and even intuitively, others only after full-scale, agonizing war. What matters is that one find how to solve problems. It is worth a great deal of time and effort. How often have you gone round and round with a problem until something flashed? Later you could scarcely believe that you didn't see how to do the problem immediately. We hope to decrease the round and round time almost to zero and increase the frequency of flashes to as close to infinity as possible.

2

PROBLEM SOLVING
BY THE SIMPLEST METHOD POSSIBLE
Comparison and Correction

Many people find the method of comparison and correction uniquely usable and valuable in problem solving. This method can generally be used when a known factor, called a *base factor,* is changed to a new, unknown value as a result of a known change in another factor. The two values of this other factor constitute the *correcting fraction* or *correcting factor.* The trick is to find the base factor, to find what affects the base factor, and to find the nature of the relationship between the base factor and the factor whose change affects it.

Be sure not to confuse comparison and correction with proportion. Proportion is really a sophisticated and often treacherous method; other methods should be learned first.

BASIC PRINCIPLES OF COMPARISON AND CORRECTION

Problem solving by comparison and correction is best explained by illustration. The following examples are therefore presented in considerable detail.

Direct Relationship, One Variable Factor

A *direct relationship* is one in which an increase in one factor causes an increase in another factor or a decrease in one factor causes a corresponding decrease in another factor.

EXAMPLE 2–1

Five children can eat 10 quarts (qt) of ice cream in a given time. How much ice cream could 20 children eat in the same time?

1. What are you looking for? A quantity of ice cream.
2. Then what must you operate on mathematically? A quantity of ice cream.
3. What is your *base factor*? A quantity of ice cream.
4. What affects the quantity of ice cream? The *changing* number of children. (Time is a constant factor.)
5. What is the nature of the relationship between quantity of ice cream and number of children? A direct relationship. More children, all other things being equal, can eat more ice cream.
6. What is the direction of the change? An increase.
7. What is the effect of the change here? An increase in quantity of ice cream.
8. What will the *correcting fraction* be composed of? The values of the factor whose change causes a change in the base factor, in this case the different numbers of children, that is, 5 and 20.
9. What will the actual correcting fraction be? You know you need an increase; therefore the fraction must be 20/5 rather than 5/20.
10. What is the setup for this problem?

Base factor × correcting fraction: $\dfrac{10 \text{ qt} \times 20 \text{ children}}{5 \text{ children}} = 40 \text{ qt}$

Note that a unit is attached to each figure. The units cancel out to give quarts, a not exactly startling fact. Form the habit of attaching units to all figures in problems of this sort.

Direct Relationship, Two or More Variables

If changes in two or more different factors affect the base factor, it is absolutely necessary to consider the effect of the change in each factor *on the base factor*. The approach is the same as before. Consider the following example.

EXAMPLE 2–2

Five children can eat 10 qt of ice cream in 1 day. How much ice cream could 17 children eat in 9 days?

1. Factor sought: quantity of ice cream.
2. Base factor: quantity of ice cream.
3. Factors affecting quantity of ice cream:

Correcting factor	Nature of relationship	Direction of change	Effect on base factor
number of children	direct	increase	increase
number of days	direct	increase	increase

4. Setup:

$$\frac{10 \text{ qt} \times 17 \text{ children} \times 9 \text{ days}}{5 \text{ children} \times 1 \text{ day}} = 306 \text{ qt}$$

Remember to consider the effect of each variable on the base factor. The setup used here is a *single-line setup*. There is no point in first setting up a problem to find the amount of ice cream needed for more children and then doing another problem with the new quantity of ice cream to find out how much ice cream is needed for the longer time period.

EXAMPLE 2–3

Five children can eat 20 qt of ice cream in 2 days. At this rate, how much ice cream could 27 children eat in 1 day?

$$\frac{20 \text{ qt} \times 1 \text{ day} \times 27 \text{ children}}{2 \text{ days} \times 5 \text{ children}} = 54 \text{ qt}$$

Here the changing time and the changing number of children produced opposite effects on the base factor. Problems in which this happens are common and cause trouble only if one deals with the effect of the variables on one another rather than on the base factor.

Notice that all figures in the problems so far have borne units. This procedure may seem needlessly cumbersome now, but you should later find that a mere check of units in a complex setup will often reveal that you have made an error. The habit of always attaching units to all figures should pay dividends in the future.

Direct Relationship, Multiple Variables, Need to Change Unit

EXAMPLE 2–4

Five children can eat 20 qt of ice cream in 2 days. How much ice cream could 2 children eat in 3 hr if they ate half as fast as the first group of children?

Here the changing number of children, the changing period of time, and the changing rate constitute the correcting fractions. However, the time factors are in dissimilar units. Time must be in the same unit, but it is immaterial which unit is chosen.

$$\frac{20 \text{ qt} \times 2 \text{ children} \times 3 \text{ hr}}{5 \text{ children} \times 2 \text{ days} \times 24 \frac{\text{hr}}{\text{day}}} \times \frac{1}{2} = 0.25 \text{ qt}$$

Rate has no units attached here; it is a dimensionless figure.

Inverse Relationship, One Variable

An *inverse relationship* is one in which an increase in one factor causes a decrease in another factor or, conversely, a decrease in one factor causes an increase in another factor. For example, the more a man spends from his salary the less he can save, but the more he saves the more money he has to invest if he wishes. There is an inverse relationship between spending and saving from one's salary and a direct relationship between saving and possible investment.

EXAMPLE 2–5

At a pressure of 1 pound per square inch ($lb/in.^2$) the thickness of a sponge was 17 millimeters (mm). What would be the thickness of the sponge if the pressure were increased to 40 $lb/in.^2$? Assume that the thickness of the sponge decreases uniformly and regularly as the pressure increases.

1. Factor sought: thickness of sponge.
2. Base factor: thickness of sponge.
3. Factor affecting thickness of sponge: changing pressure.
4. Type of relationship: inverse.
5. Direction of change: increase in pressure.
6. Effect on base factor: decrease in thickness.
7. Setup:

$$\frac{17 \text{ mm} \times 1 \text{ lb}}{\text{in.}^2 \times 40 \ \dfrac{\text{lb}}{\text{in.}^2}} = 0.42 \text{ mm}$$

EXAMPLE 2–6

Forty liters of oxygen gas were under a pressure of 70 atmospheres (atm). If the pressure were changed to 35 atm, what would be the volume? Temperature remained constant.

Background information: Within limits, increasing pressure on a gas decreases its volume.

1. Base factor: volume of gas.
2. Correcting factor: changing pressure.
3. Type of relationship: inverse.
4. Direction of change: decrease in pressure.
5. Effect on base factor: increase in volume.
6. Setup:

$$\frac{40 \text{ liters} \times 70 \text{ atm}}{35 \text{ atm}} = 80 \text{ liters}$$

Multiple Variables, Direct and Inverse Relationships

EXAMPLE 2–7

At 300°K and 2 atm pressure a certain quantity of gas had a volume of 270 milliliters (ml). Find the volume at 250°K and 5 atm pressure.

Fact: Volume of a gas is directly related to absolute temperature (°K)* and inversely related to pressure.
Assumption: The gas will still be a gas under the new conditions.

Correcting factor	Nature of relationship	Direction of change	Effect on base factor
temperature	direct	decrease	decrease
pressure	inverse	increase	decrease

$$\frac{270 \text{ ml} \times 250°\text{K} \times 2 \text{ atm}}{300°\text{K} \times 5 \text{ atm}} = 90 \text{ ml}$$

---

*See Chapter 15 for discussion of absolute temperature and degrees Kelvin (°K).

Note that we considered the effect of the changing variables on the base factor, not on one another. True, there is a relationship between temperature and pressure, but you have both temperature and pressure for the old and new conditions. Not only do you have no way, but there is no need, to calculate the effect of changing temperature and pressure on one another. You want the effect of changing pressure on the volume and the effect of changing temperature on the volume.

MINOR COMPLICATIONS IN THE USE OF COMPARISON AND CORRECTION

The Base Factor Is Missing

By now, we hope you think this method of base factor times correcting fraction may have some merit. Perhaps you're thinking of a number of occasions when you would have been delighted to use this method if only you had had a base factor. Consider this perhaps too simple example.

EXAMPLE 2–8

Seventeen silkworms working 8 hr per day for 15 days could produce 4000 grams (g) of silk. How many hours would it take 80 worms working 12 hr per day to produce 3800 g of silk?

You want hours. You have hours per day. The base factor is missing. You must supply hours yourself.

$$\frac{8 \text{ hr}}{\text{day}} \times 15 \text{ days}$$

gives hours, a not exactly startling revelation. Now let's *reword* the problem:

Seventeen silkworms could produce 4000 g of silk in 120 hr. How many hours would it take 80 silkworms working 12 hr per day to produce 3800 g of silk?

$$\frac{8 \text{ hr}}{\text{day}} \times 15 \text{ days} \times \frac{3800 \text{ g} \times 17 \text{ silkworms}}{4000 \text{ g} \times 80 \text{ silkworms}} = 24.2 \text{ hr*}$$

You'll notice we did not work on 120 hr despite the fact that we reworded the problem for our own benefit. The 120 hr is a derived figure, and a derived figure can easily become untraceable if some slight arithmetical

---

*Not in significant figures. Significant figures are taken up in Chapter 8.

slip is made. It is generally considered poor practice to use derived figures in setups.

Don't be misled by excess information. The second group of silkworms worked 12 hr each day. After you had found the total time, did the total time required (that is, the total hours required here) have anything at all to do with the number of hours that must be worked each day? No. Therefore, the 12 hr per day just does not enter the picture. Had you been asked time in days, in terms of 12-hr working days, you would naturally have had to use it.

The Problem Is Right; the Units Are Wrong

You will occasionally find that units must be introduced and that other units that are no longer really involved in a problem must be removed. Consider this example.

EXAMPLE 2–9

It takes 10 men working 8 hr per day 15 days to carry out a certain excavation. How long would it take 1 man working 8 hr per day to carry out this same excavation?

Obviously, it would take 10 times as long, 150 days. Now check this by finding the total hours in each instance.

$$\frac{8 \text{ hr} \times 15 \text{ days} \times 10 \text{ men}}{\text{day}} = 1200 \text{ hr} \quad \text{(False)}$$

$$\frac{8 \text{ hr} \times 150 \text{ days} \times 1 \text{ man}}{\text{day}} = 1200 \text{ hr} \quad \text{(False)}$$

Cancellation of units gives man-hours, not the hours requested in checking the correctness of 150 days as an answer. To find the answer in the units requested, the setups should have been:

$$\frac{8 \text{ hr} \times 15 \text{ days} \times 10 \text{ men}}{\text{day} \quad \text{man}} = 1200 \text{ hr} \quad \text{(True)}$$

$$\frac{8 \text{ hr} \times 150 \text{ days} \times 1 \text{ man}}{\text{day} \quad \text{man}} = 1200 \text{ hr} \quad \text{(True)}$$

You accuse us of introducing a unit to make the answer turn out right. Guilty. Didn't each man work 15 days? Therefore, can't we say 15 days per man? We did this so that we could get an answer in hours. It is quite true that man-hours here would not have been misleading, but we're trying to teach a technique, and man-hours is not the same as hours, the unit requested in the problem check.

The Problem Is Vague

EXAMPLE 2–10

If 17 silkworms working 8 hr per day for 15 days could produce 4000 g of silk, *how long* would it take 80 silkworms working 12 hr per day to produce 3800 g of silk?

"How long?" is vague. It could mean either hours (total hours), days, or even years. Here, however, we'd be restricted to days of 12 working hours, and years made up of 12-working-hour days. It would seem quite logical that you could solve for any time unit. You would obviously convert the time given in the problem to the new time unit and proceed as usual. Let's find days.

$$\frac{15 \text{ days} \times 17 \text{ silkworms} \times 8 \text{ hr}}{80 \text{ silkworms} \quad \dfrac{\text{day} \times 12 \text{ hr}}{\text{day}}} \times \frac{3800 \text{ g}}{4000 \text{ g}} = 2.02 \text{ days*}$$

You'll note this checks with the solution to Example 2–8 on page 10:

$$\frac{2.02 \text{ days} \times 12 \text{ hr}}{\text{day}} = 24.2 \text{ hr}$$

The Need to Make Assumptions

EXAMPLE 2–11

Lewis Carroll, an Oxford mathematician, developed the precursor of Metrecal and described it in a paper titled "Alice in Wonderland." Each of the subjects of the study, a girl named Alice and a rabbit, was 4 ft tall and weighed 60 lb at the beginning of the study. At 8:00 A.M. on May 1, 1867, Alice drank 1 thimbleful of Metrecal precursor. At the same time the rabbit drank 2 thimblefuls. Alice immediately shrank to 2 ft and shot up to 100 lb. The rabbit stretched to 8 ft and wasted away to 7 lb. What would be the effect on Alice's height of another thimbleful of Metrecal precursor?

---

*Not in significant figures.

Obviously, this problem really cannot be solved. You are not given the nature of the relationship. You must know the relationship, be able to find it in references, or perform a series of experiments to find it. Very often in problem solving you will have to make assumptions and then base the solution to a problem on the assumptions. Naturally, assumptions can only be made on a reasonable basis; otherwise there would literally be no problem to which there was not a solution.

We are interested in the techniques to be used once a reasonable assumption has been made. We will leave the discussion of assumptions and the basis for them where it most properly belongs, in specific subject matter courses, and deal here just with the techniques to be used once an assumption has been made. Be sure to remember that even—or especially —when making assumptions, you must work with facts, making sure that the facts apply in the specific situation and that you have enough facts.

Consider the effect on Alice's height of a second thimbleful of Metrecal precursor. Did the first thimbleful

(1) Decrease her height by 2 ft?
(2) Cut her height in half?
(3) Cause her height to go down *to* its square root?
(4) Cause her height to go down *by* its square root?

You would have to make an assumption of some sort before attempting to find her height after taking another thimbleful. If the assumption were

(1) —her height would be 0 ft after a second thimbleful.
(2) —she'd be 1 ft tall.
(3) —she'd be 1.4 ft tall (the square root of 2 is 1.4).
(4) —she'd be 0.6 ft.

Choose an assumption, state the assumption, and then base your solution on that assumption. The validity of the assumption would obviously have to be tested in a real problem.

Why not use these techniques, realizing that this is merely an exercise, to find the rabbit's height and weight after taking another 2 thimblefuls or even after having taken just 1 rather than 2 thimblefuls of Metrecal precursor? Incidentally, do not be disturbed by the fact that the material had opposite effects on Alice and the rabbit. You will often encounter apparent contradictions of this sort. Certain bacteria, for example, need air to live, but others perish in air.

Confusing Relationships

EXAMPLE 2–12

If 103 crocodiles can eat 47 rhinoceroses in 30 min, how many crocodiles would be required to eat 250 rhinoceroses in 3 hr? Assume that the rate of eating per crocodile remains the same.

If more rhinos must be eaten by a fixed number of crocodiles, then more time must be allowed. There is a direct relationship between rhinos and the time required to eat them. But if more crocodiles are going to eat a fixed number of rhinos, then less time need be allowed. There is an inverse relationship between number of crocodiles and time. Perhaps this is not so much a matter of confusing relationships as it is a matter of confusion about which relationship is involved. We are concerned with the relationship between time and crocodiles. There is obviously a direct relationship between number of rhinos to be eaten and number of crocodiles required to do the eating.

Base factor: number of crocodiles.

Correcting factor	Nature of relationship	Direction of change	Effect on base factor
number of rhinos	direct	increase	increase
time	inverse	increase	decrease

$$\frac{103 \text{ crocodiles} \times 250 \text{ rhinos} \times 30 \text{ min}}{49 \text{ rhinos} \times 3 \text{ hr} \times \dfrac{60 \text{ min}}{\text{hr}}} = \text{about 88 crocodiles}$$

Relationships Involving Squares, Cubes, Roots, etc.

In solving a problem, one looks for the base factor, the factors that affect the base factor, and the relationships of these factors to the base factor. *After this,* one takes into account cubes, square roots, etc. The basic relationship is the same. If the correcting factor is 8/1 rather than 1/8 to give an increase, then, if the exact relationship involves a cube root, the factor would be $\sqrt[3]{8/1}$ rather than $\sqrt[3]{1/8}$ because, of the two forms, only the first would give the wanted larger value.

EXAMPLE 2–13

The frequency of mosquito bites was found to be directly related to the age of the mosquito, inversely related to the square root of the age of the person being bitten, directly related to the square of the speed of the mosquito approaching the target, and inversely related to the fourth power of the speed at which the person is walking. (The conditions are admittedly absurd.) A 7-day-old mosquito flying exactly 10 mi per hour bit a 24-year-old man walking 3 mi per hour 17 times in 1 hour. How many times per hour could a 4-day-old mosquito flying 15 mi per hour bite a 20-year-old man walking 2 mi per hour?

Base factor: Bites per hour. It would be incorrect to use bites as the base factor.

Correcting factor	Nature of relationship	Direction of change	Effect on base factor	Correcting fraction
age of mosquito	direct	decrease	decrease	$\dfrac{4}{7}$
age of man	inverse to square root	decrease	increase	$\dfrac{\sqrt{24}}{\sqrt{20}}$
speed of mosquito	direct to square	increase	increase	$\dfrac{15^2}{10^2}$
speed of man	inverse to fourth power	decrease	increase	$\dfrac{3^4}{2^4}$

You will notice that we handled each relationship just as we had done previously, but this time we took into account the fact that there is a power or a root of something involved. You would put the problem together by multiplying base factor times correcting fractions as usual. Time does not here enter into the calculations since it is constant.

$$\frac{17 \text{ bites} \times 4 \text{ days} \times \sqrt{24 \text{ yr}} \times \left(15 \dfrac{\text{mi}}{\text{hr}}\right)^2 \times \left(3 \dfrac{\text{mi}}{\text{hr}}\right)^4}{\text{hr} \quad \times 7 \text{ days} \times \sqrt{20 \text{ yr}} \times \left(10 \dfrac{\text{mi}}{\text{hr}}\right)^2 \times \left(2 \dfrac{\text{mi}}{\text{hr}}\right)^4} = ? \frac{\text{bites}}{\text{hr}}$$

The problem is fantastic. We just wanted a vehicle for demonstration purposes.

Quick Review

- 10 to the second power is written 10^2. It is 10×10. Similarly, 2 to the fourth power is written 2^4. It is $2 \times 2 \times 2 \times 2$ or 16.
- $\sqrt{64}/\sqrt{4}$ is the same as $\sqrt{64/4}$. Each equals 4.
- $6^3/2^3$ is the same as $(6/2)^3$. Each equals 27.

COMPARISON AND CORRECTION APPLIED TO MORE COMPLICATED PROBLEMS

You may be saying to yourself that this is all well and good, but it doesn't really help. The difficulty is somewhere else. Let's explore further.

You have in mind a problem you can't do. Ask yourself specifically what you're looking for. Clearly identify the unknown. This seems too obvious to say, but in complicated problems what you are really looking for may seem impossible to find, or you may be looking for the wrong thing. Reword the problem. Get rid of all excess words. Put it into more precise English if necessary.

When you are sure of the unknown, make a list of what you're given in the problem, and look for the relationships. If you don't see any relationships, try these: Dismantle the problem. Make up little problems with parts of the data. Or imitate. In an attempt to jog your mind, look at solved problems that have some or all of the elements of the problem under consideration. Looking at previously solved problems is a decidedly helpful and valid tool if one does this in an attempt to understand the problem.

If you still don't see any relationship between what you're given and what you're looking for, try other sources—textbooks, dictionaries, technical dictionaries, handbooks, etc. Find definitions and discussions of both what you're seeking and the given factors. List this information in some orderly fashion. Look for connecting links. Look up definitions of concepts in the definitions just found. Now you have extra information, but something you need may still be missing. Keep looking. If there are relationships, you are bound to find them if you proceed in an orderly fashion. You may eventually find that the problem cannot be solved. Knowing why it cannot be solved is obviously every bit as important as actually solving the problem.

Consider the following example, which illustrates some of what we have been discussing.

EXAMPLE 2-14

At a given temperature, a gas with a relative mass of 39 had a velocity of 250 centimeters per second (cm/sec). Find the velocity of a gas with a relative mass of 7 at the same temperature.

1. What are you looking for? The velocity of the lighter gas.
2. What do you have? Mass, velocity, and temperature of one gas; mass and temperature of the other gas; and the fact that the temperature is the same for both gases.
3. What are the relationships?

Logically the lighter gas should have a higher velocity. What seems logical is not necessarily so. It would be wise to search a chemistry or physics book or technical dictionary for something about gases and the mass, velocity, and temperature thereof. You would find these pertinent items:

a. That rate of diffusion is inversely proportional (inversely related) to the square root of the molecular mass.* (Check *diffusion* in a dictionary if necessary.)
b. That there is a direct proportion (direct relationship) between the rate of diffusion of a gas and the average speed of molecules.

It would thus seem logical to think that the velocity of molecules is inversely proportional to the square root of the relative mass, but

● Do *speed* and *velocity* mean the same thing?
● Do *relative mass* and *molecular mass* mean the same thing, or can they be used interchangeably?

On consulting a technical dictionary or other reference, you would find that there is indeed a difference between speed and velocity, but that it does not apply here. You would also find that in this situation relative mass and molecular mass can be used interchangeably. We have here a good example of *indirect relationships:*

● Diffusion and molecular mass are inversely related.
● Diffusion and average speed of molecules are directly related.
● Average speed of molecules and average velocity of molecules are directly related.
● Molecular mass and relative mass are directly related.

---

*The word *proportional* is used here as a synonym for *relationship*. It has no connection with the method of proportion, a method that should not be confused with the method of comparison and correction. *Directly related, directly proportional, proportional to,* and *varies with* all mean the same thing here, just as *inversely related, inversely proportional,* and *varies inversely,* in effect, all mean the same thing.

Therefore velocity of molecules should be inversely related to the relative mass. Specifically, average velocity of molecules is inversely related to the square root of the relative mass of the molecules.

Now let's do this problem in classic fashion.

Fact: Average velocity of molecules of a gas is inversely related to the square root of the relative mass of the molecules.

Assumption: Temperature, which is constant, does not affect relationships.

1. Base factor: velocity of the gas.
2. Factor affecting base factor: changing mass.
3. Type of relationship: inverse.
4. Direction of change: relative mass decreases.
5. Effect on base factor: increase.
6. Setup:

$$\frac{250 \text{ cm} \times \sqrt{39}}{\text{sec} \quad \sqrt{7}} = 590 \text{ cm/sec}$$

Mass bears no unit because it is relative mass.

Let's try another, similar problem.

EXAMPLE 2–15

At 30.0°C, gas molecules with a relative mass of 64 have an average velocity of 50,000 cm/sec. For another gas at the same temperature the average molecular velocity is 58,000 cm/sec. Find the relative mass of the other gas.

Fact: The average velocity of a gas is inversely related to the square root of the relative mass, so the square root of the relative mass is inversely related to the velocity of a gas. If both the square root of the relative mass and the velocity are squared, the relationship becomes: Relative mass of a gas is inversely related to the square of the average velocity.*

Now let's analyze this problem in classic fashion.

1. Base factor: relative mass of gas.
2. Factor affecting base factor: changing velocity (temperature constant)

---

*$\left(\sqrt{16}\right)^2$ is 16. Proof: $4^2 = 16$. Thus $\left(\sqrt{\text{relative mass}}\right)^2 = $ relative mass.

3. Type of relationship: an inverse one involving mass and square of velocity.
4. Direction of change: increase.
5. Effect on base factor: decrease.
6. Setup:

$$\frac{64 \times (50{,}000 \text{ cm/sec})^2}{(58{,}000 \text{ cm/sec})^2} = 48$$

Again, relative mass bears no unit.

Dimensional Analysis

Dimensional analysis is a term used to describe the practice of putting all units into a problem. *Analysis* of the units involves canceling units to find the units of the answer. If you have the right units, your answer may be right, but with the wrong units, you know it is wrong.

The necessity of attaching all units to all numbers at all times cannot be stressed too much. In fact, this whole book is intended to be an example of dimensional analysis at work.

Suppose you have to find the number of yards in 15 ft. You know very well the answer is 5 yd. Suppose you were required to put this down on paper.

$$\frac{15 \text{ ft}}{3 \text{ ft}} = 5 \text{ yd}$$

This is quite wrong. From your setup, it is really a dimensionless ratio. Now put the figures down in this fashion, showing all units.

$$\frac{15 \text{ ft}}{\dfrac{3 \text{ ft}}{\text{yd}}} = 5 \text{ yd}$$

You object. It is patently ridiculous to put down these simple units. Not so. Anyone who has successfully dealt with complex problems will certainly vouch for the advantage of always putting down all units, of having developed the habit of instinctively putting down all units.

If the reason why the preceding problem bears the unit *yards* puzzles you, here is a brief review of equalities. If both sides of a fraction line, or both sides of an equation, are multiplied by the same thing, nothing really changes. Consider the equality:

$$\frac{1}{2} = \frac{2}{4}$$

a. If you multiply both numerators by 2, you have

$$\frac{1 \times 2}{2} = \frac{2 \times 2}{4} \quad \text{or} \quad \frac{2}{2} = \frac{4}{4}$$

The result is still an equality. Obviously, this would hold with any number, not just with 2.

b. If you multiply the numerator and the denominator on the right by 2, you have

$$\frac{1}{2} = \frac{2 \times 2}{4 \times 2} \quad \text{or} \quad \frac{1}{2} = \frac{4}{8}$$

This is still an equality.

c. If you multiply both denominators by 2 (or divide both numerators by 2, which is really the same thing), you have

$$\frac{1}{2 \times 2} = \frac{2}{4 \times 2} \quad \text{or} \quad \frac{1}{4} = \frac{2}{8}$$

d. But if you multiply the *numerator* on the *left* by 2 and *denominator* on the *right* by 2 (in other words, if one numerator is multiplied by 2 and the other numerator is divided by 2, two obviously different operations), you have

$$\frac{1 \times 2}{2} \neq \frac{2}{4 \times 2} \quad \text{or} \quad \frac{2}{2} \neq \frac{2}{8}$$

The result is not an equality.

Now consider this example:

$$\frac{1}{\frac{1}{2}} = 2 \quad (1 \text{ divided by } \tfrac{1}{2} \text{ has to equal } 2.)$$

Multiply both the numerator and the denominator on the left by 2 and cancel suitably.

$$\frac{1 \times 2}{\frac{1 \times \cancel{2}}{\cancel{2}}} = 2 \quad \text{or} \quad 2 = 2$$

This is an equality.

Now take

$$\frac{ft}{\frac{ft}{yd}}$$

Multiply both the numerator and the denominator by yards and cancel suitably.

$$\frac{\cancel{ft} \times yd}{\dfrac{\cancel{ft} \times \cancel{yd}}{\cancel{yd}}} = yd$$

You will often encounter problems in which this type of unit handling is necessary.

The Unbelievable Problem (The Relationships Seem Illogical; Therefore, You Cannot Solve the Problem)

Certain *facts* cannot be readily believed by the average person. The facts *are*, but how *can* they be? There are supposedly six laws of conservation of energy. Some of them involve space and time. There is such a thing as curved space, perhaps curved time, too. Fantastic. They are beyond the ordinary person's experience. The mind refuses to accept them with so little insurance against fantasy.

Only yesterday the idea of inertia—the tendency of objects to stay in motion if in motion and to stay still if still—was partly unbelievable. Now, as a result of television and film coverage of satellites and astronauts, we really do know that objects in motion tend to stay in motion.

Perhaps future developments will make various ideas about time and space simple and believable. In the meantime, imagination is a faculty to be developed. Perhaps it is necessary to suspend mental judgment, perhaps even to suspend good sense and reason once in a while, in order to deal with facts that are beyond belief merely because they are out of our range of experience. Certainly we don't want to urge you to abandon reason, but once in a while odd methods are needed to jog the mind. Reason is fine, but without imagination it starves. Working with the imaginary can sometimes help to make the real believable.

All of us must deal with things we cannot fully understand, often even with things that seem illogical. Work with the given facts. Do your best to understand the relationships, then branch out and *use the facts,* use the known relationships. This may sound like a most unscientific approach. Yet if men had always worked only with what they fully understood, people might still be shivering in caves. Please don't think we are advocating complacency about lack of understanding or lack of knowledge, however; the search for reasons and understanding should never stop.

Here is a seemingly absurd problem. *Work with the known or given conditions,* even though your mind says the relationship is false, illogical, etc. We want to illustrate an idea here.

EXAMPLE 2–16

On planets in the antiuniverse Metsys Ralos, force is directly proportional to the square root of the distance between the centers of masses attracting one another and inversely proportional to the masses of the bodies. Water flows uphill twice as fast as it flows downhill, for a given slope. Heating of materials decreases molecular motion, and increasing the pressure on a gas causes the gas to expand. On the planet Sram in this particular antiuniverse, a given object O weighed 8900 tons. How much would it weigh on Noom, another planet in the same antiuniverse? Noom's mass is 1/8 that of Sram; Noom's diameter is 77 times that of Sram. Assume that the diameter of object O is negligible with respect to those of Sram and Noom.

Given: The relationship between weight and the masses of attracting bodies, the relationship between weight and the distance between attracting bodies, the fact that the diameter of object O is insignificant with respect to that of the planets.

Possible major objection: We have switched from force to weight. Weight is one kind of force (see Chapter 14). Here we can use weight and force interchangeably.

1. Factor sought: weight of O on Noom.
2. Base factor: weight of O on Sram.
3. Factors affecting weight: changing diameter* of major attracting body, changing mass of major attracting body.

Changing factor	Nature of relationship	Direction of change with respect to effect on O
diameter*	direct (square root)	increase
mass	inverse	increase

---

*You may object to diameter here. The proportion involves distance between centers of attracting bodies. The distance between the center of a body (presuming some sort of sphere is involved here) and the surface is the radius. However, radius and diameter are directly proportional to one another.

4. The solution:

$$\frac{8900 \text{ tons} \times \sqrt{77} \times 8}{\sqrt{1} \times 1}$$

Absurd? Yes. We cannot think of a real problem with such unbelievable data, despite the fact that such problems surely do exist.

Complicating factors: Actual masses and diameters were not given; we had to use relative ones.

If we let mass of Sram $= 1$, then

mass of Noom $= \frac{1}{8}$ or 0.125

It is easier this way:

Let mass of Sram $= 8$ (as we did), then

mass of Noom $= 1$

Similarly,

Let diameter of Sram $= 1$

diameter of Noom $= 77$

You may think we should have used 0.5 and 38.5 in place of 1 and 77, but 38.5/0.5 is really the same as 77/1, and 77/1 is a more convenient form to use.

Need to Work Within Limits of Known Facts

After having told you to use your imagination, occasionally to suspend what seems like good sense, we are going to be contrary and tell you to hold your imagination in check.

EXAMPLE 2–17

At the age of 4 a child gained 0.5 lb for every 10 lb of his body weight during a year. Between his fifth and sixth birthdays he gained 0.6 lb for every 10 lb of his body weight. Find the weight he gained during the year he was 80.

This problem is absurd. You know it cannot be solved. Information about weight gain at age 4 or 5 would have no relationship to weight gain at age 80. There is no reasonable basis on which to make an assumption about what the weight gain would be out of the age range for which you have information. Any assumption would be meaningless. The only point of making an assumption here would be to provide a basis for demonstrating problem-solving techniques.

There is a difficulty in determining when an assumption can be made. Assumptions—when to make them, when they are reasonable—are affected by the specific subject matter. In general, though, it can be said that one could make an assumption, and then base solutions to problems on the assumption, when the assumption is reasonable in terms of knowledge of the subject, literature search, experimentation, etc. Stretching this to the absolute limit one could say it would be reasonable to make an assumption (in the absence of information even after diligent searching) when the assumption does not involve anything known to be false.

PROBLEMS

Set up each problem, but do not work it through to the answer unless specifically directed to do so. Show all units. List any assumptions you must make in solving a problem. Give the reasons why a problem cannot be solved if it cannot be solved. Work with the conditions given in the problem. A number of problems with unreal, ridiculous, or generally impossible conditions have been set forth to encourage use of the method presented in this chapter. If conditions governing the factors in the problem are not given, then they are either within the realm of experience or common sense or "findable" in ordinary references.

1. The rate at which a certain *Neurospora* mutant grows in a certain medium is directly related to the concentration of adenine. At a concentration of 0.004 mole per liter (symbol: *M*), the *Neurospora* grew at a rate of 0.33 gram per hour (g/hr).
    a. Find the rate at which the *Neurospora* would grow in 0.008 *M* adenine.
    b. Find the weight gain after 12 hr in 0.004 *M* adenine.
    c. If the weight gain was 1 g/hr, what must have been the concentration of adenine?
2. Now, traces of chloride ion inhibit *Neurospora* growth. The rate of growth in a certain medium was found to be inversely proportional to concentration of chloride ion if the adenine concentration was constant. With a set concentration of adenine in the medium and a chloride ion concentration of 0.00009 *M, Neurospora* grew at a rate of 0.1 g/hr.
    a. Find the growth rate in 0.04 *M* chloride ion in the given medium.

b. Find the chloride ion concentration in this medium that would give a growth rate of 0.001 g/year.

3. Suppose that in a standard medium containing adenine at 0.004 *M* and chloride ion at 0.0007 *M*, the *Neurospora* gained 3 g in 7 hr. Remember that the rate of growth is directly proportional to the adenine concentration and inversely proportional to the chloride ion concentration.

a. Find the rate at which *Neurospora* would grow in 0.0009 *M* adenine and 0.00009 *M* chloride ion.

b. Find the weight gain in 25 hr under the conditions given in problem 3a.

4. In 30 min, 103 men dug 49 trenches. Presume that each man's rate of digging remains the same.

a. How many trenches could be dug by 10 men in 2 months?

b. How many men would be required to dig 17 trenches in 3 hr?

c. How long would it take 1 man to dig 100 trenches?

5. Working 8 hr/day, 50 IBM machines can process 3,000,000 accounts in 15 days. Each machine works at the same constant rate.

a. How many accounts could be processed if 5 machines worked 15 hr a day for 20 days?

b. How many hours would it take 80 machines to process 28,000 accounts working 24 hr/day?

c. How many hours per day must 220 machines work to process 800,000 accounts in 10 days?

6. Rolling friction is directly proportional to load and inversely proportional to the radius of the wheel. With a load of 2000 lb and wheels 3 ft in diameter, the friction was 89 friction units. (The units are as imaginary as the problem, but we have method in mind here.) Find the friction units when the load is 500 lb and the wheel diameter is 1 ft.

7. The speed of a wave along a wire or string is directly proportional to the square root of the tension and inversely proportional to the square root of the mass per unit length. A wave traveled along a guitar string at a rate of 70 ft/sec when the tension was 17 tension units (another imaginary unit) and the mass was 2 g/yd. Find the speed at which a wave could travel along a guitar string under a tension of 80 tension units and with a mass of 7 g/yd.

8. The area of a circle is proportional to the square of the radius. A certain circle has a radius of 2 ft and an area of 12.6 ft^2.

a. Find the area of a circle with a 6-ft radius.

b. Find the radius of a circle with an area of 78.5 ft^2.

(Please use the relationships given here, not the probably readily remembered formula for the area of a circle.)

9. In a *hypothetical* survey of students of a foreign language, it was found that the length of time of study was inversely proportional to the number of words learned. In 2 hr, 140 new words were learned. Considering the data presented and the *conditions specified,* find:

    a. The number of words that could be learned in 3 hr.
    b. The number of new words that could be learned in 20 min.
    c. The number of days it would take to learn 800 new words.
    d. The number of minutes required to learn 50 new words.

10. Suppose that another fictitious study of the rate of learning foreign words showed that the rate of learning words was inversely proportional to increasing temperature in the range 50°F to 70°F, directly proportional to the square of the time spent studying the words in the range 1 to 8 hr, and inversely proportional to the age of the student in the range of 17 to 69 years of age. It was found that the average student 20 years of age could learn 40 new words in 1 hr in a room at 61°F.

    a. How many words could a 22-year-old student learn in 3 hr in a room at 69°F?
    b. How long would it take a student aged 45 to learn 75 new words if the room temperature is 52°F?
    c. How long would it take a student 12 years old to learn 500 words in a 75°F room?

11. Captain Ahab found that a dolphin's appetite was directly proportional to the depth to which it had dived to dine, inversely proportional to the temperature of the water, directly proportional to the square of the velocity of the water currents, inversely proportional to the seventh power of the length of fish available for food. *Considering these stated conditions,* answer each of the following.

    a. A dolphin ate 4 lb of fish in 2.0°C water. How much fish could he eat in 30.0°C water during the same time interval if all other conditions were the same? In 1.0°C water if all other conditions were the same?
    b. A dolphin ate 999 lb of fish in 20.0°C water at a depth of 7 fathoms. How much fish could this dolphin eat at 30.0°C and 9 fathoms, all other conditions constant?
    c. At 19.0°C in water flowing 90 mi/hr 7 fathoms below the surface, a certain dolphin ate 99 lb of fish. How much could this dolphin eat in water flowing 40 mi/hr at a depth of 3 fathoms and a temperature of 19.0°C (size of fish constant)?

  d. At a depth of 4 fathoms in 2.0°C water with a 90-mi/hr current, a dolphin ate 120 lb of fish from a school of sardines in which the sardines were 8 ft long. How much could this dolphin eat in 20.0°C water, 19 fathoms down, if the current is 3 mi/hr and the sardines in the school are 1½ in. long?

  e. At what temperature was the water in which a dolphin ate 90 lb of fish under the conditions given in problem 11a?

12. The Earth takes a year to travel around the sun. In other words, the Earth's period is 1 year. The square of the period of a planet is directly related to the cube of its average distance from the sun.

  a. How long would the period be on a planet that, on the average, is twice as far from the sun as is the Earth?

  b. If summer on a given planet were 210 days, how far would the planet be (in terms of average distance, of course) from the sun? From the Earth? (The sun is about 93,000,000 mi from the Earth on the average.)

  c. If another planet were 23,250,000 mi from the sun, what would be the length of its period? (See problem 12b for Earth-to-sun distance.) What would be the distance between this planet and the Earth?

13. The distance that Jack could climb up a beanstalk was directly proportional to his total climbing weight. He climbed from ground level to 4000 ft in 2 hr while wearing a 9-lb climbing outfit. He himself weighed 150 lb.

  a. How far could he have climbed in 2 hr had he worn an 11-lb climbing outfit?

  b. How long would he take to climb 5000 ft if he lost 20 lb of his own weight before starting the climb and if he wore a 5-lb climbing outfit?

  c. Modify problem 13b to 40 years later. What is the distance now?

3

PROBLEM SOLVING BY ANALOGY

or How to Decide When to Multiply and When to Divide

The alternate title of this chapter may sound absurd, but this is at the heart of the difficulty that many students have when they encounter unfamiliar units. There are methods at which people with fine mathematical ability leap with joy but at which students generally look with horror. Among these methods one finds that of analogy, a totally respectable and useful method.

Just what is analogy? It is a type of reasoning in which from certain observed and known relations or resemblances others are inferred. Still Greek? No help? Let's see.

Do these problems, showing all units.*

(a) How many pounds in 5 tons?
(b) How many feet in 7 yd?

You obviously got

(a) $\dfrac{5 \text{ tons} \times 2000 \text{ lb}}{\text{ton}} = 10,000 \text{ lb}$

(b) $\dfrac{7 \text{ yd} \times 3 \text{ ft}}{\text{yd}} = 21 \text{ ft}$

(c) How many miles in 10,560 ft?
(d) How many yards in 144 in.?

---

*Unit handling is discussed on pages 19–21.

Here you got

(c) $\dfrac{10,560 \text{ ft}}{5,280 \dfrac{\text{ft}}{\text{mi}}} = 2 \text{ mi}$ (d) $\dfrac{144 \text{ in.}}{36 \dfrac{\text{in.}}{\text{yd}}} = 4 \text{ yd}$

Note that in (a) and (b) you were changing a bigger unit into a smaller one. Consider (a). In a given, unchanging weight there are always numerically more pounds than tons. You must have a numerically larger answer whenever you change a given quantity from a large unit to a small unit. In (c) and (d) you were changing from a small unit to a large unit. You had to have a numerically smaller answer.

Now let's add a dash of confusion.

In making unit conversions, you want to focus on the *effect* rather than on the method. In other words, concentrate on the idea that you want an increase or a decrease rather than on the method of getting such increase or decrease.

Do you multiply to effect an increase? Of course? Of course not? Sometimes? The last is the answer.

EXAMPLE 3–1

$8 \times 2 = 16$

$\dfrac{8}{0.5} = 16$

$\dfrac{8}{\dfrac{1}{2}} = 16$

To effect an increase you multiply by a number greater than one and divide by a number less than one.

Do you divide to effect a decrease?

EXAMPLE 3–2

$8 \times 0.5 = 4$

$8 \times \dfrac{1}{2} = 4$

$\dfrac{8}{2} = 4$

So to effect a decrease, you multiply by a number less than one and divide by a number more than one.

In the preceding chapter we urged you to operate on the mathematical counterpart of the factor you were seeking. If you want a quantity of ice cream, you must work on a quantity of ice cream. In unit conversion problems you have just one thing, the unit to be converted. Of necessity, you must operate on it. In converting 9 ft to inches you must operate on 9 ft. You cannot operate on the desired unit, inches, because you do not have inches; you must operate on feet.

Consider this example.

EXAMPLE 3–3

How many inches are there in 9 ft?

Obviously,

$$\frac{9 \text{ ft} \times 12 \text{ in.}}{\text{ft}} = 108 \text{ in.}$$

Suppose you had been given this relationship:

1 in. = 0.083 ft

You *know* the foot is larger than the inch. You *know* that in converting 9 ft to inches you are going from a larger unit to a smaller unit and that you need a numerically larger answer. With a decimal conversion factor less than one (0.083 ft/in.) you must divide to effect an increase. So

$$\frac{9 \text{ ft}}{\dfrac{0.083 \text{ ft}}{\text{in.}}} = 108 \text{ in.}$$

EXAMPLE 3–4

Now convert 108 in. to feet.

You *know* you need a smaller answer, so

$$\frac{108 \text{ in.}}{\dfrac{12 \text{ in.}}{\text{ft}}} = 9 \text{ ft} \quad \text{or} \quad \frac{108 \text{ in.} \times 0.083 \text{ ft}}{\text{in.}} = 9 \text{ ft}$$

If you just remember how to solve foot-inch problems, you should have no trouble with other conversions. You merely have to cope with the fact that the units might be unfamiliar. We want to present a method of attack on conversions, so we have chosen rather uncommon units in the hope that they cannot be cracked by tricks of memory.

EXAMPLE 3–5

Convert 99 British bushels to U.S. bushels.

Handbook information: 1 British bushel (bu) = 1.032 U.S. bu.

Which is the larger unit? More than one U.S. bushel will fit into a British bushel. Obviously, the British bushel is larger. By analogy,

from 1 ft = 12 in. you *know* the foot is the larger unit,
so if 1 British bu = 1.032 U.S. bu, you similarly *know* the British bushel is the larger unit.

You are going from a larger unit to a smaller unit. You know the answer must be larger, so here, with a conversion factor greater than one, you multiply

$$\frac{99 \text{ British bu} \times 1.032 \text{ U.S. bu}}{\text{British bu}} = 102 \text{ U.S. bu}$$

You object to 1.032 U.S. bu/British bu? You don't object to 12 in./ft.

EXAMPLE 3–6

How many British bags are there in 17 cubic meters (m^3)?

Handbook value: 1 British bag = 0.1091 m^3.

Which is the bigger unit? One British bag could hold only 0.1 (one-tenth) of a cubic meter. The other 0.9 m^3 would have to be left out. The cubic meter must be a bigger unit than a British bag.

If 1 in. = 0.083 ft, you *know* the foot is the larger unit.
If 1 British bag = 0.1091 m^3, you *know* the cubic meter is the larger unit.

In converting 17 m^3 to British bags, you have to go from a big unit to a small one. You know you need a numerically larger answer. With a decimal conversion factor that is less than one, you effect an increase by dividing.

$$\frac{17 \text{ m}^3}{\dfrac{0.1091 \text{ m}^3}{\text{British bag}}} = 160 \text{ British bags}$$

EXAMPLE 3–7

How many cubic meters are there in 33 British bags?

You are going from a small unit to a large unit. You need a numerically smaller answer. Since the conversion factor is a decimal less than one, you effect a decrease by multiplying.

$$\frac{33 \text{ British bags} \times 0.1091 \text{ m}^3}{\text{British bag}} = 3.6 \text{ m}^3$$

EXAMPLE 3–8

Convert 91 British bu to cubic meters.

Facts: 1 British bag = 3 British bu; 1 British bag = 0.1091 m³.

You don't know the relationship between British bushels and cubic meters, but you do know the relationship of each of these to British bags. Convert British bushels to British bags, and then convert British bags to cubic meters.

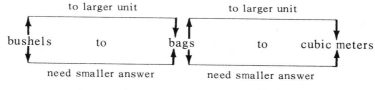

$$\frac{91 \text{ British bu} \times 0.1091 \text{ m}^3}{\dfrac{3 \text{ British bu}}{\text{British bag}} \quad \text{British bag}} = 3.3 \text{ m}^3$$

For the first transformation you had to divide to effect a decrease, since you had a conversion factor larger than one. For the second transformation, you had to multiply to effect a decrease, since the conversion factor was less than one. You would follow the procedure we have just shown no matter how many transformations you might have. Just plot the route from unit to unit on the path from the unit you have to the unit you want.

Table 3–1. Some Relationships of Units

1 inch (in.) = 2.54 centimeters (cm)

1 meter (m) = 39.37 in.

1 mile (mi) = 5280 feet (ft)

1 yard (yd) = 3 ft

1 grain (gr) = 1/7000 pound avoir-
             dupois (lb av)

1 gr = 1/5760 lb Troy (lb T)

1 gram (g) = 0.06480 gr

1000 g = 1 kilogram (kg)

1 kg = 2.2 lb av

1 lb av = 454 g

1 pennyweight (pwt) = 24 gr

1 lb av = 16 ounces (oz)

1 lb av = 0.07143 stone

1 ton = 2000 lb av

1 horsepower (hp) = 745.2 watts (w)

1 metric horsepower = 0.9863 hp

1 w = 10^7 ergs per second (ergs/sec)

1 British bag = 3 British bushels (bu)

1 British bag = 0.1091 cubic meter (m^3)

1 British bu = 1.032 U.S. bu

1 British gallon (gal) = 1.201 U.S. gal

1 dry British barrel (bbl) = 0.1637 m^3

1 liter = 1000 milliliters (ml)

1 liter = 1.06 quarts (qt)

1 qt = 4 cups

1 U.S. bu = 9.309 U.S. gal

1 U.S. gal = 4 qt

PROBLEMS

Provide only the setups to solve these problems, unless expressly directed also to find the answers. Show all units always (see Table 3–1). Unless otherwise specified, pound means pound avoirdupois.

1. Express 8450 g in pounds.
2. How many quarts are there in 49 liters?
3. How many grains are there in 91 g?
4. How many stone in 50 g?
5. How many inches are there in 5.8 m?
6. Convert 450 cm to inches.
7. How many dry British barrels are there in 71 m³?
8. How many British gallons are there in 0.8 U.S. bu?
9. How many grams in 91 pwt?
10. Express 91 oz in terms of grams.
11. Express 99 g in pounds Troy.
12. How many dry British barrels are there in 71 British bu?
13. Convert 88 British bags to British barrels.

14. How many pennyweight in 0.3 gr?

15. How many cubic meters in 5 British bags?

16. How many liters in 5 British bags?

17. Convert 10 mi to centimeters.

18. What is the difference in inches per hour between 14 ft/day and 100 ft/day?

19. What is the difference in ergs per second between horsepower and metric horsepower?

20. Exactly 1.00 ml of pyridine (C_5H_5N) weighs 0.983 g at 20°C. What is the weight in pounds of 155 U.S. gal of pyridine?

4

HOW TO TURN WORD PROBLEMS
INTO EQUATION FORM
and a Brief Review of Algebra

Very often, with just the briefest review, students can solve quite complicated algebraic setups, quadratic equations in two unknowns, and other equally exotic beasts. Yet these same students often have moderate to severe difficulty in putting word problems into mathematical form for solution. Consequently, we will pay more attention to putting word problems into equation form than to the mechanics of algebra. There is, however, a review of the mechanics of algebra at the end of the chapter.

In solving problems, first read the problem carefully. It cannot be reiterated too often that students commit about as many errors because of misreading problems as for any other reason. Talk to yourself. Ask yourself questions. Make a start. If you are absolutely stymied and can't think of a thing to do, start writing. Even if you only write what you are given and what you are looking for, you have started the mental train. Look at the problem again. What assumptions can or must you make to get started. Precisely define the thing you are looking for. If possible, define it in more than one way. Still no help? Put the problem away for a while. Let your subconscious mind or something or other work on it. Take up the problem again. Start doing little problems related to the problem. Use very simple numbers. Where possible, make an estimate of the answer and work backward to see how far off you are. Does this sound dreadful? Perhaps. However, it is a legitimate means of tricking the mind onto the right track.

We have done something that may surprise you. We have included incorrect solutions to various problems. Students very often want to know why something is wrong. They see why another solution is correct, but they do not really see why their own solution is wrong. Understanding why a particular solution is wrong can be just as helpful and as important as seeing why another solution is correct.

Let's take some examples.

EXAMPLE 4–1

Building A is twice as tall as building B. Building C is 5 times as tall as building B. Express the height of each in terms of a single unknown.

Where do you start?

Let x = height of A
then $0.5x$ = height of B (since A is twice as tall as B)
and $2.5x$ = height of C (since C is 5 times as tall as B)

Or let x = height of B
$2x$ = height of A (since A is still twice as tall as B)
$5x$ = height of C

Which is better? Neither.

EXAMPLE 4–2

Suppose building C is 800 ft tall. Find the heights of the other buildings in Example 4–1.

Obviously, this problem need not be done with algebra. But let's start with something simple.

$5x$ = 800 ft (height of C)
$$x = \frac{800 \text{ ft}}{5} = 160 \text{ ft (height of B)}$$
$2x = 2 \times 160$ ft = 320 ft (height of A)

Or, using the first notation given in Example 4–1:

$2.5x$ = 800 ft (height of C)
$$x = \frac{800 \text{ ft}}{2.5} = 320 \text{ ft (height of A)}$$
$0.5x = 0.5 \times 320$ ft = 160 ft (height of B)

Now let's modify this same problem a little bit.

EXAMPLE 4–3

Suppose all three buildings have a combined height of 1280 ft. Find the height of each building. Now, unless you want to work several "by guess and by golly" problems (not a tool to be laughed at, incidentally), you will want to use algebra.

Using the second notation of Example 4–1,

$$2x + x + 5x = 1280 \text{ ft}$$
$$8x = 1280 \text{ ft}$$
$$x = \frac{1280 \text{ ft}}{8} = 160 \text{ ft} \quad \text{(B's height)}$$
$$2x = 2 \times 160 \text{ ft} = 320 \text{ ft} \quad \text{(A's height)}$$
$$5x = 5 \times 160 \text{ ft} = 800 \text{ ft} \quad \text{(C's height)}$$

Simple addition proves you are right.

EXAMPLE 4–4

The area of a given building's basement is 5000 ft^2. It would take 5000 ft^2 of tile to cover the floor, assuming there were no spaces between the tiles and no overlap. If each tile were 1 ft square, the number of tiles would be 5000. Now, if the area were doubled, how many tiles would be needed?

Background information: Area = length × width.

There is a direct relationship between the number of tiles and the area of the floor. If the area were doubled, the number of tiles would be doubled. In this case you did not need the background information, but it is the sort of thing that should slip into your mind automatically when you think of area.

EXAMPLE 4–5

Suppose the basement in Example 4–4 was known to have a length of 100 ft. Suppose the length was increased by a certain amount and the width increased by twice that amount. As a result, 7700 tiles measuring 1 ft on each edge (area = 1 ft^2) were needed for the floor. Find the new dimensions of the floor.

We don't know who would be doing such a silly problem, but it illustrates the point we want to put across.

(100 ft) (what) = 5000 ft^2 (before expansion)

$$\text{what} = \frac{5000 \text{ ft}^2}{100} = 50 \text{ ft}$$

Now (100 + something) (50 + twice that same something) = 7700.

Let x = something

$2x$ = twice something

Then $(100 + x) (50 + 2x) = 7700$

$\qquad 5000 + 250x + 2x^2 = 7700$

$\qquad\qquad\qquad x = 10$

(Solution of quadratic equation in one unknown is reviewed on page 60.)

The new dimensions are 110 ft by 70 ft.
Proof: 110 ft × 70 ft = 7700 ft^2.

We have thus far stressed the importance of always attaching all units to all figures. To be contrary we now suggest you do this with some discrimination. If only one unit (for example, feet) is involved in a problem, it becomes cumbersome, tedious, and really unnecessary to use this unit throughout the problem. There is no possible confusion in omitting the unit in such cases. For convenience we have omitted carrying such single units throughout algebraic setups in this chapter.

A number of students may have thought of solving Example 4–5 by working with the increased dimensions and the increased area alone. Suppose you had written:

Let $\quad x$ = the increase along one edge (the length)

$\qquad 2x$ = the increase along the other edge (the width)

If $\ 7700 - 5000 = 2700$ = increase in area

then $(x) (2x) = 2700$

$\qquad\quad 2x^2 = 2700$

$\qquad\quad\ x = 36.7$

$\qquad\ 2x = 73.4$

Now try this in the original problem:

(100 + 36.7) (50 + 73.4) = 16,869

This is a far cry from 7700. What is wrong? You wanted the amount by which the edge lengths were to be increased. Instead you did a totally different problem. You found the edge lengths of a separate rectangle whose edges bore a 2 : 1 ratio to one another, that is, a rectangle with one side twice the length of the other and whose area was equal to the increased area of the floor. You wanted to know the dimensions when a given rectangle had one edge *increased* twice as much as the other edge. Perhaps drawings will be far clearer than words here (see Figure 4-1).

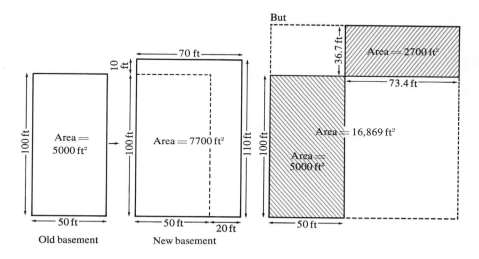

Figure 4-1

EXAMPLE 4-6

By how much must a swimming pool $40 \times 18 \times 10$ ft be uniformly enlarged along each dimension in order to double the volume?

Background information: Length × width × depth = volume.

Let x = the amount by which each dimension must be increased

Then $40 \times 18 \times 10$ = volume (under old conditions)

$(40 + x) (18 + x) (10 + x)$ = volume (under new conditions)

That is,

$$(40 + x) (18 + x) (10 + x) = 2(40 + 18 + 10)$$

This now becomes an algebraic monstrosity. We do not have the patience to bother actually working this out. You know it will eventually give the answer.

There is, however, an area of doubt here. Did the word "uniformly" mean that every dimension must be increased by the same amount? If it did not, then the solution is not necessarily the only one.

EXAMPLE 4–7

Determine the length and width of a rectangle whose area is 1400 ft^2 and whose perimeter is 180 ft.

Background information: Area = length × width
and perimeter = 2 lengths + 2 widths
= 2 (length) + 2 (width)

Then   length = $\dfrac{\text{perimeter} - 2\ (\text{width})}{2} = \dfrac{\text{perimeter}}{2} - \text{width}$

Now, here length = 180/2 − width.

Let x = the width

then $\dfrac{180}{2} - x$ = the length

$90 - x$ = the length

Since area = length × width,

$$x(90 - x) = 1400$$
$$90x - x^2 - 1400 = 0$$
or $-90x + x^2 + 1400 = 0$ or $x^2 - 90x + 1400 = 0$

(See algebraic signs on page 55 if necessary.)

$$x = 20 \text{ (the width)}$$
$$90 - 20 = 70 \text{ (the length)}$$

(Solution of quadratic equations on page 60.)

Proof: 20 ft × 70 ft = 1400 ft^2; 2(20 ft) + 2(70 ft) = 180 ft.

EXAMPLE 4–8

A man had $1.52 worth of change in the form of dimes and pennies. He had 17 coins. How many dimes and how many pennies did he have?

Pennies and dimes add up to $1.52 or 152¢ value. Pennies and dimes together add up to 17 coins.

Let x = number of pennies
then $17 - x$ = number of dimes

Now, can you say "$x + (17 - x) = 152$¢"? No, you cannot. The sum of x and $(17 - x)$ is equal to the number of coins, not to the value of the coins. But x times the value of a penny and $(17 - x)$ times the value of a dime would be equal to the total value, 152¢. In other words, coins +

coins can only equal total coins, here 17, but value of coins + value of coins = total value in cents or dollars. That is,

$$x(1¢) + (17 - x)10¢ = 152¢$$
$$x + 170 - 10x = 152$$
$$- 9x = -18$$
$$x = 2$$

There are 2 pennies; $17 - x = 15$, so there are 15 dimes.

Now, why did we use the value in cents rather than dollars? For convenience. We could have taken dollars and had $x(\$0.01) + (17 - x)\$0.10 = \$1.52$; the answer would be the same.

EXAMPLE 4–9

Suppose a bank had a practice of keeping pennies, nickels, dimes, quarters, and half dollars in the ratio of $20 : 15 : 10 : 1 : 2$. If it had \$64,000 in change on hand, how many coins of each kind would it have?

Let x = number of quarters
$2x$ = number of half dollars
$10x$ = number of dimes
$15x$ = number of nickels
$20x$ = number of pennies

Now this is solved in exactly the same way that Example 4–8 was solved.

EXAMPLE 4–10

Henry VIII's barge could go down the Thames from Hampton Court to the Tower of London, a distance of 21 mi, in 3 hr. It took the same barge with the same royal rowers 7 hr to return. The speed of the Thames was 2 mi/hr. (We are disregarding the fact that the Thames is a tidal river.) Find the time the round trip would have taken had the river been preternaturally still, that is, not flowing anywhere to any appreciable extent.

What do you know?

- The river ran 2 mi/hr.
- The distance one way was 21 mi, round trip 42 mi.
- Time down was 3 hr, time back 7 hr, total time 10 hr.

What must you assume?

- Rate of royal rowers was constant.

- River flow constant.

What do you want to know?

- Time to make the trip if there had been no river current.

How do you get time? If you knew the total distance and the rate you could get time because

$$\frac{\text{distance in miles}}{\dfrac{\text{number of miles}}{\text{unit of time}}} = \text{time}$$

The rate downstream to the Tower was assisted by the current; the rate upstream was slowed by the current. Remember, we are assuming that the rowers rowed at a constant rate in both directions and that the current was constant so that the amount of assistance or interference by the current was the same.

Let x = the rate of the royal rowers
Therefore $x + 2$ = rate downstream
$x - 2$ = rate upstream

Now, look again at the expression that you know gives you time.

time down + time back = total time

$$\text{time down} = \frac{21 \text{ mi}}{(x + 2) \dfrac{\text{mi}}{\text{hr}}} \qquad \text{time back} = \frac{21 \text{ mi}}{(x - 2) \dfrac{\text{mi}}{\text{hr}}}$$

You know the unit for the answer must be miles per hour, so for simplicity let's work with the figures alone.

$$\frac{21}{(x + 2)} + \frac{21}{(x - 2)} = 10$$
$$21(x - 2) + 21(x + 2) = 10[(x - 2)(x + 2)]$$

Now you solve a quadratic equation in one unknown and find:

$x = 5$ mi/hr

(See pages 58 and 60 for mechanics of solving this setup.)

You could probably have guessed what x was once you had the setup. This would have been a perfectly valid trick.

This solution was dreadfully and unnecessarily complicated. You worked through the known *time* factors. Could you perhaps have worked through the known *distance* factors?

Distance = rate × time

You have the distance and you have the time. You have already said rates would be $(x + 2)$ and $(x - 2)$.

So $\dfrac{3 \text{ hr} \times (x + 2) \frac{\text{mi}}{\text{hr}} + 7 \text{ hr} \times (x - 2) \frac{\text{mi}}{\text{hr}}}{} = 42 \text{ mi}$

$$3x + 6 + 7x - 14 = 42$$
$$10x = 50$$

(See page 55 for gathering of terms, etc.)

$$x = 5 \frac{\text{mi}}{\text{hr}}$$

This is right, but it too is unnecessarily complicated. Why use both rates and both times, that is, total time? Suppose we use only the time down the river and the distance down.

$$\frac{3 \text{ hr} \times (x + 2) \frac{\text{mi}}{\text{hr}}}{} = 21 \text{ mi}$$

$$x = 5 \frac{\text{mi}}{\text{hr}}$$

Don't stop now. This is the rowers' rate. You needed it, but what you really wanted was the round trip time when there was no current. Total distance was 42 miles; therefore,

$$\frac{42 \text{ mi}}{5 \frac{\text{mi}}{\text{hr}}} = 8.4 \text{ hr}$$

If there is any moral to this story, it is that the first way to do a problem is likely to be too complicated. Cast about for the easiest, apparently least sophisticated method. Careful reading of a problem, followed by quiet reflection and a careful rereading, often leads to discovery of a more direct method for solving the problem.

EXAMPLE 4–11

In order to sell coffee at 50¢/lb wholesale, how much 20¢/lb and 90¢/lb coffees must be mixed together?

What are you looking for? Quantity of 90¢ coffee and quantity of 20¢ coffee to be combined as 50¢ coffee. Note that you do *not* have the amount of coffee to be prepared. You would thus seem to be allowed to choose the amount of coffee to be prepared. How about 1 lb?

Now you can phrase the problem more precisely: How many pounds of 90¢/lb coffee and how many pounds of 20¢/lb coffee must be mixed to make 1 lb of 50¢ coffee? (The phrase "how many pounds" here does not necessarily imply more than 1 lb of such coffee. To us, it means that so much 90¢ coffee plus so much 20¢ coffee equals 1 lb of 50¢ coffee.)

Let x = the amount of 90¢ coffee
y = the amount of 20¢ coffee

But why introduce so many unknowns? Since $x + y = 1$ lb,

if x = amount (lb) of 90¢ coffee
$(1 - x)$ = amount (lb) of 20¢ coffee

You now have only one symbol for an unknown.

Together the two amounts, x lb of 90¢ coffee and $(1 - x)$ lb of 20¢ coffee, must equal 1 lb of 50¢ coffee. Omitting the units for convenience, since you know the answer must be in pounds:

$$(x)90 + (1 - x)20 = 1 \times 50$$
$$90x + 20 - 20x = 50$$
$$70x = 30$$
$$x = 0.43 \text{ (lb 90¢ coffee)}$$
$$(1 - x) = 0.57 \text{ (lb 20¢ coffee)}$$

This problem could also be solved by means of a graph (see Chapter 12).

EXAMPLE 4-12

May is 12, her mother 37. In how many years will the mother be twice as old as May?

What are you looking for? The number of years in which the mother will be twice as old as May. You're really looking for a time span.

What do you have? The mother's age, May's age, the present difference in their ages, the fact that this difference in age will always be constant.

You also know that the time span from now until the time when the mother will be twice as old as May is the same as the time span for May from now until the time when she is half as old as her mother. We have a common factor, the time span. We don't know what it is, but that is immaterial. The heart of the matter here is that at some time in the future the mother's age plus this span has to equal twice the quantity of May's age plus this span.

At the time in the future when the mother is twice May's age the mother's age would be (37 + the span), and May's age would be 2(12 + the span). Be sure you see this is so.

Let s = the span
$$(37 + s) = 2(12 + s)$$
$$s = 13$$

Proof: 37 + 13 = 50 and 12 + 13 = 25. So in 13 years the mother will be twice as old as May.

EXAMPLE 4–13

Two cars approach one another. They are traveling toward one another between Nice and Paris, a distance of about 450 mi. How long will it be before car A going north at 90 mi/hr meets car B going south at 60 mi/hr?

What are you looking for? Time interval before cars meet.

Assumptions: The speed of each car will be constant; there will be neither stops nor delays en route.

What do you have? Really, you are losing patience. It is quite obvious what you have here. But have you thought of the fact that the cars will have traveled a total of 450 mi when they meet and that each car will have been traveling the same amount of time?

The distance must equal time (hr) × speed (mi/hr). Let t = the time interval.

$$t \left(90 \, \frac{mi}{hr}\right) + t \left(60 \, \frac{mi}{hr}\right) = 450 \text{ mi}$$
$$t \left(150 \, \frac{mi}{hr}\right) = 450 \text{ mi}$$
$$t = 3 \text{ hr}$$

Car A should meet car B 3 hr after their common starting time.

EXAMPLE 4–14

Car A was going 125 mi/hr. It passed car B, which was going 60 mi/hr. After 1 hr the first car slowed down and the second car speeded up. They then met again 3 hr later after having traveled nonstop at the new speeds. Find the speed at which each car was traveling at the time of the second meeting.

What are you looking for? Speed of each car at time of second meeting.
What do you have?

- Initial speeds.
- Time before speed changes.
- Time after speed changes.
- Total time involved.
- That speeds after changes were constant.
- Distance apart at time of speedup.
- That B traveled 65 mi more than A after the speedup.
- That car B speeds up and car A slows down.
- That cars meet again (or B catches A, if you prefer) 3 hr after speed changes.
- That each car traveled the same distance in 4 hr.

What you do not know.

- Did A and B slow down and speed up by the same or different amounts?
- Is there a unique solution to this problem, or are there several sets of conditions that would meet the requirements of this problem?

Let's first solve this on the basis of the possibility that A and B changed speeds by the same amount.

Let x = the amount by which A slowed down
  x = the amount by which B speeded up

$$(time)(speed) = distance \quad or \quad (hr)\left(\frac{mi}{hr}\right) = mi$$

In 3 hr after the speedup, B must travel 65 mi more than A, but in 4 hr the distance traveled by both is the same. Let's work through this approach first.

distance traveled by B in 4 hr = 60 + (3 × new rate)
distance traveled by A in 4 hr = 125 + (3 × new rate)

new rate for B = (60 + x)
new rate for A = (125 − x)

So 60 + 3(60 + x) = 125 + 3(125 − x)
                $6x = 260$
                 $x = 43.3$

Proof: Distance covered by B = 60 + 3(60 + 43.3) = 369.9*; distance covered by A = 125 + 3(125 − 43.3) = 370.1.*

---

*Not in significant figures; see Chapter 8.

At time of second meeting A was traveling 81.7 mi/hr; B, 103.3 mi/hr.

Suppose you had wanted to work just with the 3-hr span. B had to travel 65 mi more than A after the speedup to catch A. Thus, after speed changes

distance covered by A = (distance covered by B) − 65
distance covered by B = (distance covered by A) + 65
distance covered by A = 3(125 − x)
distance covered by B = 3(60 + x)

Now $3(125 - x) = 3(60 + x) - 65$
$$-6x = -260$$
$$x = 43.3$$

This checks with your preceding solution. Again you would have to say that at the time of second meeting A was traveling 81.7 mi/hr and B 103.3 mi/hr (again, not in significant figures).

If you think about it, you will probably agree that if the cars do not speed up or slow down by numerically the same amount, there must be, within limits, an infinite number of possible different new speeds for A and B. We are governed by the requirement that A must slow down and B must speed up. If A merely slowed to 124.99999..., it would have met the requirement that it slow down; and if B merely speeded up to 60.000...1, then it, too, would have met its requirement. We will work with 124.9 and 60.1 for convenience. Neither is a significant figure, but we're interested in an idea here.

A and B must still cover the same total distance in 4 hr. So, taking A's new speed as 124.9 mi/hr, we have

$125 + 3(124.9) = 499.7$
         = total distance covered by A
         = total distance covered by B

Therefore new speed for B is

$$\frac{499.7 - 60}{3} = 146.6$$

If the new speeds of A and B were 124.9 and 146.6 mi/hr, respectively, the conditions set forth in the problem would be satisfied.

But if B's new speed is 60.1 mi/hr, then

$60 + 3(60.1) = 240.3$
         = total distance covered by B
         = total distance covered by A

Therefore new speed of A is

$$\frac{240.3 - 125}{3} = 38.4$$

If the new speeds of A and B were 38.4 and 60.1 mi/hr, respectively, the conditions set forth in the problem would also be satisfied.

It would thus seem that there could be an infinite number of possibilities between 38.4 and 124.9 (infinitesimally more and infinitesimally less for each) for A and between 144.9 and 60.1 (infinitesimally less and infinitesimally more, respectively) for B. Obviously, there is not a unique solution to the problem if A and B change speed by numerically different amounts.

It is occasionally possible, as a result of a handy series of errors, to arrive at a beautiful solution that apparently checks but is actually wrong. Careful reading of the problem and exact statement of what symbols stand for make such solutions virtually impossible. They are obviously impossible if all definitions and operations are correct. But look at this.

Let x = amount by which the initially fast car (A) slowed down
y = amount by which the initially slow car (B) speeded up
Then $(125 - x)$ = new rate for A
$(60 + y)$ = new rate for B

Now, no matter how you try to solve this, using the relationships you successfully used when you were having A and B change speeds by the same amount, you cannot solve it. This setup involves the assumption that there is still a definite amount by which A slows down and a definite amount by which B speeds up. You *know* from the material just preceding this there is a wide variety of amounts by which the speeds of the two cars can change if they do not change by the same amount. Under these circumstances there is not a unique solution to the problem. The equations fail to yield to your best efforts; they are telling you there is not a unique solution.

Now let's commit a few more errors and see how this helps to produce a nice if incorrect solution. Forgetting that there is not a unique answer to the problem if the speeds change by different amounts, you say the following:

The only difference in rate is that the initially slower car must somehow make up 65 mi in 3 hr. So (forgetting that you have just confused rate and distance with one another), you say

$$y = x + \frac{65}{3} \quad \text{or} \quad y = x + 21.7$$

Here's another error: You defined x and y as the amount by which A and B slowed down and speeded up, respectively, and now you're using them as the rates themselves. But let's see what happens when you use the equation just given:

$$(125 - x)3 + 65 = (60 + y)3$$
$$y = x + 21.7$$

Now $260 - 3x - 3y = 0$
$$y - x - 21.7 = 0$$

Multiply the second equation by 3 and add the two equations together.

(See page 59 for solution of simultaneous linear equations in two unknowns.)

$$
\begin{array}{r}
260 - 3x - 3y = 0 \\
-\ 65 - 3x + 3y = 0 \\
\hline
+\ 195 - 6x \qquad = 0 \\
x = 32.5
\end{array}
$$

Therefore $(125 - x) = (125 - 32.5) = 90$ mi/hr.

$$y = x + 21.7$$
$$= 32.5 + 21.7 = 54.2$$

Therefore $(60 + y) = 60 + 54.2 = 114.2$ mi/hr.

If you substitute these values in the equations, you will find that they work! The pair of new speeds are among the infinite number that we have already said were possible. Despite the fact that this problem checks, it is very wrong. There was a major confusion—in fact, a change— in definition of symbols. Your setups check; mathematics is not capricious. However, your setups were wrong.

EXAMPLE 4–15

A ferryboat traveled 18 mi/hr against an ebb tide of 15 mi/hr. Find how long it would take to go from Point Bonita to Hunter's Point, a distance of 7 mi, presuming the absurd, that the tide was constant.

Assumption: That 18 mi/hr is the speed at which the boat covers the distance—the effective speed—and not the speed at which the boat would travel if there were no tide.

So $\dfrac{7 \text{ mi}}{18 \dfrac{\text{mi}}{\text{hr}}} = 0.4 \text{ hr}$

EXAMPLE 4–16

Let's suppose Example 4–15 was worded this way: A ferryboat used enough fuel to develop enough power to go 18 mi/hr in still water, but this ferryboat was going against a 15-mi/hr tide (that same impossible constant tide). Find the time the boat would take to travel from Point Bonita to Hunter's Point, a distance of 7 mi.

Find the effective speed of the boat.

$$\dfrac{18 \text{ mi} - 15 \text{ mi}}{\text{hr} \qquad \text{hr}} = 3 \, \dfrac{\text{mi}}{\text{hr}}$$

Then $\dfrac{7 \text{ mi}}{3 \dfrac{\text{mi}}{\text{hr}}} = 2.3 \text{ hr}$ (not in significant figures)

EXAMPLE 4–17

Suppose the same boat, operated at the still-water speed of 18 mi/hr, went with the tide and covered the 7 mi in 15 min. Find the speed of the tide (again presume the impossible, a constant tide).

The effective speed of the boat was

$$\dfrac{7 \text{ mi}}{\dfrac{15 \text{ min}}{60 \dfrac{\text{min}}{\text{hr}}}} = 28 \, \dfrac{\text{mi}}{\text{hr}}$$

The tide was

$$\dfrac{28 \text{ mi} - 18 \text{ mi}}{\text{hr} \qquad \text{hr}} = 10 \, \dfrac{\text{mi}}{\text{hr}}$$

EXAMPLE 4–18

Now suppose this same boat that can go 18 mi/hr in slack water could go 8 mi against the tide and 15 mi with the tide in a given time interval. Find the tide speed, again presuming that it could be constant.

Note the difference between this problem and the preceding one. In Example 4–17 you were given the miles traveled per hour (or fraction of an hour). Here you are given the absolute distances, 8 and 15 mi, and told that these distances were traveled in the same interval of time.

$$\text{Let } x = \text{the tide speed}$$

$$\text{then } (18 - x)\,(\text{hr}) = 8 \text{ mi} \quad \left[\left(\frac{\text{mi}}{\text{hr}}\right)(\text{hr}) = \text{mi}\right]$$

$$\text{and } (18 + x)\,(\text{hr}) = 15 \text{ mi}$$

What can be set equal?

$$8 \neq 15$$

$$\text{therefore } (18 - x)\,(\text{hr}) \neq (18 + x)\,(\text{hr})$$

The distances are different. But the tidal speed is the same, and the time is the same. What is the time?

$$\text{speed} = \frac{\text{distance}}{\text{time}}$$

$$\text{therefore } \text{time} = \frac{\text{distance}}{\text{speed}}$$

We have the distance. We have the speed. We know that time = time. So

$$\frac{8}{(18 - x)} = \frac{15}{(18 + x)}$$

$$8x + 144 = 270 - 15x$$

(See page 58 for algebraic mechanics.)

$$x = 5.48 \text{ mi/hr} \quad (\text{the tide speed})$$

Thus $18 - 5.48 = 12.52^*$ mi/hr effective speed against tide
and $18 + 5.48 = 23.48^*$ mi/hr effective speed with tide

$$\frac{15 \text{ mi}}{23.48 \dfrac{\text{mi}}{\text{hr}}} = 0.64 \text{ hr}$$

$$\frac{8 \text{ mi}}{12.52 \dfrac{\text{mi}}{\text{hr}}} = 0.64 \text{ hr}$$

We seem to be able to prove that the tidal speed must be 5.48 mi/hr.

---

*We have again neglected the niceties of significant figures.

EXAMPLE 4-19

Suppose that 4 years ago Wallie was 12 times as old as Willie. In 16 years Wallie will be twice Willie's age. How old are Wallie and Willie at this moment?

Let x = Willie's age
and $12x$ = Wallie's age

Do you see the flaw? These were the ages 4 years ago. So $x + 16$ could not equal $2(12x + 16)$. Instead,

let x = Willie's present age
    y = Wallie's present age

Four years ago Wallie was 12 times Willie's age, so

$(y - 4) = 12(x - 4)$

In 16 years Wallie will be twice Willie's age, so

$(y + 16) = 2(x + 16)$

Or $y - 4 = 12x - 48$
       $y + 16 = 2x + 32$

Subtracting the second equation from the first to eliminate y (see page 59 for solution of simultaneous linear equations), we find

$-20 = 10x - 80$
$-10x = -60$
   $x = 6$

Then, substituting in one of the equations (let's arbitrarily use the first one), we find

$y - 4 = (12 \times 6) - 48$
   $y = 24 + 4$
   $y = 28$

Wallie is now 28 and Willie 6. We could have done this problem with just one unknown, but we wanted to show the thought involved in working with two unknowns.

BRIEF REVIEW OF THE MECHANICS OF ALGEBRA

Simple Operations

1. Algebraic addition: Add up the figures with like signs, find the difference, and affix the sign of the larger sum.

23 + (+29) + (−33) + (−99) = ?

The difference between +52 and −132 is −80.

2. Algebraic subtraction: Mentally change the sign of the subtrahend (the figure to be subtracted) and proceed as in addition.

+42 − (−27) becomes +42 + (+27) = 69
+42 − (+27) becomes +42 + (−27) = 15

3. Multiplication and division of signed quantities: Multiplication or division of quantities with like signs gives a product or quotient with a plus (+) sign. Multiplication or division of quantities with unlike signs gives a product or quotient with a minus (−) sign.

$+2 \times +4 = +8 \qquad +2 \times -4 = -8$
$-2 \times -4 = +8$
$$\frac{+8}{+2} = +4 \qquad \frac{-8}{+2} = -4$$
$$\frac{-8}{-2} = +4$$

Use of Parentheses, Brackets, and Braces

1. In the expression 2(4 + 9), the 2 applies to everything inside the parentheses. This expression means

2(13) = 26   or   (2 × 4) + (2 × 9) = 26

2. In the expression 3{4(16 + 8) − 5[8 − (−9)]}
   a. The 4 applies to everything inside the first pair of parentheses:

   4(16 + 8) = 4(24) = 96

   b. The 5 applies to everything inside the brackets:

   5[8 − (−9)] = 5(17) = 85

   c. The 3 applies to everything inside the braces:

   3{4(16 + 8) − 5[8 − (−9)]} = 3[4(24) − 5(17)]
   $$= 3(96 - 85) = 3(11) = 33$$

Addition and Subtraction Across Equal Signs

1. Give a + b = c, obviously,

   a = c − b

   You apparently changed the sign on b on crossing the equation sign; you really subtracted b from both sides. The +b and −b on the left canceled one another out.

2. Now look at this:

$$e - f = g$$
$$e = g + f$$

You really added f to both sides.

3. Now solve for x in this setup:

$$x + \frac{c}{(a^2 - b)} = \frac{d}{(a^2 - b)}$$

$$x = \frac{d}{(a^2 - b)} - \frac{c}{(a^2 - b)}$$

You subtracted $c/(a^2 - b)$ from both sides.

Simplifying Expressions

1. $2a = 3b$: To express a most simply in terms of b, it is necessary to eliminate the 2. To do this, divide both numerators by 2 and cancel.

$$\frac{2a}{2} = \frac{3b}{2}$$

$$a = \frac{3b}{2}$$

2. $\frac{c}{3} = d$: To express c in terms of the other factors—that is, to get c alone, not $\frac{1}{3}c$—multiply both numerators by 3 and cancel.

$$\frac{3c}{3} = 3d$$

$$c = 3d$$

3. $\frac{2e}{3} = f$: To express e in terms of the other factors, both the 2 and the 3 must be eliminated. Divide both sides of the equation by 2, multiply both sides of the equation by 3, and cancel.

$$\frac{3 \times 2e}{2 \times 3} = \frac{3f}{2}$$

$$e = \frac{3f}{2}$$

4. $\frac{gh}{i} = \frac{j}{kl}$: To express g in terms of everything else, divide both sides of the equation by h, multiply both sides by i, and cancel suitably. Then

$$g = \frac{ij}{hkl}$$

5. $\dfrac{\frac{m}{n}}{o} = pq$ There is more than one way to get the expression for m in terms of everything else because this equation includes a complex fraction.

   a. Multiply both sides of the equation by the fraction n/o and cancel suitably.

$$\dfrac{\frac{m \times n}{n \times o}}{o} = \dfrac{pq \times n}{o} \quad \text{gives} \quad m = \dfrac{pqn}{o}$$

   b. Multiply or divide as needed to get a simple fraction and then further simplify. This is obviously less efficient than method a.

     (1) Multiply both sides of the main fraction line on the left by o:

$$\dfrac{\frac{m \times o}{n \times o}}{o} = pq \quad \text{gives} \quad \dfrac{mo}{n} = pq \quad \text{gives} \quad m = \dfrac{pqn}{o}$$

Note which o's were canceled. Canceling the topmost and bottommost o's would be a gross error. You would be dividing the numerator of the main fraction but the denominator of a different fraction. These are surely dissimilar operations.

     (2) Divide the numerators on both sides of the equation by o:

$$\dfrac{\frac{m}{n \times o}}{o} = \dfrac{pq}{o} \quad \text{gives} \quad \dfrac{m}{n} = \dfrac{pq}{o} \quad \text{gives} \quad m = \dfrac{pqn}{o}$$

6. Application to more complicated equations.

   a. Consider the expression $2 + 4/8 = 2.5$. If you want this without any fraction, you have to eliminate the 8. Suppose you did this.

$$2 + \dfrac{4 \times 8}{8} = 2.5 \times 8$$

Then $2 + 4 = 20$, but $6 \neq 20$. You multiplied on both sides; what is wrong? You did not really multiply both sides. You multiplied all of one side and only part of the other side. The correct operation is

$$\left(2 + \dfrac{4}{8}\right) \times 8 = 2.5 \times 8$$
$$(2 \times 8) + \dfrac{4 \times 8}{8} = 2.5 \times 8$$
$$16 + 4 = 20$$

   b. Put this in nonfractional form:

$$17x + \dfrac{12}{x} = 100 \qquad 17x^2 + \dfrac{12x}{x} = 100x \qquad 17x^2 + 12 = 100x$$

c. Now simplify this one:

$$88 + \frac{180}{(35 + 55)} = 90$$

$$88(35 + 55) + \frac{180(35 + 55)}{(35 + 55)} = 90\,(35 + 55)$$

$$88(35 + 55) + 180 = 90(90)$$

$$7920 + 180 = 8100$$

Naturally, you would never have worked with $180(35 + 55)$; you would have called it $180/90$ or 2, but we're interested in the technique here.

d. Simplify this:

$$x + \frac{7}{a + b} = z$$

$$x(a + b) + \frac{7(a + b)}{(a + b)} = z(a + b)$$

$$x(a + b) + 7 = z(a + b)$$

e. Solve for x here:

$$x(r^2 - j) = dg$$

$$\frac{x(r^2 - j)}{(r^2 - j)} = \frac{dg}{(r^2 - j)}$$

$$x = \frac{dg}{(r^2 - j)}$$

Check: Let $x = 8$, $r = 3$, $j = 2$, $d = 8$, $g = 7$.* Then

$$8 = \frac{8 \times 7}{9 - 2} = \frac{56}{7} = 8$$

f. Solve for x here:

$$x(r^2 - j) + c = ef$$

$$\frac{x(r^2 - j) + c}{(r^2 - j)} = \frac{ef}{(r^2 - j)}$$

or

$$\frac{x(r^2 - j)}{(r^2 - j)} + \frac{c}{(r^2 - j)} = \frac{ef}{(r^2 - j)}$$

---

*In order to have a means of checking changes we arbitrarily chose 8, 3, and 2 for x, r, and j. Use of these values gave us 56 as a product of dg. We then arbitrarily took 7 as the value for g, giving us 8 for d.

Which is right? Check with numbers. Let x, r, j, and c arbitrarily equal 2, 3, 1, and 32, respectively, making ef equal 48. Let $e = 12$, making $f = 4$.

$$2(8) + 32 = 48$$
$$\frac{2(8) + 32}{8} = \frac{48}{8}$$
$$\frac{16 + 32}{8} = \frac{48}{8}$$
$$6 = 6$$

and
$$\frac{2(8)}{8} + \frac{32}{8} = \frac{48}{8}$$
$$2 + 4 = 6$$
$$6 = 6$$

Obviously, each above is correct. Proceed as usual.

Two Unknowns (or Simultaneous Linear Equations)

1. Find x and y if

$$x + y = 7$$
$$x - y = 3$$

You have no doubt already made the correct guess here, but we want to illustrate procedures.

a. Add the equations:

$$x + y = 7$$
$$\underline{x - y = 3}$$
$$2x = 10 \quad (+ y - y = 0)$$
$$x = 5$$

Then $5 + y = 7$ or $5 - y = 3$
$$y = 7 - 5 \qquad -y = 3 - 5$$
$$y = 2 \qquad -y = -2$$
$$y = 2$$

b. Subtract the equations:

$$x + y = 7$$
$$\underline{x - y = 3}$$
$$2y = 4$$
$$y = 2$$

Then $x + 2 = 7$ or $x - 2 = 3$
$$x = 7 - 2 \qquad x = 3 + 2$$
$$x = 5 \qquad x = 5$$

c. Substitute one unknown for the other:
From $x + y = 7$ you get $x = 7 - y$. Then, using $x - y = 3$, you write

$$(7 - y) - y = 3$$
$$7 - 2y = 3$$
$$-2y = 3 - 7$$
$$-y = -2$$
$$y = 2$$

2. Now suppose you had this set of equations:

$$3x + y = 34$$
$$x + 2y = 23$$

These equations cannot be added or subtracted in their present form to eliminate one unknown. (You can, of course, substitute the value of one unknown in terms of the other unknown in one of the equations.) But there is another way. Multiply the first equation by 2, and then subtract the second equation from the first.

$$6x + 2y = 68$$
$$\underline{x + 2y = 23}$$
$$5x = 45$$
$$x = 9$$

If $x = 9$, then from $x + 2y = 23$ we get

$$9 + 2y = 23$$
$$y = \frac{23 - 9}{2} = 7$$

You could have done any number of multiplications followed by suitable additions or subtractions to get a single unknown.

A Quadratic Equation in One Unknown

An equation such as $x^2 + 3x = 19$ is a classic quadratic equation in one unknown. It is generally given in the form $ax^2 + bx + c = 0$. A quadratic equation is solved by finding the values of x that satisfy the equation. Such values are called the *solutions* or *roots* of the equation. For example, $x^2 + 9 = 0$ has these roots: $x = +3$, $x = -3$. There are various methods of solving a quadratic equation, among them completing the square, factoring, using a graph, and solving by formula. We regret having to ignore the first three methods and present only the last one, the least interesting one, and it without any theory, because of the limitations of space.

The formula for solving quadratic equations is

$$x = \frac{-b \pm \sqrt{b^2 - 4ac}}{2a}$$

a, b, and c are taken from the general equation: $ax^2 + bx + c = 0$. An equation such as $+90x - x^2 - 1400 = 0$ presents an obvious difficulty. What is the square root of $-x^2$? In such a case just change the sign of everything to get $-90x + x^2 + 1400 = 0$. You have not changed anything really by doing this. Consider these examples:

$$12 = 8 + 4 \quad \text{and} \quad -12 = -8 + (-4)$$
$$+12 - (+12) = 0 \qquad -12 - (-12) = 0$$
$$+12 + (-12) = 0 \qquad -12 + (+12) = 0$$

Find the values of x in the equation $x^2 - 4x = 32$.

First, rearrange the equation into the general form for convenience:
$x^2 - 4x - 32 = 0$.*

$$x = \frac{-(-4) \pm \sqrt{4^2 - 4[1(-32)]}}{2 \times 1}$$

$$= \frac{4 \pm \sqrt{144}}{2}$$

$$= \frac{4 + 12}{2} = 8 \quad \text{and} \quad \frac{4 - 12}{2} = -4$$

Thus x in this particular equation has roots of $+8$ and -4. You can also say that x has two solutions: $+8$ and -4.

In some cases you will have to choose a root. There are examples of this in Chapter 27, "Equilibrium," where many problems have to be solved by quadratic equation. The following generalizations should prove useful in choosing roots:

If $b^2 - 4ac > 0$, the roots are real and unequal (as they were in the preceding problem).

If $b^2 - 4ac = 0$, the roots are real and equal (for example, in $x^2 + 6x + 9$, x is equal to $+3$ and only to $+3$).

If $b^2 - 4ac < 0$, the roots of the equation are imaginary.

---

*You might want to review the chapters on logarithms and slide rule if you have forgotten how to find a square root.

PROBLEMS

Translate these problems into algebraic expressions. The problems have deliberately been phrased in less than straightforward English to provide practice in interpreting problems, to provide the necessity of making assumptions. Not all problems have enough information to provide a numerical answer. Identify such problems and indicate what additional information would be needed to find a numerical answer.

1. Put the following statements into algebraic form.

    a. A box weighed 5 lb when empty and 40 lb when filled with an unknown number of steel spheres. Find the weight of each sphere.

    b. N is 3 times as old as M and 20 years younger than R. Express the age of M in terms of N's age. In terms of R's age.

    c. J is 7 times as heavy as K. L is 1/3 as heavy as J. Find the weights of J and L.

    d. S gained weight 3 times as fast as T, and U gained weight 0.7 times as fast as T. Find the weight gains for S and U after a given interval.

    e. Two years ago D was half as heavy as E. D is now 16 times as heavy as E. Over the past 2 years E's weight has quadrupled. Find the weights of D and E now and 2 years ago.

    f. A rectangle increased its length 4 times as much as its width. The area was then 800 ft². Find the new and old perimeters, the old area.

2. Check your setup for problem 1b. Suppose R is now 30. Find the ages of N and M. Obviously this can be done with simple arithmetic. Check your algebraic expressions.

3. Suppose the ages of N, M, and R (problem 1b) add up to 50 years. Find the ages of N, M, and R.

4. In problem 1d suppose that S, T, and U each weigh 25 lb. What would S and U weigh at the end of a year if T then weighed 100 lb?

5. Suppose S, T, and U (problem 1d) weighed 25, 30, and 35 lb, respectively, at a given time. After an interval their total weight was 1030 lb. Find the weights of S, T, and U at the end of this interval.

6. In problem 1e, suppose that E now weighs 100 lb.

    a. Find the weight of D now and D's and E's weights 2 years ago.

    b. Find the amount by which D's weight increased in 2 years.

7. A square tripled its dimensions. It then had an area of 50 ft². Find the original dimensions. (See Chapters 6 and 7 for methods of finding square roots if necessary.)

8. What amounts of $5.00/lb and $1.00/lb materials should be mixed to give 100 lb of a product to be sold for $228?

9. What increase in length and width must occur if a rug measuring 50 × 70 ft is to fit an area of 4000 ft^2 if for every foot increase in length there must be an 8-ft increase in width?

10. At 20.0°C, 1.00 liter of benzene weighs 879 g and 1.00 liter of acetone weighs 791 g. What weights of benzene and acetone must be used to make exactly 1.00 liter of benzene-acetone solution that will weigh 825 g. (Assume no volume change on mixing.)

5

EXPONENTIAL QUANTITIES

An exponent is the power to which one quantity must be raised to equal yet another quantity. In the following table the 4 in 10^4 and the 1 in 10^{-1} etc. are exponents.

Table 5–1   Some Powers of 10

$10^4 = 10,000$	$10^0 = 1*$	$10^{-1} = 0.1$
$10^3 = 1,000$		$10^{-2} = 0.01$
$10^2 = 100$		$10^{-3} = 0.001$
$10^1 = 10$		$10^{-4} = 0.0001$

*Any number to the zero power is equal to 1.

EXPONENTIAL NOTATION

Numbers such as 1,250,000 and 0.00069 are often expressed in exponential form, that is, as a product of two numbers, one of which is an integer power of 10.

EXAMPLE 5–1

1,250,000 could be expressed exponentially in the following ways:

$$1{,}250{,}000 = 1250 \quad \times \quad 1{,}000 = 1250 \quad \times 10^3$$
$$= \ 125 \quad \times \quad 10{,}000 = \ 125 \quad \times 10^4$$
$$= \ 12.5 \quad \times \ 100{,}000 = \ 12.5 \quad \times 10^5$$
$$= \ 1.25 \ \times \ 1{,}000{,}000 = \ 1.25 \ \times 10^6$$
$$= \ 0.125 \times 10{,}000{,}000 = \ 0.125 \times 10^7$$

All of the forms on the right are in exponential notation, but one of them, 1.25×10^6, is also in scientific notation, perhaps the most common form of exponential notation.

SCIENTIFIC NOTATION

A number expressed in scientific notation has the form

$$M \times 10^n$$

where M is a number between 1 and 10 (that is, a number in which there is only one digit to the left of the decimal point), and n is the power to which 10 must be raised.

EXAMPLE 5–2

$$250 \quad = 2.5 \times 100 \quad = 2.5 \times 10^2$$
$$25 \quad = 2.5 \times \ 10 \quad = 2.5 \times 10^1$$
$$2.5 \quad = 2.5 \times \quad 1 \quad = 2.5 \times 10^0$$
$$0.25 \quad = 2.5 \times \quad 0.1 \quad = 2.5 \times 10^{-1}$$
$$0.025 \ = 2.5 \times \quad 0.01 \ = 2.5 \times 10^{-2}$$
$$0.0025 = 2.5 \times \quad 0.001 = 2.5 \times 10^{-3}$$

Each expression on the right is in scientific notation.

You have probably noticed a quick way to convert a given number into scientific notation. For a number greater than one, the power to which 10 must be raised is one less than the number of digits to the left of the decimal point. For a number less than one, the negative power of 10 is the number of the first place to the right of the decimal point in which a digit other than zero appears.

MATHEMATICAL OPERATIONS INVOLVING EXPONENTIAL NUMBERS

Addition and Subtraction

In order to add or subtract exponential numbers, each number must be expressed to the same power and referred to the same base. For example, 10^2 is the base 10 raised to the second power. You can add or subtract 5×10^2 and 40×10^2 or 0.5×10^3 and 4×10^3, but you cannot add or subtract 5×10^2 and 4×10^3.

Multiplication and Division

In multiplication the exponents are added algebraically. In division they are subtracted algebraically.

EXAMPLE 5–3

$$100 \quad \times 1000 \quad = 100{,}000 \qquad 10^2 \times 10^3 = 10^5$$
$$0.01 \times \quad 0.001 = \quad 0.00001 \qquad 10^{-2} \times 10^{-3} = 10^{-5}$$
$$1000 \quad \times \quad 0.1 \quad = \quad 100 \qquad 10^3 \times 10^{-1} = 10^2$$

$$\frac{100{,}000}{100} = 1{,}000 \qquad \frac{10^5}{10^2} = 10^3$$

$$\frac{0.001}{0.01} = 0.1 \qquad \frac{10^{-3}}{10^{-2}} = 10^{-1}$$

$$\frac{0.01}{0.001} = 10 \qquad \frac{10^{-2}}{10^{-3}} = 10^1$$

$$\frac{0.1}{100} = 0.001 \qquad \frac{10^{-1}}{10^2} = 10^{-3}$$

$$\frac{100}{0.1} = 1{,}000 \qquad \frac{10^2}{10^{-1}} = 10^3$$

Nonexponential figures are handled in an ordinary arithmetical fashion.

EXAMPLE 5–4

$$24 \times 10^{-9} \times 2 \times 10^{11} = 48 \times 10^2 = 4.8 \times 10^3$$

$$\frac{24 \times 10^{-9}}{2 \times 10^{11}} = 12 \times 10^{-20} = 1.2 \times 10^{-19}$$

$$\frac{7.3 \times 10^3 \times 1.8 \times 10^{-4}}{2.5 \times 10^{-7}} = 5.4 \times 10^6$$

SHIFTING THE DECIMAL POINT

Each shift of the decimal point one place to the right involves multiplication by 10, that is, by 10^1.

EXAMPLE 5–5

$6.6 \times 10 = 66$ or $6.6 \times 10^0 \times 10^1 = 6.6 \times 10^1$

$0.66 \times 10 = 6.6$ or $6.6 \times 10^{-1} \times 10^1 = 6.6 \times 10^0$

Each shift of the decimal point one place to the left involves division by 10.

EXAMPLE 5–6

$\dfrac{66}{10} = 6.6$ or $\dfrac{66 \times 10^0}{10^1} = 66 \times 10^{-1}$ or 6.6×10^0

$\dfrac{6.6}{10} = 0.66$ or $\dfrac{6.6 \times 10^0}{10^1} = 6.6 \times 10^{-1}$

These techniques can be applied to put any exponential figure into scientific notation.

EXAMPLE 5–7

$660 \times 10^9 = 6.60 \times 10^2 \times 10^9 = 6.60 \times 10^{11}$

$660 \times 10^{-9} = 6.60 \times 10^2 \times 10^{-9} = 6.60 \times 10^{-7}$

$0.0660 \times 10^9 = 6.60 \times 10^{-2} \times 10^9 = 6.60 \times 10^7$

$0.0660 \times 10^{-9} = 6.60 \times 10^{-2} \times 10^{-9} = 6.60 \times 10^{-11}$

In each case nothing is actually changed. In the first equation, for example, 660 was divided by 10^2 and 10^9 was simultaneously multiplied by 10^2. There is only an apparent change, a change in form. For each move of the decimal point to the right the exponent increases by 1, reflecting the multiplication by 10. For each move of the decimal point to the left the exponent decreases by 1, reflecting the division by 10. Obviously, 10^3 is greater than 10^2, but it is easy to forget that 10^{-2} is greater than 10^{-3}.

A FEW OTHER ASPECTS OF EXPONENTIAL FIGURES

1. $(2^2)^3$ is the same as 2^6.

$(4)^3 = 64$ and $2 \times 2 \times 2 \times 2 \times 2 \times 2 = 64$

Therefore the form $(N^a)^b$ must be the same as N^{ab}. Note that this is *a* times *b*, not *a* plus *b*.

2. $(2 \times 3)^2$ is the same as $2^2 \times 3^2$.

$6^2 = 36$ and $4 \times 9 = 36$

3. $(6/2)^2$ is the same as $6^2/2^2$.

$3^2 = 9$ and $\dfrac{36}{4} = 9$

4. The form $8^{2/3}$ is the same as $\sqrt[3]{8^2}$

5. Exponents can also be used with words, for example, 5 miles hour^{-1} (or mi hr^{-1}). Notations of this sort often confuse students. But $1/10^2 = 10^{-2}$ (that is, 1/100 does equal 0.01), does it not? Similarly, 5 mi/hr can just as well be written 5 mi hr^{-1}.

PROBLEMS

1. Express each of the following in scientific notation.
   a. 6,800,000
   b. 7200
   c. 7020
   d. 7002
   e. 7000
   f. 22.9
   g. 16
   h. 3.8
   i. 0.05
   j. 0.005
   k. 1.005
   l. 0.008
   m. 0.00803
   n. 6

2. Express each of the following in arithmetical form.
   a. 5×10^3
   b. 6.2×10^3
   c. 6.02×10^3
   d. 4.3×10^1
   e. 4.3×10^0
   f. 9×10^{-4}
   g. 9.1×10^{-3}

3. Express each of the following in scientific notation.
   a. 75×10^3
   b. 781×10^9
   c. 0.5×10^6
   d. 0.008×10^4
   e. 0.00005×10^6
   f. 481×10^{-5}
   g. 69×10^{-7}
   h. 0.7×10^{-4}
   i. 0.00092×10^{-7}
   j. 392×10^{-8}
   k. 481×10^{-2}
   l. 14.8×10^{-1}
   m. 148×10^{-1}
   n. 1995×10^{-4}
   o. 759×10^2
   p. 0.00821×10^3

6

THE SLIDE RULE

There is no trick to learning to use the slide rule beyond accurate reading of the scales. Once the reading of just one scale has been mastered, it is a simple matter to learn to read the other scales, and it is then just as simple to learn to multiply and divide.

READING THE SCALES

Find the D scale on your slide rule (Figure 6-1). Notice the large numerals 1, 2, 3, 4, 5, 6, 7, 8, 9, and 1 that appear at progressively smaller intervals from left to right. In locating a number on the slide rule you need consider only the digit sequence, not the magnitude of the number. Any number beginning with 1, no matter how large or small it is, is located between the large 1 and the large 2 on the scale. Any number beginning with 2 is located between the large 2 and the large 3, and so on.

Now look at the portion of the scale between the large 1 and the large 2. There are ten subdivisions indicated by small numerals 1, 2, 3, etc. Any number between 10 and 11 (for example, 108—remember we said only digit sequence, not size of the number, need be considered) is located between the large 1 and the small 1. Similarly, any number between 15 and 16 (such as 153) is between the small 5 and the small 6.

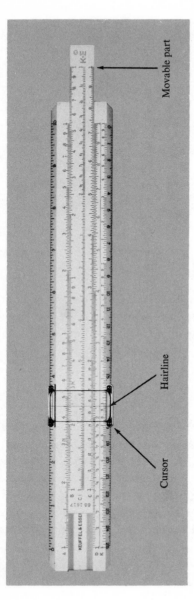

Figure 6-1

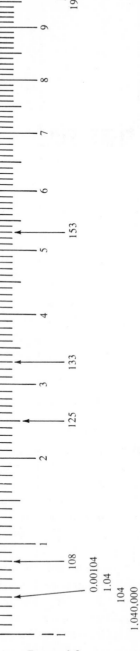

Courtesy of Keuffel & Esser Company

Figure 6-2

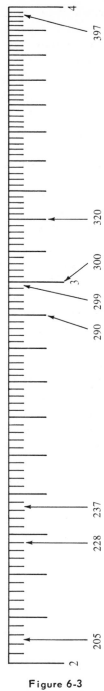

Figure 6-3

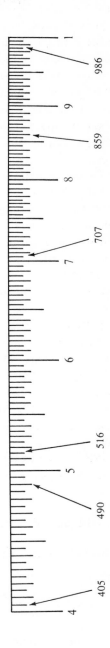

Figure 6-4

Now notice that between the small numerals just mentioned there are still smaller divisions. The lines are unnumbered, but the middle one (5) is slightly longer than the others. The third digit of a number beginning with 1 is located on these lines. The relative magnitude of a number has nothing to do with its location, as we have said before, but this bears repeating because students cannot quite believe this at first. Thus, 0.00104 is in exactly the same place as 1.04, 104, 1,040,000, etc., that is, at the fourth short line to the right of the large numeral 1. In each case the digit sequence was 104, as shown on Figure 6-2. Now locate 133, 153, 108, 198, and 125 on your slide rule. Check your readings against Figure 6-2.

Now concentrate your attention between large 2 and large 3 on the D scale. Notice that there are ten major unnumbered divisions between 2 and 3; the lines correspond to 21, 22, 23, etc. Between each two of these lines there are five small divisions. Reading each successive line to the right of large 2, you would read 202, 204, 206, 208, 210 (the first major line), 212, etc. Now locate 299, 237, 205, 228, and 290. Compare your locations with Figure 6-3. The decimal point still has nothing to do with the location on the scale. The same system is used between large 3 and large 4. Locate 300, 320, and 397 and again compare with Figure 6-3.

In the space between large 4 and large 5 you find ten smaller unnumbered divisions, which represent 41, 42, 43, etc., but these are separated by only one shorter line. The lines beginning at large 4 are read 400, 405, 410, 415, 420, etc. You can readily estimate the position of a number such as 417. This system also applies between 5 and 6, between 6 and 7, and so on to the end of scale. Locate 405, 490, 516, 707, 859, and 986 (Figure 6-4).

Needless to say, all numbers must be located exactly on the scales, and all alignments must be exact.

USING THE SLIDE RULE

Simple Multiplication

EXAMPLE 6–1

$2 \times 3 = 6$

1. Slide the hairline over 2 on D.
2. Slide the *index* (the large 1 on the C scale) under the hairline.
3. Slide the hairline to 3 on C.
4. Read the answer under the hairline on D (Figure 6-5).

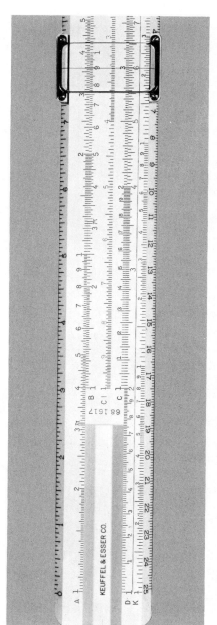

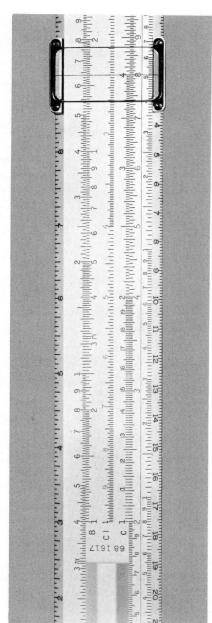

Courtesy of Keuffel & Esser Company

Figure 6-5

Figure 6-6

EXAMPLE 6–2

$2 \times 9 = 18$

For step 3 you find 9 out in thin air. In such cases, slide the right-hand index under the hairline in step 2, and then proceed with steps 3 and 4.

Simple Division

EXAMPLE 6–3 (Figure 6-6)

$\dfrac{8}{4} = 2$ (8 is the dividend; 4 is the divisor; 2 is the quotient)

1. Put the hairline over the dividend on D.
2. Slide the divisor on C under the hairline.
3. Read the quotient on D below the index.

Multiplication of Several Numbers

EXAMPLE 6–4

$8 \times 3 \times 7 = 168$

1. Slide the hairline over 8 on D.
2. Slide the index under the hairline.
3. Move the hairline to 3 on C.

The answer to 8×3 appears under the hairline on D, and this is the number you must multiply by 7. In multiplying you put the hairline over the number on D to be multiplied, and that is where your hairline is now, so—

4. Slide the index under the hairline.
5. Slide the hairline to 7 on C.
6. Read the answer on D under the hairline.

You could continue this process indefinitely depending upon the number of numbers to be multiplied together.

Division by More Than One Number

EXAMPLE 6–5

$\dfrac{2}{8 \times 6} = 0.0417$

1. Slide the hairline over 2 on D.
2. Slide 8 on C under the hairline.

Your quotient is below the index on D, but you want to divide further. Your dividend for the next division, which must be on D under the hairline, is already below the index.

3. Slide the hairline over the index.
4. Slide 6 on C under the hairline.
5. Read the final answer on D below the index.

You have been given a cumbersome method here, but it seems to be the easiest to learn. Once you know how to use the slide rule, you will find it very easy to play with and will discover simpler methods of using it. Then, too, most slide rule direction booklets give more sophisticated methods.

Multiplication and Division by Several Numbers in the Same Problem

EXAMPLE 6-6

$$\frac{7 \times 9 \times 16}{30 \times 17}$$

You can solve problems such as this one by finding the numerator product and the denominator product (the divisor) separately and then dividing. Or you can find the numerator product and then divide by 30 and 17 in sequence. We will divide 7 by 30, multiply by 9, divide again by 17, and finally multiply by 16, to illustrate still another approach (perhaps the least simple).

1. Slide the hairline over 7 on D.
2. Slide 30 on C under the hairline.
3. Move the hairline over the index.
4. Slide the right-hand index under the hairline; then slide the hairline to 9 on C.
5. Slide 17 on C under the hairline.
6. Slide the hairline to 16 on C.
7. Read the answer under the hairline on D.

The answer would seem to be 1.98 (not in significant figures).

Estimation of Answer

How does one know the magnitude of the answer? One makes an educated guess by looking at the numbers involved and then uses the slide rule to find the exact number.

EXAMPLE 6-7

a. $\dfrac{2859.9}{12.9}$ is equal to approximately $\dfrac{3000}{13}$

3000/13 is somewhere around 200 (certainly not 20 or 2000). The slide rule gives the digit sequence. The exact answer is 222.

b. 48×0.0895 is equal to approximately 50×0.1.

50×0.1 would be about 5; the slide rule answer is 4.3.

Most slide rule setups in practical use are a little more complicated than the preceding examples. The method to be presented now is tiresome at first, but it soon becomes automatic and "mental" with practice.

EXAMPLE 6–8

$$\frac{785 \times 1500 \times 0.04}{159 \times 1700 \times 6000}$$

Convert to *approximate* powers of 10.

$$\frac{8 \times 10^2 \times 1.5 \times 10^3 \times 4 \times 10^{-2}}{1.6 \times 10^2 \times 1.7 \times 10^3 \times 6 \times 10^3}$$

Gather the arithmetical part and cancel.

$$\frac{8 \times 1.5 \times 4}{1.6 \times 1.7 \times 6} = \text{approximately } 3$$

Now go back and take care of the powers of 10.

$$\frac{10^2 \times 10^3 \times 10^{-2}}{10^2 \times 10^3 \times 10^3} = \frac{10^3}{10^8} = 10^{-5}$$

Now you know the answer is approximately 3×10^{-5}. The slide rule digit sequence is 291, making the answer 2.91×10^{-5}.

Suppose you had estimated that an answer would be 1×10^8, but the slide rule gave you 998. You would know that the answer was 9.98×10^7, since this figure would be very close to 10×10^7, which is 1×10^8; 9.98×10^8 would be tenfold off. You similarly would make adjustments if your answer seemed to be 1×10^{-8} and the slide rule gave 998. Here the adjustment would naturally be in the opposite direction. The answer would have to be 9.98×10^{-9}. This is very close to 10×10^{-9}, which is equal to 1×10^{-8}.

Square Roots and Squares

To find square roots and squares, use the A and D scales. Note that the A scale is not divided in the same way that the D scale is and that each half of the A scale has the same marks and numerals.

EXAMPLE 6–9

a. Place the hairline over 4 on the left side of the A scale. Read 2 under the hairline on D. You know the square root of 4 is 2. Voilà!

b. Place the hairline over the right-hand 25 on the A scale; read 5 on D under the hairline. $\sqrt{25} = 5$ (Figure 6-7).

c. Place the hairline over 144 on the left A scale; read 12 on D under the hairline. $\sqrt{144} = 12$.

d. Place the hairline over 2025 on the right A scale; read 45 under the hairline on D. $\sqrt{2025} = 45$.

By now you must have concluded that the left side of the A scale is used to find the square root of a number with an odd number of digits to the left of the decimal point and the right side of the scale to find the square root of a number with an even number of digits on the left of the decimal point. Now suppose you want to find the square root of 0.09. You know it is 0.3. To find the square root of a decimal number, point off two places at a time to the right of the decimal point. If zero is the first digit to the right of the decimal, it is not counted. Therefore 0.09 is considered a one-digit number, and you use the left side of the A scale. For 0.90 you would look on the right side of the A scale. To find the square root of 0.144 you first point off by pairs and fill in the empty space with zero. The figure to deal with is 0.1440. Thus you look at the right side of the scale in this case to get a square root of about 0.38.

To square a number, place the hairline over it on the D scale. Read its square under the hairline on the A scale.

Cube Roots and Cubes

Locate the K scale and notice that it is really three identical scales one after the other.

EXAMPLE 6–10

a. Put the hairline over 8 on the extreme left K scale; read 2 on D under the hairline (Figure 6-8).

b. Put the hairline over 27 on the middle K scale; read 3 under the hairline on D.

c. Put the hairline over 125 on the extreme right K scale; read 5 on D under the hairline.

The numbers 2, 3, and 5 are the cube roots of 8, 27, and 125, respectively.

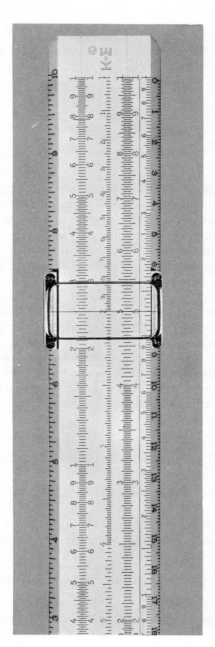

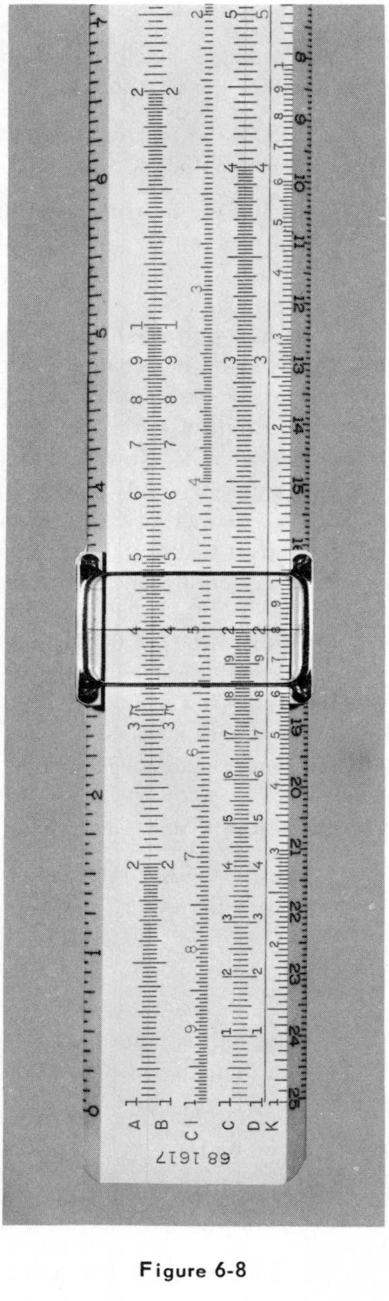

Courtesy of Keuffel & Esser Company

Figure 6-7

Figure 6-8

You use the left K scale for numbers with 1, 4, 7, etc., digits to the left of the decimal point, the middle K for numbers with 2, 5, 8, etc., digits to the left of the decimal point, and the right K scale for numbers with 3, 6, 9, etc., such digits.

To cube a number, place the hairline over it on D. Read its cube under the hairline on K.

PROBLEMS

Estimate each answer first; then use the slide rule to obtain the actual answer.

1. 3×7

2. 98×6

3. 43×8

4. 39×21

5. 76×17

6. 317×8

7. 839×7

8. 839×11

9. $6.29 \times 781,000$

10. 0.00117×609

11. $14 \times 41.5 \times 9.98$

12. 0.332×2156

13. $\dfrac{72}{6}$

14. $\dfrac{490}{52}$

15. $\dfrac{83}{129}$

16. $\dfrac{0.0297}{803}$

17. $\dfrac{93}{0.000338}$

18. $\dfrac{142}{685}$

19. $\dfrac{68 \times 23.5}{95}$

20. $\sqrt[3]{\dfrac{73}{605 \times 0.0259}}$

21. $\sqrt{\dfrac{73}{605 \times 0.0259}}$

22. $\dfrac{843 \times 2.09 \times 0.0031}{43.5}$

23. $\dfrac{22.4 \times 735 \times 245 \times 81.5}{760 \times 215}$

24. 16^2 $(16)^2$

25. $(253)^2$

26. $(8)^3$

27. $(29)^3$

28. Find the square root of each of the following:
a. 9
b. 63.6

28. **c.** 295

   d. 6810

29. Find the cube root of each number in problem 28.

30. $\dfrac{381 \times 69}{81 \times 0.08}$

31. $\dfrac{4^3 \times 0.016}{75 \times 0.59}$

7

LOGARITHMS

The *logarithm* of a number is the power to which another number, called a *base*, must be raised to equal the first number. For example,

$10^2 = 100$ (exponential form)

Read this equation as the base 10 raised to the second power equals the number 100. With 10 as the base, the exponent, 2, is the logarithm, and the logarithm of 100 is 2. Now re-read the definition just given and see whether it makes more sense.

We could also have written this as

$2 = \log_{10} 100$ (logarithmic form)

Here 2 is the logarithm, and it is the logarithm of the number 100 to the base 10.

This material can be written in a general form by replacing the logarithm (2) with x, the base (10) with b, and the number (100) with N;

$b^x = N$ (exponential form)
$x = \log_b N$ (logarithmic form)

It would be rather surprising if you didn't find this a bit confusing at first. Keep before you the symbol form and an example in nonhostile numbers.

EXAMPLE 7-1

Exponential form	Logarithmic form
$5^2 = 25$	$2 = \log_5 25$
$2^3 = 8$	$3 = \log_2 8$
$\left(\dfrac{1}{2}\right)^4 = \dfrac{1}{16}$	$4 = \log_{1/2} \dfrac{1}{16}$
$x^y = z$	$y = \log_x z$

Here 2, 3, 4, and y are logarithms (exponents), which are represented by symbol x in the general model; 5, 2, $\frac{1}{2}$, and x are bases, which are represented by symbol b in the general model. 25, 8, 1/16, and z are the numbers—symbol N in the general model—of which the exponents are the logarithms.

Operations Involving Logarithms

Since logarithms are exponents, the facts presented in Chapter 5 on exponential figures should be valid here too.

1. The logarithm of the product of two numbers equals the sum of the logarithms of the two numbers.

   a. $2^3 = 8$ and $2^4 = 16$

$$8 \times 16 = 128$$
$$2^{3+4} = 2^7 = 128$$

   b. $10^3 = 1000$ and $10^2 = 100$

$$1000 \times 100 = 100,000$$
$$10^{2+3} = 10^5 = 100,000$$

In symbol form:
$$\log_b M = x \qquad \log_b N = y$$
$$b^x = M \qquad b^y = N$$
$$b^{x+y} = MN$$

2. The logarithm of the quotient of two numbers is equal to the logarithm of the dividend minus the logarithm of the divisor.

   a. $\dfrac{10^5}{10^2} = 10^3$ $\dfrac{100,000}{100} = 1000$

   b. $\dfrac{2^4}{2^3} = 2^1$ $\dfrac{16}{8} = 2$

In symbol form:

$$\log_b M = x \qquad \log_b N = y$$
$$b^x = M \qquad b^y = N$$
$$b^{x-y} = \frac{M}{N}$$

3. The logarithm of the zth power of a number is equal to z times the logarithm of the number.

$$\log_{10} 100 = 2$$
$$100^3 = 1,000,000$$
$$\log_{10} 1,000,000 = 3 \log_{10} 100 = 3 \times 2 = 6$$

$$\log_b N = x$$
$$b^x = N$$
$$b^{xz} = N^z$$
$$\log_b N^z = zx = z \log_b N$$

4. The logarithm of the yth root of a number is equal to the logarithm of that number divided by y.

$$\log_{10} 1,000,000 = 6$$
$$1,000,000^{1/3} = 100$$
$$\log_{10} 1,000,000^{1/3} = \frac{1}{3} \log_{10} 1,000,000 = \frac{6}{3} = 2$$

$$\log_b N = x$$
$$b^x = N$$
$$b^{x/y} = N^{1/y}$$
$$\log_b N^{1/y} = \frac{1}{y} \log_b N = \frac{\log_b N}{y}$$

COMMON LOGARITHMS

By now you have gathered that logarithms can be the exponents for virtually any base. In actual practice, 10 is most often the base. Logarithms to the base 10 are *common logarithms,* and these are usually meant when one refers to logs or logarithmic tables. The common log of a number is the power to which the base 10 must be raised to equal that number.

EXAMPLE 7–2

Exponential form	*Logarithmic form* (base 10 understood)
10^4 = 10,000	log 10,000 = 4
10^3 = 1,000	log 1,000 = 3
10^2 = 100	log 100 = 2
10^1 = 10	log 10 = 1
10^0 = 1	log 1 = 0
10^{-1} = 0.1	log 0.1 = -1
10^{-2} = 0.01	log 0.01 = -2
10^{-3} = 0.001	log 0.001 = -3

It is probably obvious that the number 250 is somewhere between 10^2 and 10^3, so that its logarithm is 2 plus something. The "2 part" of the logarithm is called the *characteristic*. The "plus part" (when it is given in actual figures) is called the *mantissa* and is found in tables of logarithms, more commonly called log tables, such as the one on pages 88–89. The characteristic and the mantissa together constitute the *logarithm*.

Finding the Characteristic

1. The characteristic for a number greater than one is one less than the number of digits to the left of the decimal point. The characteristic is naturally the same as the exponent that would be used on 10 if the number were expressed in scientific notation.

Number	*Scientific notation*	*Characteristic*
250	2.50 $\times 10^2$	2
2	2 $\times 10^0$	0
2500	2.5 $\times 10^3$	3
2599.9	2.5999 $\times 10^3$	3

2. The characteristic for a number less than one is the negative of the number of the decimal place in which a digit other than zero first appears. Note the relationship of the characteristic to the exponent of the number expressed in scientific notation.

Number	*Scientific notation*	*Characteristic*
0.03	3 $\times 10^{-2}$	-2 or $\bar{2}$
0.008	8 $\times 10^{-3}$	-3 or $\bar{3}$
0.0012	1.2 $\times 10^{-3}$	-3 or $\bar{3}$
0.000809	8.09 $\times 10^{-4}$	-4 or $\bar{4}$

Finding the Mantissa

Numbers with the same sequence of digits have the same mantissa.

log 127   = 2.1038
log 1.27   = 0.1038
log 1,270,000 = 6.1038

1. Forget about the magnitude of the figure.
2. Forget about the characteristic.
3. Forget about decimal points.
4. Work only with the particular digit sequence involved.

EXAMPLE 7–3

Digit sequence	Position in table on page 88	Mantissa
229	line 22 under column 9	3598
209	line 20 under column 9	3201
200	line 20 under column 0	3010
2	line 20 under column 0	3010

Finding the Logarithm of a Number

Find the characteristic, write a decimal point, write the mantissa for the digit sequence after the decimal point.

EXAMPLE 7–4

Find the logarithm of 291.

characteristic: 2
mantissa: 0.4639
logarithm: 2.4639

EXAMPLE 7–5

Find the logarithm of 0.00291 (that is, 2.91×10^{-3}).

characteristic: $\bar{3}$
mantissa: 0.4639
logarithm: $\bar{3}.4639$ or $7.4639 - 10$ if you prefer.

It is very important to remember that only the characteristic is negative here. To indicate this a bar is placed over the 3 only, or else the form

Four-Place Logarithms

No.	0	1	2	3	4	5	6	7	8	9
10	0000	0043	0086	0128	0170	0212	0253	0294	0334	0374
11	0414	0453	0492	0531	0569	0607	0645	0682	0719	0755
12	0792	0828	0864	0899	0934	0969	1004	1038	1072	1106
13	1139	1173	1206	1239	1271	1303	1335	1367	1399	1430
14	1461	1492	1523	1553	1584	1614	1644	1673	1703	1732
15	1761	1790	1818	1847	1875	1903	1931	1959	1987	2014
16	2041	2068	2095	2122	2148	2175	2201	2227	2253	2279
17	2304	2330	2355	2380	2405	2430	2455	2480	2504	2529
18	2553	2577	2601	2625	2648	2672	2695	2718	2742	2765
19	2788	2810	2833	2856	2878	2900	2923	2945	2967	2989
20	3010	3032	3054	3075	3096	3118	3139	3160	3181	3201
21	3222	3243	3263	3284	3304	3324	3345	3365	3385	3404
22	3424	3444	3464	3483	3502	3522	3541	3560	3579	3598
23	3617	3636	3655	3674	3692	3711	3729	3747	3766	3784
24	3802	3820	3838	3856	3874	3892	3909	3927	3945	3962
25	3979	3997	4014	4031	4048	4065	4082	4099	4116	4133
26	4150	4166	4183	4200	4216	4232	4249	4265	4281	4298
27	4314	4330	4346	4362	4378	4393	4409	4425	4440	4456
28	4472	4487	4502	4518	4533	4548	4564	4579	4594	4609
29	4624	4639	4654	4669	4683	4698	4713	4728	4742	4757
30	4771	4786	4800	4814	4829	4843	4857	4871	4886	4900
31	4914	4928	4942	4955	4969	4983	4997	5011	5024	5038
32	5051	5065	5079	5092	5105	5119	5132	5145	5159	5172
33	5185	5198	5211	5224	5237	5250	5263	5276	5289	5302
34	5315	5328	5340	5353	5366	5378	5391	5403	5416	5428
35	5441	5453	5465	5478	5490	5502	5514	5527	5539	5551
36	5563	5575	5587	5599	5611	5623	5635	5647	5658	5670
37	5682	5694	5705	5717	5729	5740	5752	5763	5775	5786
38	5798	5809	5821	5832	5843	5855	5866	5877	5888	5899
39	5911	5922	5933	5944	5955	5966	5977	5988	5999	6010
40	6021	6031	6042	6053	6064	6075	6085	6096	6107	6117
41	6128	6138	6149	6160	6170	6180	6191	6201	6212	6222
42	6232	6243	6253	6263	6274	6284	6294	6304	6314	6325
43	6335	6345	6355	6365	6375	6386	6395	6405	6415	6425
44	6435	6444	6454	6464	6474	6484	6493	6503	6513	6522
45	6532	6542	6551	6561	6571	6580	6590	6599	6609	6618
46	6628	6637	6646	6656	6665	6675	6684	6693	6702	6712
47	6721	6730	6739	6749	6758	6767	6776	6785	6794	6803
48	6812	6821	6830	6839	6848	6857	6866	6875	6884	6893
49	6902	6911	6920	6928	6937	6946	6955	6964	6972	6981
50	6990	6998	7007	7016	7024	7033	7042	7050	7059	7067
51	7076	7084	7093	7101	7110	7118	7126	7135	7143	7152
52	7160	7168	7177	7185	7193	7202	7210	7218	7226	7235
53	7243	7251	7259	7267	7275	7284	7292	7300	7308	7316
54	7324	7332	7340	7348	7356	7364	7372	7380	7388	7396
	0	1	2	3	4	5	6	7	8	9

Four-Place Logarithms

No.	0	1	2	3	4	5	6	7	8	9
55	7404	7412	7419	7427	7435	7443	7451	7459	7466	7474
56	7482	7490	7497	7505	7513	7520	7528	7536	7543	7551
57	7559	7566	7574	7582	7589	7597	7604	7612	7619	7627
58	7634	7642	7649	7657	7664	7672	7679	7686	7694	7701
59	7709	7716	7723	7731	7738	7745	7752	7760	7767	7774
60	7782	7789	7796	7803	7810	7818	7825	7832	7839	7846
61	7853	7860	7868	7875	7882	7889	7896	7903	7910	7917
62	7924	7931	7938	7945	7952	7959	7966	7973	7980	7987
63	7992	8000	8007	8014	8021	8028	8035	8041	8048	8055
64	8062	8069	8075	8082	8089	8096	8102	8109	8116	8122
65	8129	8136	8142	8149	8156	8162	8169	8176	8182	8189
66	8195	8202	8209	8215	8222	8228	8235	8241	8248	8254
67	8261	8267	8274	8280	8287	8293	8299	8306	8312	8319
68	8325	8331	8338	8344	8351	8357	8363	8370	8376	8382
69	8388	8395	8401	8407	8414	8420	8426	8432	8439	8445
70	8451	8457	8463	8470	8476	8482	8488	8494	8500	8506
71	8513	8519	8525	8531	8537	8543	8549	8555	8561	8567
72	8573	8579	8585	8591	8597	8603	8609	8615	8621	8627
73	8633	8639	8645	8651	8657	8663	8669	8675	8681	8686
74	8692	8698	8704	8710	8716	8722	8727	8733	8739	8745
75	8751	8756	8762	8768	8774	8779	8785	8791	8797	8802
76	8808	8814	8820	8825	8831	8837	8842	8848	8854	8859
77	8865	8871	8876	8882	8887	8893	8899	8904	8910	8915
78	8921	8927	8932	8938	8943	8949	8954	8960	8965	8971
79	8976	8982	8987	8993	8998	9004	9009	9015	9020	9025
80	9031	9036	9042	9047	9053	9058	9063	9069	9074	9079
81	9085	9090	9096	9101	9106	9112	9117	9122	9128	9133
82	9138	9143	9149	9154	9159	9165	9170	9175	9180	9186
83	9191	9196	9201	9206	9212	9217	9222	9227	9232	9238
84	9243	9248	9253	9258	9263	9269	9274	9279	9284	9289
85	9294	9299	9304	9309	9315	9320	9325	9330	9335	9340
86	9345	9350	9355	9360	9365	9370	9375	9380	9385	9390
87	9395	9400	9405	9410	9415	9420	9425	9430	9435	9440
88	9445	9450	9455	9460	9465	9469	9474	9479	9484	9489
89	9494	9499	9504	9509	9513	9518	9523	9528	9533	9538
90	9542	9547	9552	9557	9562	9566	9571	9576	9581	9586
91	9590	9595	9600	9605	9609	9614	9619	9624	9628	9633
92	9638	9643	9647	9652	9657	9661	9666	9671	9675	9680
93	9685	9689	9694	9699	9703	9708	9713	9717	9722	9727
94	9731	9736	9741	9745	9750	9754	9759	9763	9768	9773
95	9777	9782	9786	9791	9795	9800	9805	9809	9814	9818
96	9823	9827	9832	9836	9841	9845	9850	9854	9859	9863
97	9868	9872	9877	9881	9886	9890	9894	9899	9903	9908
98	9912	9917	9921	9926	9930	9934	9939	9943	9948	9952
99	9956	9961	9965	9969	9974	9978	9983	9987	9991	9996
	0	1	2	3	4	5	6	7	8	9

7 – 10 is used. You know 0.00291 is between 0.001 and 0.01. If you use –3.4639, which is a negative log, you would have an entirely different number.*

EXAMPLE 7–6

Find the logarithm of 2.91.

characteristic:	0
mantissa:	0.4639
logarithm:	0.4639

EXAMPLE 7–7

	Number	Logarithm
a.	308	2.4886
b.	380	2.5798
c.	6210	3.7931
d.	0.00308	$\bar{3}$.4886 or 7.4886 – 10
e.	0.0000308	$\bar{5}$.4886 or 5.4886 – 10
f.	2.35	0.3711

Interpolation

If a number has more digits in it than can be directly read from the table at hand, one must interpolate, that is, find a mantissa that is between the values on the particular table.

EXAMPLE 7–8

Find the log for 2555.

Since the magnitude of the number has no effect on the mantissa, the mantissa for 2555 must be between those for 255 and 256. Thus you find:

Digit sequences for number	Mantissas from log table
256	4082
255	4065

---

*The negative log –3.4639 would have been obtained by adding –4 and +0.5361, and represents approximately 3.44×10^{-4}. According to the system being presented here the logarithm of that number would be written $\bar{4}$.5361 or 6.5361 – 10. There is an obvious difference between $\bar{3}$.4639 and $\bar{4}$.5361.

You need a fourth digit, so use 2550 and 2560 for 255 and 256, respectively.

Digit sequences for number	Mantissas
2560	4082
2550	4065
difference: 10	17

A difference of 10 digit-sequence units in the number corresponds to a difference of 17 mantissa units. Since 2555 is 5 of the 10 digits beyond 2550, the mantissa would be 5/10 of 17, or 9, units greater than 4065, specifically 4074. (You could add 8 or 9 but not 8.5 to 4065.) So logarithm of 2555 is 3.4704.

EXAMPLE 7-9

Number	Digit sequences	Mantissas	Interpolated mantissa	Logarithm of number
a. 8.219	8220	9149	$9143 + \frac{9}{10} (6) =$	
	8210	9143	$9143 + 5$	0.9148
difference:	10	6		
b. 12,140	1220	0864	$0828 + \frac{4}{10} (36) =$	
	1210	0828	$0828 + 14$	4.0842
difference:	10	36		
c. 0.0001943	1950	2900	$2878 + 0.3(22) =$	
	1940	2878	$2878 + 7$	$\overline{4}.2885$ or
difference:	10	22		$6.2885 - 10$

Many log tables include "proportional parts" along the side, making this process of interpolation unnecessary. The method used is easy to grasp.

ANTILOGARITHMS

An antilogarithm is the number of which a given set of digits is the logarithm. One just works backward to find the number represented by the given logarithm.

EXAMPLE 7–10

The log of a certain number is 2.7853. Find the antilog.

The 2 says the number is between 10^2 and 10^3, that is, between 100 and 1000. The mantissa 7853 is on line 61 in the 0 column of the log table. The antilog of 2.7853 is thus 610. In other words, the number for which the log was given is 610.

EXAMPLE 7–11

Find the antilog of 2.5746.

You must interpolate here. You cannot find the mantissa on the table.

Logarithm	Mantissas	Digit sequences in table	Digit sequences used here
2.5746	5752	376	3760
	5740	375	3750
difference:	12		10

5746 is 6 units beyond 5740, so it must be the mantissa for a number 6/12 of the way between 3750 and 3760. Since $6/12 \times 10 = 5$, the digit sequence of the number must be 3755. The characteristic is 2, so the number must be 375.5.

EXAMPLE 7–12

Find the antilog of $\bar{5}.6922$.

	Mantissas	Digit sequences in table	Our digit sequences
	6928	493	4930
	6920	492	4920
difference:	8		10

Since 6922 is 2 units beyond 6920, and $2/8 \times 10 = 2.5$ (or 3 here), the antilog of $\bar{5}.6922$ is 4.923×10^{-5}.

USES OF COMMON LOGARITHMS

Multiplication

Add logs of each of the numbers to be multiplied; find antilog of the sum of the logs.

EXAMPLE 7–13

a. 285×731

$\log 285 = 2.4548$
$\log 731 = 2.8639$
sum: 5.3187

Antilog is 208,300.

b. 0.0285×0.00731

$\log 0.0285$: $\overline{2}.4548$ or $8.4548 - 10$
$\log 0.00731$: $\overline{3}.8639$ $7.8639 - 10$
sum: 4.3187 $16.3187 - 20$ or $6.3187 - 10$

Antilog is 2.083×10^{-4}.

Division

From the log of the dividend subtract the log of the divisor; find the antilog of the difference.

EXAMPLE 7–14

a. $\dfrac{285}{731}$

2.4548 or $12.4548 - 10$
2.8639 2.8639
difference: $\overline{1}.5909$ $9.5909 - 10$

Antilog is 0.3898.

b. $\dfrac{0.0285}{0.00731}$

$\overline{2}.4548$ or $8.4548 - 10$ ("disappears" because of
$\overline{3}.8639$ $7.8639 - 10$ algebraic subtraction)
difference: 0.5909 0.5909

Antilog is 3.898.

c. $\dfrac{0.00731}{285}$

$\overline{3}.8639$ or $7.8639 - 10$
2.4548 2.4548
difference: $\overline{5}.4091$ $5.4091 - 10$

Antilog is 2.565×10^{-5}.

d. $\dfrac{731}{0.00285}$

	2.8639	or	2.8639	
	$\overline{3}$.4548		7.4548 $- 10$	(more algebraic
difference:	5.4091		5.4091 $+ 10$	subtraction)

Antilog is 256,500.

Finding a Power of a Number

Multiply log of a number by the power to which one wishes to raise the number; find the antilog of the product so obtained.

EXAMPLE 7–15

a. $(12)^3$

3(log of 12) = 3(1.0792) = 3.2376

Antilog is 1728.

b. $(9.80 \times 10^{-2})^2$

$2(\log 9.80 \times 10^{-2}) = 2(\overline{2}.9912) = \overline{3}.9824$

Antilog is 9.60×10^{-3}.

Finding a Root of a Number

Divide the log of the number by the number of the root to be found; find the antilog of the quotient so obtained. There are complications when roots of numbers less than 1 are to be found.

EXAMPLE 7–16

a. $\sqrt[4]{285}$

$$\frac{\log \text{ of } 285}{4} = \frac{2.4548}{4} = 0.6137$$

Antilog is 4.11.

b. $\sqrt[4]{0.00549}$ (In other words, find the fourth root of 0.00549.)

The method used in the preceding problem fails here. Find log 0.00549, which is $\overline{3}$.7396; convert to the form 7.7396 $- 10$ and divide separately:

$$\frac{7.7396}{4} - \frac{10}{4} = 1.9349 - 2.5000$$

Now do the actual subtraction.

1.9349
2.5000
‾‾‾‾‾‾
$\overline{1}$.4349

This difference is the logarithm of the fourth root of 0.00549. The antilog is 0.272. The fourth root of 0.00549 is 0.272.

A simpler method is to arrange to have the negative part be a whole number.

$$\frac{17.7396 - 20}{4} = 4.4349 - 5 = \overline{1}.4349$$

Antilog is still 0.272.

COLOGARITHMS

A cologarithm is the logarithm of the reciprocal of a given number.

$$\text{colog } N = \log \frac{1}{N} = \log 1 - \log N = - \log N \quad (\text{since } \log 1 = 0)$$

$$\text{colog } 16 = \log \frac{1}{16} = \log 1 - \log 16$$

$$\begin{aligned}
\log \ 1 &= 10.0000 - 10 \\
\log 16 &= \underline{1.2041} \\
\text{colog } 16 &= 8.7959 - 10 \quad \text{or} \quad \overline{2}.7959
\end{aligned}$$

Here notice that the colog of a number is equal to minus the logarithm of the number. Be sure not to confuse this with the logarithm of a number such as 0.00285 wherein the minus is connected solely with the $\overline{3}$ in $\overline{3}$.4548.

EXAMPLE 7-17

Find the cologarithm of the number 0.00016 (1.6×10^{-4}).

$$\begin{aligned}
\log 1 &= 10.0000 - 10 \\
\log 1.6 \times 10^{-4} &= \underline{6.2041 - 10} \\
&\quad 3.7959 \quad \text{is the colog for } 1.6 \times 10^{-4}
\end{aligned}$$

How does one convert a colog into an ordinary logarithm and into an ordinary number? Suppose the colog is 8.3605 − 10 or $\overline{2}$.3605.

colog N = log 1 − log N
so log N = log 1 − colog N

thus   10.0000 − 10 (log 1)
          8.3605 − 10 (colog N)
          ‾‾‾‾‾‾‾‾‾‾‾‾
          1.6395   (log N)

The antilog of 1.6395 is 43.6.

USE OF COLOGARITHMS

Division by a number is the same as multiplication by the reciprocal of this same number.

$$\frac{8}{2} = 4 \quad \text{and} \quad 8 \times \frac{1}{2} = 4$$

One can divide by subtracting the log of the divisor from the log of the dividend. One could also divide by adding the colog of the divisor to the logarithm of the dividend. Naturally one would have to look up the antilog to get the actual answer. You may well wonder who would bother with this. Be patient. Cologs as such are often used in chemistry, despite the fact that they seem a nuisance. One example is pH, which is the colog of the hydrogen ion concentration.

pH is a measure of the hydrogen ion concentration of a solution. Hydrogen ion concentration (symbol: $[H^+]$) is a measure of the acidity of a solution. The prefix p is used in chemistry to indicate minus the log, or the colog, of whatever p precedes. The H in pH represents hydrogen ion concentration.

$$pH = - \log [H^+] = \log \frac{1}{[H^+]} = \log 1 - \log [H^+]$$

EXAMPLE 7–18

Find pH when $[H^+]$ is 1.6×10^{-4} mole/liter.

pH = − log $[H^+]$ = log 1 − log $[H^+]$

           log 1 = 10.0000 − 10
log 1.6×10^{-4} = 6.2041 − 10
                    ‾‾‾‾‾‾‾‾‾‾‾‾
                    3.7959

pH here would be 3.80.

pH cannot be accurately measured to anything more precise than ±0.01

pH unit. However, here we are working with the mathematical tools, so let's use an absurdity, a four-decimal-place pH figure.

EXAMPLE 7–19

Convert pH 3.7959 to hydrogen ion concentration.

pH is just a colog, so just do whatever is necessary to convert a colog to an ordinary number, that is, first find the log of the species whose colog one has, then find the antilog of the log.

$$\log 1 - \log [H^+] = \text{colog} [H^+] = pH$$
therefore $\log 1 - pH = \log [H^+]$

so

$$
\begin{array}{ll}
10.0000 - 10 & (\log 1) \\
\underline{3.7959} & (pH) \\
6.2041 - 10 & (\log [H^+])
\end{array}
$$

$6.2041 - 10$ could also be expressed as $\overline{4}.2041$. The antilog, no matter which way you expressed the log, is 1.6×10^{-4}.

FINDING LOGARITHMS ON A SLIDE RULE (FIGURE 7–1)

Find the characteristic in the usual fashion. Locate the digit sequence for which a mantissa is needed with the hairline on the D scale. Under the same hairline on the L scale read the mantissa. To find the antilog locate the mantissa on the L scale and read the digit sequence corresponding to the antilogarithm on the D scale.

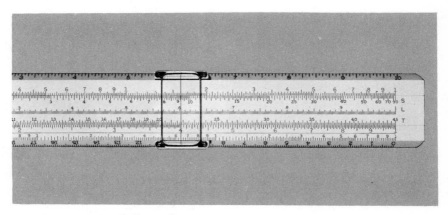

Courtesy of Keuffel & Esser Company

Figure 7-1
Log 4 = 0.602; log 40 = 1.602; etc.

PROBLEMS

1. Express in logarithmic form:

    a. $3^2 = 9$ **g.** $\sqrt[4]{81} = 3$

    b. $4^3 = 64$ **h.** $r^0 = 1$

    c. $10^4 = 10{,}000$ **i.** $c^d = e$

    d. $\left(\dfrac{1}{5}\right)^2 = \dfrac{1}{25}$ **j.** $z = 8^{3y}$

    e. $2^{-3} = \dfrac{1}{8}$ **k.** $16^{1/2} = 4$

    f. $\sqrt{25} = 5$ **l.** $2^{3/2} = 2.8$

2. Express in exponential form:

    a. $\log_5 25 = 2$ **e.** $\log_{25} 5 = \frac{1}{2}$

    b. $\log_4 256 = 4$ **f.** $\log_r r = 1$

    c. $\log_2 64 = 8$ **g.** $\log_r 1 = 0$

    d. $\log_{10} 0.00001 = -5$ **h.** $\log_{10} 0.01 = -2$

3. Find the logarithms of these numbers:

    a. 4925   **b.** 2.813   **c.** 17.89

4. Find the antilogs for these logarithms:

    a. 2.7710   **c.** 1.9559

    b. $\bar{1}.9559$ **d.** 0.0020

5. Find cologs for these numbers:

    a. 2.805   **b.** 0.00821

6. Find the antilogs for these cologs:

    a. 3.2951   **b.** $4.2951 - 10$

7. Solve by logs, interpolating where necessary:

    a. 583×0.000921 **c.** $\dfrac{0.00921}{6023}$

    b. 0.008541×0.00840 **d.** $\dfrac{4095}{0.0891}$

7. e. $\dfrac{273 \times 6.023 \times 10^{23} \times 4.821}{62.9 \times 17.5}$

f. $\dfrac{0.008992 \times 1.773 \times 4.08}{3 \times 10^{10} \times 0.00805}$

g. $\dfrac{(4 \times 10^4)^3 \times 43.9}{0.016}$

h. $\dfrac{40.8 \times (2.1)^3}{75}$

8

SIGNIFICANT FIGURES

Significant figures represent measured quantities. Any figures representing reasonably reliable values should be considered significant. However, one must remember that error is inherent in all measurements. There is a possibility—really a probability, perhaps even a certainty—of error in measurement.

Suppose a foot rule were used to measure a field. The field was found to be 285 by 225 ft. The measurements were made to within 1 ft. In science and engineering the dimensions of this field would be given as

$$285 \pm 1 \text{ ft} \times 225 \pm 1 \text{ ft}$$

In other words, the length is somewhere between 284 and 286 ft, and the width is between 224 and 226 ft.

You are quite properly objecting. You measured the field over and over again, and it really is 285 ft by 225 ft. We're setting forth the custom used in expressing scientific measurements. You would have had to use something which measured to within at least 0.1 ft to be *sure* of the last foot. As stated here, there is an uncertainty of at least 1 ft in each measurement. Notice we have not said error. We said uncertainty. We just are not sure of that last foot.

Suppose you wanted the area of a room 28 ft by 23 ft. As stated here, the figures mean

$$28 \pm 1 \text{ ft}: \quad \frac{1 \times 100}{28} = 3.6\% \text{ uncertainty}$$

$$23 \pm 1 \text{ ft:} \quad \frac{1 \times 100}{23} = 4.3\% \text{ uncertainty}$$

The area would be calculated

$$28 \text{ ft} \times 23 \text{ ft} = 644 \text{ ft}^2$$

We cannot say 644 ft². It is true that if the length and width were exactly 28 ft and 23 ft, we could put exactly 644 squares 1 ft by 1 ft over the area. However, we are dealing with conventions involving statement of measurement. From the way in which the figures are stated, we most decidedly do not know that the length was exactly 28 ft nor that the width was exactly 23 ft.

As written, 644 ft² means 644 ± 1 ft². This represents an uncertainty of 1 part in 644 or 0.16%. But mere multiplication could not improve your original measurements. The uncertainty due to the measurement of the length was 3.6% and that due to the width was 4.3%. The value for the area is limited by the uncertainty of both measurements and thus must be even greater than the uncertainty of either individual measurement. The uncertainty about the area is really 7.9%. So the area is 644 ± 51 ft². This is really a monstrous uncertainty! Measurement to 0.1 ft would obviously have reduced the uncertainty.

Students very often want to know how far to carry out mathematical operations in finding answers or how far out to weigh something in an experiment. A knowledge of significant figures and of the accuracy of all measuring instruments used is necessary to answer such questions. The methods just demonstrated are too clumsy for general use. There are some simple conventions for ordinary use.

DETERMINATION OF NUMBER OF SIGNIFICANT FIGURES

1. Any figures (digits) representing a reasonably reliably measured value should be considered significant.
   a. The diameter of the Earth on a given axis is 7926 mi. How many significant figures are there? Four significant figures. The last measured figure, here the 6, is the first uncertain figure (digit). This is really 7926 ± 1 mi. The diameter is somewhere between 7925 and 7927.
2. Zeros may or may not be significant. If a zero is used to give position value to one or more other digits, it is not significant. If it represents a measured quantity which happens to be zero, then it is significant.
   a. In the expression

      2.54 mm = 0.254 cm = 0.00254 m = 0.00000254 km

none of the zeros is significant. The zeros merely give position value to the other digits. In each case there are three significant figures. In general, any zeros to the right of a decimal point are insignificant unless there is a digit other than zero between the decimal point and the zero(s).

b. 0.008 has *one* significant figure; zeros are not significant.

c. 1.008 has *four* significant figures; zeros are significant.

d. 0.00800 has *three* significant figures. The two zeros to the right of 8 are significant because they are not needed to give position value and would not be written if they had not been measured. The three zeros to the left of 8 are not significant.

e. 1.00800 has *six* significant figures; all zeros are significant.

3. In figures presented in exponential notation ($M \times 10^n$), all of the digits in M are significant.

a. 2×10^3 ft.   One significant figure.

b. 1.25×10^4 ft. Three significant figures.

c. 100×10^5 ft. Three significant figures.

d. 100×10^0 ft. Three significant figures.

4. Some integer values are absolutely accurate. For example, a basketball team has 5 players on it. This is 5.0000... to infinity. One must have 5040 uniforms to outfit 1008 basketball teams. One could not say 5000 uniforms just because 5 players at first glance appeared to be one significant figure.

Determining the number of significant figures in a quantity which one himself measures rarely presents any difficulty. However, determining the number of significant figures really involved in numbers which one finds in reports, books, etc., can present quite a problem. This is why exponential notation is so helpful, since all digits in M in the form $M \times 10^n$ are by convention significant.

A figure such as 125 presents no problem. There are three significant figures. 350 does present a problem. If this is 350 men enrolled in a medical school, then there are three or an infinite number of significant figures, since accurate counts are made of enrollees in medical schools. If, on the other hand, this is 350 porpoises sighted from the deck of a ship, then one would be lucky to have two significant figures. True, porpoises are absolute integers, but there would be extreme difficulty in counting a school of porpoises traveling at sea.

Figures such as 5000 present particularly difficult problems. As stated, just plain 5000 is really 5000 $\pm$ 1000 with just one significant figure. Now suppose this is 5000 gal. Surely one would measure so much material to something closer than $\pm$1000 gal. If one had the statement ''a 5000-gal tank,'' one could be reasonably sure that the volume was very close to being exactly 5000 gal and could rather safely use four significant figures.

Ambiguities arising from such figures will disappear only when everyone dealing with figures of this sort either uses exponential notation or gives some indication of the number of significant digits, as in "exactly 5000 gal," "5000 ± 10 gal," "5000 ± 1 gal" etc.

EXAMPLE 8–1

How many significant figures are there in each of the following?

a. The diameter of the Earth is 8000 mi.

Only the 8 is unquestionably significant. You do not know how many figures are significant because there is insufficient information on how accurately the measurement was made. One significant figure.

b. The diameter of the Earth is 8000 ± 100 mi.

There are two significant figures. The diameter is somewhere between 7900 and 8100 mi.

c. The diameter of the Earth is 8000 ± 10 mi.

There are three significant figures. The value is somewhere between 7990 and 8010 mi.

d. The length of a rug is 180 ft.

There are two significant figures. You object. Surely anyone who measured a rug would measure it to at least 1-ft precision. This may be so, but the convention for 180 ft calls for 180 ± 1 ft in such a case. Here 180 means 180 ± 10 ft.

e. The membership is now 80 men.

Two significant figures or an infinite number of significant figures.

EXAMPLE 8–2

Express 1.500×10^3 in arithmetical notation.

To preserve the number of significant figures this must be written as 1500 ± 1 ft. If one wrote 1500, which would be 1.5×10^3 in exponential notation, significant figures would have been lost by mere mathematical manipulation.

MATHEMATICAL OPERATIONS INVOLVING SIGNIFICANT FIGURES

Addition and Subtraction

Only quantities representing like units and expressed to the same number of decimal places may be added or subtracted, regardless of the number of significant digits in the quantities. To add 13.8 g, 208.32 cg, and 885 mg (see Chapter 9, "The Metric System"), first express all quantities in the same unit; which unit is a matter of choice.

$$13.8 \text{ g} = 13.8 \text{ g}$$
$$208.32 \text{ cg} = 2.0832 \text{ g}$$
$$885 \text{ mg} = 0.885 \text{ g}$$

You do not know the second decimal place for the 13.8 g. Therefore no sum including the 13.8 could have a second decimal place that had any meaning. Therefore you would add

$$\begin{array}{r} 13.8 \text{ g} \\ 2.1 \text{ g} \\ \underline{0.9 \text{ g}} \\ 16.8 \text{ g} \end{array}$$

Multiplication and Division

In multiplication and division the number of significant digits retained in the product or quotient is the same as the least number of significant digits occurring in any of the quantities involved.

$$\frac{789 \times 15 \times 189,568}{895 \times 19.6 \times 1500} = \text{an answer with but two significant digits}$$

It is probably obvious that measurements should be made to similar significance. It would make little sense to measure one factor to seven agonizing digits if elsewhere in the data there are figures known only to two or three digits.

An additional word is perhaps needed. Determination of significant figures is really neither as hard and fast nor as simple as this presentation has indicated. One has to use a good deal of judgment in dealing with significant figures. For example,

$$\frac{98 \times 171}{821 \times 19.3} = ?$$

How many significant figures would there seem to be in the answer? Following the rule we have given here, the answer at first glance would seem to be 1.1. However, that answer would be 1.1 ± 0.1 with a built-in uncertainty of 9% (0.1/1.1 × 100 = 9%). But the least significant figure in the setup (98) has a built-in uncertainty of about 1% (98 ± 1). Now if the answer to the problem is taken as 1.06, the built-in uncertainty would be just 0.9%, a figure much closer in uncertainty to the least certain figure in the original setup. Therefore the answer to the problem should probably be 1.06.

Rounding Off Significant Figures

Ordinarily mathematical operations are carried out with one digit more than is significant. Rounding off to the correct number of significant figures is done at the end. If the first nonsignificant digit is more than 5, the last significant figure is increased; if the first nonsignificant digit is less than 5, the last significant digit is not changed. When the first nonsignificant digit is 5, the last significant digit is raised only if it is an odd number. Examples are:

Calculated value	*Number of significant figures*	*Value expressed in significant figures*
1.066	3	1.07
1.064	3	1.06
1.075	3	1.08
1.065	3	1.06

PROBLEMS

1. How many significant figures are there in the answers to problem 7 on pages 98–99.
2. How many significant figures in each of the following?
   a. 8 silver dollars
   b. $50,000
   c. 35,000 pores per finger
   d. 1000
   e. 1000×10^6
   f. 0.001×10^9
3. How many significant digits would there be in the answer to each of the following?
   a. $62 \times 0.0152 \times 7,850,000$
   b. $78.85 \times 0.08509 \times 1509.2$
   c. $\dfrac{308.25 \times 5.31 \times 10^{-9} \times 6,543,210}{7.852 \times 395}$
4. To have a quotient with four significant figures, by which of the following numbers should 13.598 be divided: 8.309, 8.31, 8.3092, or none of these?

9

THE METRIC SYSTEM

There seems to be little point in discussing the historical or political aspects of the metric system here in view of the number of easily obtainable references on the subject. Suffice it to say that this marvelously simple and widely used decimal system of measurement was devised at the instigation of Napoléon I.

METRIC UNITS

The fundamental dimensions are length, mass, and time, measured by the meter, the gram, and the second in the metric system. Volume, a derived unit, is measured in liters in the metric system. Larger and smaller units are derived by using the appropriate prefix. (There can be some confusion about the symbol μ. Alone, μ stands for a micron, a millionth of a meter. As a prefix, μ stands for a millionth of the indicated unit; for example μ liter would be 10^{-6} liter.)

Some of the more common units and their relationships to the three fundamental units are given in Table 9-2. The liter was intended to be the volume of a cube 10 cm on every edge, thereby making the milliliter and the cubic centimeter equal to one another. An error was made, and they were not quite equal. In 1964 the Twelfth General Conference on Weights and Measurements reduced the size of the liter by 28 parts per million in order to make the milliliter and the cubic centimeter equal to one another.

Table 9-1   Metric Prefixes

Prefix	Symbol	Value
tera	T	10^{12}
giga	G	10^{9}
mega	M	10^{6}
*kilo	k	10^{3}
hecto	h	10^{2}
deka	da	10^{1}
*deci	d	10^{-1}
*centi	c	10^{-2}
*milli	m	10^{-3}
*micro	μ	10^{-6} (μ is the Greek letter mu)
nano	n	10^{-9}
pico	p	10^{-12}

*These are rather more commonly used than the others in ordinary scientific work.

Table 9-2   Metric Equivalents

1 meter (m) = 10^{1} decimeters (dm)	1 dm = 10^{-1} m
= 10^{2} centimeters (cm)	1 cm = 10^{-2} m
= 10^{3} millimeters (mm)	1 mm = 10^{-3} m
= 10^{6} microns (μ)	1 μ = 10^{-6} m
= 10^{-3} kilometer (km)	1 km = 10^{3} m
1 gram (g) = 10 decigrams (dg)	1 dg = 0.1 g
= 100 centigrams (cg)	1 cg = 0.01 g
= 1000 milligrams (mg)	1 mg = 0.001 g
= 1,000,000 micrograms (μg or γ)	1 μg = 0.000001 g
= 0.001 kilogram (kg)	1 kg = 1000 g
1 liter (l) = 1000 milliliters (ml)	1 ml = 0.001 l
= 1000 cubic centimeters (cm^{3} or cc)	1 cm^{3} = 0.001 l
= 10^{6} microliters or lambda (μl or λ)	1 λ = 10^{-6} l

Examples of some of the less common prefixes are:

1 pg = 10^{-12} g   1 g = 10^{12} pg (picogram)
1 ng = 10^{-9} g
1 μg = 10^{-6} g
1 dag = 10^{1} g   1 g = 10^{-1} dag (dekagram)
1 hg = 10^{2} g
1 Mg = 10^{6} g (Mg is megagram, not to be confused with mg, milligram)
1 Gg = 10^{9} g
1 Tg = 10^{12} g

CONVERSION OF UNITS

Now let's take some typical metric conversion problems. The method used is exactly the same as that presented in Chapter 3, "Problem Solving by Analogy."

EXAMPLE 9–1

Convert 5 g to decigrams.

1 g = 10 dg

You are going to a smaller unit; consequently you need a numerically larger answer.

$$\frac{5 \text{ g} \times 10 \text{ dg}}{\text{g}} = 50 \text{ dg}$$

EXAMPLE 9–2

Convert 90 dm to meters.

A meter is larger than a decimeter. You must get a numerically smaller answer.

a. Using the relationship 1 m = 10 dm,

$$\frac{90 \text{ dm}}{10 \frac{\text{dm}}{\text{m}}} = 9 \text{ m}$$

b. Using the relationship 1 dm = 0.1 m,

$$\frac{90 \text{ dm} \times 0.1 \text{ m}}{\text{dm}} = 9 \text{ m}$$

Note that in Examples 9.1 and 9.2b you multiplied by the number of new units per old unit. This method can unfortunately be used mechanically without really knowing anything about the processes involved. This may be fine if the goal is getting an answer to a metric conversion problem, but it isn't much help if the goal is problem solving.

Conversions When Unit Relationship Is Not Given

EXAMPLE 9-3

Convert 19 dg to milligrams.

You do not have a relationship between decigrams and milligrams. Find a unit to which each is related, obviously the gram here.

1 g = 10 dg   and   1 g = 1000 mg

so   10 dg = 1000 mg
      1 dg = 100 mg

a. $\dfrac{19 \text{ dg} \times 1000 \frac{\text{mg}}{\text{g}}}{10 \frac{\text{dg}}{\text{g}}} = 1.9 \times 10^3$ mg

b. or $\dfrac{19 \text{ dg} \times 100 \frac{\text{mg}}{\text{dg}}}{} = 1.9 \times 10^3$ mg

c. or $\dfrac{19 \text{ dg} \times 0.1 \frac{\text{g}}{\text{dg}} \times 1000 \frac{\text{mg}}{\text{g}}}{} = 1.9 \times 10^3$ mg

In solutions a and c you converted to and from the common unit, the gram. In solution b you used a derived conversion factor.

EXAMPLE 9-4

How many kilograms are there in 6 cg?

Common unit to which both kilogram and centigram are related? The gram.

1 g = 100 cg   and   1 g = 0.001 kg

Therefore 100 cg = 0.001 kg (10^2 cg = 10^{-3} kg)
                1 cg = 10^{-5} kg
                1 kg = 10^5 cg

$\dfrac{6 \text{ cg}}{100 \frac{\text{cg}}{\text{g}} \times 1000 \frac{\text{g}}{\text{kg}}} = 6 \times 10^{-5}$ kg

or $\dfrac{6 \text{ cg} \times 10^{-5} \frac{\text{kg}}{\text{cg}}}{} = 6 \times 10^{-5}$ kg $\left[\dfrac{\frac{1}{1}}{\text{kg}} = \text{kg}\right.$

or $\dfrac{6 \text{ cg} \times 0.01 \frac{\text{g}}{\text{cg}} \times 0.001 \frac{\text{kg}}{\text{g}}}{} = 6 \times 10^{-5}$ kg   (see algebra review $\left.\text{in Chapter 4}\right]$

Conversions Involving English and Metric Units

EXAMPLE 9-5

Convert 17 U.S. gal to milliliters (see table of units on page 34).

You do not know the relationship between gallons and milliliters, but you do know the relationships between milliliters and liters, between liters and quarts, and between quarts and U.S. gallons.

$$\frac{17 \text{ gal} \times 4 \text{ qt}}{\text{gal} \times 1.06 \dfrac{\text{qt}}{\text{liter}}} \times 1000 \frac{\text{ml}}{\text{liter}}$$

or $\dfrac{17 \text{ gal} \times 4 \text{ qt}}{\text{gal} \times 1.06 \text{ qt}} \times 1 \dfrac{\text{liter}}{} \times 1000 \dfrac{\text{ml}}{\text{liter}}$

Conversions Involving Areas and Volumes

EXAMPLE 9-6

Find the area of a room 16 ft × 14 ft in square inches.

a. $\left(16 \text{ ft} \times 12 \dfrac{\text{in.}}{\text{ft}}\right)\left(14 \text{ ft} \times 12 \dfrac{\text{in.}}{\text{ft}}\right) = 3.2 \times 10^4 \text{ in.}^2$

b. $(16 \text{ ft} \times 14 \text{ ft}) \left(12 \dfrac{\text{in.}}{\text{ft}}\right)^2 = 3.2 \times 10^4 \text{ in.}^2$

Note that the quantity (12 in./ft) was squared to give 144 in.^{2}/ft^2. It would have been totally wrong to have multiplied by 12 in.^{2}/ft^2.

EXAMPLE 9-7

Find the volume of a cube 6.0 in. on every edge in (a) cubic centimeters, (b) cubic meters, and (c) liters.

volume of a cube = (edge length)^3
1 in. = 2.54 cm = 0.0254 m
1 liter = 1000 cm^3

a. $(6.0 \text{ in.})^3 \times \left(2.54 \dfrac{\text{cm}}{\text{in.}}\right)^3 = 3500 \text{ cm}^3$

b. $(6.0 \text{ in.})^3 \times \left(2.54 \dfrac{\text{cm}}{\text{in.}}\right)^3 \times \left(0.01 \dfrac{\text{m}}{\text{cm}}\right)^3$

   or $(6.0 \text{ in.})^3 \times \left(0.0254 \dfrac{\text{m}}{\text{in.}}\right)^3 = 3.5 \times 10^{-3} \text{ m}^3$

c. One could either convert the volume in cubic centimeters or start from the beginning to find the volume in liters.

$$\frac{3500 \text{ cm}^3 \times 0.001 \text{ liter}}{\text{cm}^3} = 3.5 \text{ liters}$$

or $\dfrac{3500 \text{ cm}^3}{1000 \dfrac{\text{cm}^3}{\text{liter}}} = 3.5 \text{ liters}$

or $\dfrac{(6.0 \text{ in.})^3 \left(\dfrac{2.54 \text{ cm}}{\text{in.}}\right)^3 \times 0.001 \dfrac{\text{liter}}{\text{cm}^3}}{} = 3.5 \text{ liters}$

EXAMPLE 9–8

Find the height of a room with a volume of 1920 ft^3 and floor dimensions of 12 ft × 16 ft.

volume = length × width × depth

therefore depth (or height) $= \dfrac{\text{volume}}{\text{length} \times \text{width}} = \dfrac{1920 \text{ ft}^3}{16 \text{ ft} \times 12 \text{ ft}} = 10 \text{ ft}$

EXAMPLE 9–9

Now find the height to which 9000 gal of water would fill a rectangular swimming pool 12 ft by 16 ft on the bottom and 10 ft deep.

First convert the gallons to cubic feet, presuming U.S. gallons. A handbook shows that 1 ft^3 = 7.48 U.S. gal. To find how high 9000 gal of water would fill the pool:

$$\frac{9000 \text{ gal}}{7.48 \dfrac{\text{gal}}{\text{ft}^3} \times 12 \text{ ft} \times 16 \text{ ft}} = 6 \text{ ft}$$

Division by 7.48 gal/ft^3 gave an answer of cubic feet in the numerator of the main fraction; then

$$\frac{\text{ft}^3 \text{ (cubic feet)}}{12 \text{ ft} \times 16 \text{ ft}} = \underline{\qquad} \text{ ft}$$

You will have noticed we did not use the 10 ft. The pool was not full. We wanted to know what height when multiplied by the length and width (16 ft and 12 ft) would give the number of cubic feet in 9000 U.S. gal.

Conversions Involving Rather Unfamiliar Units and Seemingly Unusual Prefixes

Do each of the following problems, checking the solution for each problem as you go along. You will defeat the whole purpose of this section if you just read through the solutions.

EXAMPLE 9–10

How many microns are there in 7 cm?

You know the relationship of each unit here to meters, so

$$\frac{7 \text{ cm} \times 10^6 \, \frac{\mu}{m}}{10^2 \, \frac{cm}{m}} \quad \text{or} \quad \frac{7 \text{ cm} \times 10^{-2} \, \text{m} \times 10^6 \, \frac{\mu}{m}}{cm} = 7 \times 10^4 \, \mu$$

or $1 \text{ m} = 10^2 \text{ cm}$ $10^2 \text{ cm} = 10^6 \, \mu$
    $1 \text{ m} = 10^6 \, \mu$ $1 \text{ cm} = 10^4 \, \mu$

so $\dfrac{7 \text{ cm} \times 10^4 \, \mu}{cm} = 7 \times 10^4 \, \mu$

EXAMPLE 9–11

How many centimeters are there in 7 μ?

$$\frac{7 \, \mu \times 10^2 \, \frac{cm}{m}}{10^6 \, \frac{\mu}{m}} \quad \text{or} \quad \frac{7 \, \mu \times 10^{-6} \, \text{m} \times 10^2 \, \frac{cm}{m}}{\mu} = 7 \times 10^{-4} \, \text{cm}$$

Analogy: $\$1 = 100¢$ $1¢ = \$0.01$
             $\$1 = 10^2¢$ $1¢ = \$10^{-2}$
          $1 \text{ m} = 10^6 \, \mu$ $1 \, \mu = 10^{-6} \text{ m}$

EXAMPLE 9–12

Convert 8 Ångstroms (1 Å $= 10^{-8}$ cm) to microns. You have the relationships of Ångstroms to centimeters, centimeters to meters, and meters to microns, so

$$\frac{8 \text{ Å} \times 10^6 \, \frac{\mu}{m}}{10^8 \, \frac{Å}{cm} \times 10^2 \, \frac{cm}{m}} = 8 \times 10^{-4} \, \mu$$

or $\dfrac{8 \text{ Å} \times 10^{-8} \, \frac{cm}{Å} \times 10^{-2} \, \text{m} \times 10^6 \, \frac{\mu}{cm}}{} = 8 \times 10^{-4} \, \mu$

If one regularly converted Ångstroms to microns (or vice versa), one would develop a conversion factor in this fashion:

$1 \text{ m} = 10^2 \text{ cm}$ and $1 \text{ m} = 10^6 \mu$

$10^2 \text{ cm} = 10^6 \mu$

$1 \text{ cm} = 10^4 \mu$

$1 \text{ cm} = 10^8 \text{ Å}$

$10^4 \mu = 10^8 \text{ Å}$

$1 \mu = 10^4 \text{ Å}$ or $1 \text{ Å} = 10^{-4} \mu$

Then $\dfrac{8 \text{ Å} \times 10^{-4} \mu}{\text{Å}} = 8 \times 10^{-4} \mu$

EXAMPLE 9–13

How many liters are there in 9 μl?

$\dfrac{9 \ \mu l}{10^6 \dfrac{\mu l}{\text{liter}}}$ or $\dfrac{9 \ \mu l \times 10^{-6} \text{ liter}}{\mu l} = 9 \times 10^{-6} \text{ liter}$

EXAMPLE 9–14

Find the volume of a box 7 by 10 by 17 Å in (a) cubic centimeters, (b) lambdas, and (c) microliters.

a. $(7 \text{ Å} \times 10 \text{ Å} \times 17 \text{ Å}) \left(10^{-8} \dfrac{\text{cm}}{\text{Å}}\right)^3 = 1 \times 10^{-21} \text{ cm}^3$

b. You know the relationships of lambdas to liters and cubic centimeters to liters. You can get centimeters from Ångstroms, so

$\dfrac{7 \text{ Å} \times 10 \text{ Å} \times 17 \text{ Å}}{\left(10^8 \dfrac{\text{Å}}{\text{cm}}\right)^3} \dfrac{\times 10^6 \lambda}{10^3 \dfrac{\text{cm}^3}{\text{liter}} \quad \text{liter}} = 1.2 \times 10^{-18} \lambda$

or $7 \text{ Å} \times 10 \text{ Å} \times 17 \text{ Å} \times \left(10^{-8} \dfrac{\text{cm}}{\text{Å}}\right)^3 \times 10^3 \dfrac{\lambda}{\text{cm}^3}$

Here the (new unit)/(old unit) conversion really is quite respectable. Anyone making a conversion of this sort would very likely know how to make conversions, so the simplest method possible would be the best.

c. Conversion to microliters would be made in exactly the same fashion as conversion to lambdas since $1 \ \lambda = 1 \ \mu$l.

See Table 3-1 (page 34) for other units.

$$1 \text{ astronomical unit} = 9.29 \times 10^7 \text{ mi}$$
$$= 1.50 \times 10^8 \text{ km}$$
$$= 4.85 \times 10^{-6} \text{ parsec}$$
$$= 1.58 \times 10^{-5} \text{ light yr}$$

$$1 \text{ ft} = 1.64 \times 10^{-4} \text{ nautical mi}$$
$$= 1.89 \times 10^{-4} \text{ statute mi}$$

$$1 \text{ Ångstrom (Å)} = 10^{-8} \text{ cm}$$

PROBLEMS

See Tables 9-2 (page 108) and 3-1 (page 34). Give setup only unless specifically directed to find answers to these problems. Show all units at all times. (Unless otherwise specified, miles are statute miles.)

1. Perform the following conversions:
   a. 17 dm to meters.
   b. 4.8 kg to grams.
   c. 4 liters to milliliters.
   d. 73 cm to millimeters.
   e. 420 mm to kilometers.
   f. 79 kg to decigrams.
   g. 59 cg to kilograms.
   h. 17 cg to micrograms.
   i. 49 km to miles.
   j. 5 km/sec to miles per hour.
   k. 7 μ to millimeters.
   l. 14 μ to millimicrons.
   m. 45 cm to microns.
   n. 11 mμ to millimeters.
   o. 45 cm to nanometers.
   p. 14 μ to Ångstroms.
   q. 41 pm to gigameters.
   r. 9 Tm to microns.
   s. 5 Å to picometers.
   t. 14 Tm/millenium to microns per millisecond.
   u. 45 liters to lambdas.
   v. 0.17 cm^3 to microliters.

2. How many particles 13 Å wide could stand shoulder to shoulder along 17 Micron Drive in Van Diemen's Land? How swiftly could the road be cleared of particles if 100 particles per second were blown off the road?

3. How many milliliters are there in 5700 gal?

4. Find:
   a. The volume of a cube 5.00 cm on each edge.
   b. The volume of a unit cube of NaCl, edge length 5.63 Å.

5. Find:
   a. The edge length of a cube of 1.500×10^3 cm^3 volume.
   b. The edge length of a unit cube of sodium bromide. Volume of unit cube of sodium bromide is 2.10×10^{-22} cm^3.

6. What is the volume in cubic inches and in cubic centimeters of a box 2 in. by 6 in. by 7 in.?
7. How many minutes would it take to empty a full reservoir 108 m × 155 m × 35 m if it lost water at a uniform rate of 525 gal/min?
8. How high will 220 m^3 fill a box 3 × 7 m × 100 m deep?
9. How high will 200 British gal fill a box 3 by 7 m and 100 m deep?
10. How high would 200 British gal fill a cylinder with a radius of 100 cm? (Volume of a cylinder is $\pi r^2 h$, where π is 3.14, r is radius, and h is height.)
11. How many cubic centimeters are there in 1 μ^3?
12. How many lambdas are there in 1 μ^3?
13. Find the volume in microliters of a box that measures 10 × 10 × 5 mμ.
14. To what depth could 1 ml of liquid fill a box 10 cm × 10 cm? Express the answer in Ångstroms.
15. How many lambdas of liquid would be needed to fill a steel sphere whose inside diameter is 16 μ? (The volume of a sphere is 1.33 πr^3, where π is 3.14 and r is radius.)
16. How many microliters would be required to coat the sphere in the preceding problem to a depth of 1 μ all over if the outside diameter is 17 μ?
17. How many light years are there in 41 parsec?
18. Convert 208 nautical mi to light years.
19. What is the difference in astronomical units between 1 statute mi and 1 nautical mi?

10

PERCENTAGE

Percentage means parts per hundred. Most students know how to do percentage, but why not follow the method presented here to be sure you understand what you are really doing.

EXAMPLE 10–1

If 7 out of 10 men this year will buy a suit, what percentage of men will buy a suit this year? In other words, how many men out of 100 would buy a suit?

We are seeking men per 100; therefore we must mathematically operate on men. Logically, more men in a group of 100 would buy suits than in a group of 10. The changing total number of men in the group constitutes the correcting fraction.

$$\frac{7 \text{ men} \times 100 \text{ men}}{10 \text{ men}} = 70 \text{ men}$$

This is 70 men out of a new total of 100 men; it is 70 parts per 100 or 70%. As more commonly written,

$$\frac{7 \text{ men} \times 100}{10 \text{ men}} = 70\%$$

EXAMPLE 10-2

A $600 investment in a speculative stock increased $24,000 in value. What percent profit does this represent?

Had the value merely increased $600 there would have been a 100% profit. In essence this is the problem:

If a $600 increase in value represents a 100% profit, what percent profit would a $24,000 increase in value represent?

You want percent, that is, parts per hundred, so operate on percent. Therefore

$$\frac{100\% \times \$24,000}{\$600} = 4000\%$$

EXAMPLE 10-3

A $600 investment in a speculative stock increased to a paper value of $24,000. Find the percent profit if sold immediately. Find the percentage increase in paper value.

Before finding the percent profit one must find the profit.

$24,000 − $600 = $23,400 profit

$600 of the $24,000 is not profit but merely recovery of the original investment. Now

$$\frac{100\% \times (\$24,000 - \$600)}{\$600} = 3900\% \text{ profit}$$

Wouldn't the percent increase in paper value be the same numerical value as the percent profit?

EXAMPLE 10-4

Anhydrous copper sulfate is 40% copper. What weight of copper could be obtained from 150 lb of anhydrous copper sulfate?

Always focus your attention on the result you want. You *know* there's less than 150 lb of copper. Out of 100 parts of anhydrous copper sulfate only 40 parts are copper. You want weight, so operate on the only weight you have, 150 lb. This would be

$$\frac{150 \text{ lb} \times 40}{100} \text{ or } 150 \text{ lb} \times 0.40 = 60 \text{ lb}$$

However, perhaps one could think of this problem in the following fashion.

You want to know the total parts (in pounds) of copper in the 150-lb sample. The 40% says that out of 100 total parts (or 100 lb) of sample there would be 40 parts (or 40 lb) of copper. In the 150 total parts (150 lb) there would be more copper than in 100 total parts (100 lb).

So $\dfrac{40 \text{ lb} \times 150 \text{ lb}}{100 \text{ lb}} = 60 \text{ lb}$

EXAMPLE 10–5

A ton of a certain ore contained 0.035% gold. Find the weight of gold in 24 tons of this ore.

$\dfrac{24 \text{ tons} \times 0.035}{100}$ or $24 \text{ tons} \times 0.00035 = 0.0084 \text{ ton}$

EXAMPLE 10–6

What weight of 50%-pure gold bars would you need to obtain 48 lb of pure gold?

Focus on the result. You know that you need more than 48 lb of the gold bars to get 48 lb of gold. The bars are only 50% gold.

$48 \text{ lb} \times 2 = 96 \text{ lb}$ (you know this is right)

$\dfrac{48 \text{ lb} \times 100}{50}$ or $\dfrac{48 \text{ lb}}{0.50} = 96 \text{ lb, too}$

You want to be careful not to confuse the preceding problem with this one.

EXAMPLE 10–7

What weight of gold could be obtained from a 48-lb bar known to contain 50% gold?

$\dfrac{48 \text{ lb} \times 50}{100}$ or $48 \text{ lb} \times 0.50 = 24 \text{ lb}$

EXAMPLE 10–8

In 1900 the city of X had 409 people over 40 years of age. In 1964 it had 617 such people. Find the number of people in this age category in 1836 and in 2028.

One would not actually try to make population predictions—or any other kind of predictions—without much more data. However, we are interested in demonstrating problem-solving techniques here. For our present purposes, therefore, we will make two quite unreasonable assumptions and solve the problem separately on the basis of each assumption. These are the assumptions:

1. The absolute change in population for successive 64-year periods is constant.
2. The percent change in population for successive 64-year periods is constant.

First of all, what would be the absolute change? There are (617 − 409) or 208 more people in 1964 than there were in 1900. If the absolute change was constant, then in 2028 there would be 208 more than in 1964, making the number (617 + 208) or 825. In 1900 there must have been 208 more than there had been in 1836. The 1836 population must have been 201.

Now what would have been the percentage change in population from 1900 to 1964? Percentage can be somewhat treacherous. You have to know what percentage you want.

A. The 1900 population is $\dfrac{409 \times 100}{617}$ or 66.3% of the 1964 population.

B. The 1964 population is $\dfrac{617 \times 100}{409}$ or 151% of the 1900 population.

C. The 1900 population is $\dfrac{208 \times 100}{617}$ or 33.7% less than 1964 population.

D. The 1964 population is $\dfrac{208 \times 100}{409}$ or 50.9% more than 1900 population.

You will naturally have noticed that we have four different percentages here. Each is correct. One just can't give a percentage. One has to qualify it, explain what it is. Let's demonstrate that no matter which type of percentage operation you chose, you would get the same answers for the 1836 and 2028 populations, presuming percent change for successive 64-year periods is constant.

Considering A, find the populations in 1836 and 2028. If 1900's population is 66.3% of the 1964 population, then the 1964 population must be 66.3% of the 2028 population.

Let x = 2028's population

Then 66.3% of what is equal to 617? That is,

$$0.663x = 617$$
$$x = \frac{617}{0.663} = 931$$

Similarly, 1836's population was 66.3% of the 1900 population, or

$$0.663(409) = 271$$

Considering B, find the populations in 1836 and 2028. If the 1964 population is 151% of the 1900 population, then the 2028 population must be 151% of the 1964 population.

$$1.51(617) = 932$$

The 1900 population could only have been 151% of the 1836 population (according to the limited data we have and assuming the same percentage changes occurred).

Let x = the 1836 population

$$1.51x = 409$$
$$x = 271$$

Considering C, find the populations for 1836 and 2028. The 1964 population must be 33.7% less than the 2028 population.

Let x = the 2028 population

$$x - 0.337x = 617$$
$$0.663x = 617$$
$$x = 931$$

Similarly the 1836 population must be 33.7% less than the 1900 population.

$$409 - 0.337(409) = 271$$

Considering D, find the populations for 1836 and 2028. The 2028 population must be 50.9% more than the 1964 population.

$$617 + 0.509(617) = 1.509(617) = 931$$

The 1900 population is 50.9% more than the 1836 population.

Let x = the 1836 population

$$x + 0.509x = 409$$
$$1.509x = 409$$
$$x = 271$$

Before you think that our statement has not been proved because we have 931 and 932 for the 2028 population, remember that we have only three significant figures with which to get the answer. There is an uncertainty in the third figure. So, depending on the exact figures used, one would expect to get a variation of one; 931 is 931 $\pm$ 1, and 932 is 932 $\pm$ 1.

Perhaps you're wondering why we made such a song and dance of this? All too often problems such as this are done in haste, and just because the 1964 population is 50.9% more than the 1900 population one hastily jumps to the conclusion that the 1836 population is 50.9% less than the 1900 population. No one is likely to phrase it in such fashion, but problems are often solved as if this were what the person solving the problem had in mind. Let's try this just to see the result.

$$409 - 0.509(409) = 201$$
$$409 + 0.509(617) = 931$$

The figure for the 2028 population is the same, but we're hopelessly in error for the 1836 population. The 1964 population is 50.9% greater than the 1900 population, but the 1900 population is 33.7% less than the 1964 population—not 50.9% less.

EXAMPLE 10–9

Find the volume of fluid that must be poured into a 40.00-liter tank in cool morning weather so that the tank will be completely filled but not overflowing after a 10% expansion of the fluid during the warmest part of the day. Presume that the tank is made of something whose expansion is negligible and that the fluid has a negligible evaporation.

Let x = volume of the fluid to be put into the container

Then $x + 0.10x = 40.00$ liters
$$1.10x = 40.00 \text{ liters}$$
$$x = 36.36 \text{ liters}$$

Do you see that it would be quite wrong to say that the volume must be 36.00 liters (10% less than 40.00 liters)? 36.00 liters would be the volume that 40.00 liters would have if it shrank 10%. This is not what happened. You have to *add* 10% *of* the original volume *to* the original volume to get 40.00 liters.

Proof: 36.36 liters + (0.10 $\times$ 36.36 liters) = 40.00 liters
36.00 liters + (0.10 $\times$ 36.00 liters) = 39.60 liters

Let's modify Example 10–9 in this fashion.

EXAMPLE 10-10

How much fluid must be poured into a 40.00-liter container in the cool of the morning so that it will be filled but not overflowing after the fluid has expanded 10% and the container has expanded 0.8%?

Will you have a 40.00-liter container? No. The container will hold ... now, wait. If the container expands, it presumably expands in all directions. We would seem to need more information.

For example, if a $10 \times 10 \times 10$ tank (units immaterial) expanded 10% on every edge (linearly only, let's say, for simplicity here), then the volume would be

$11 \times 11 \times 11 = 1331$ cubic units

But if it expanded so that the net volume was 10% more, then it would hold

$10 \times 10 \times 10 + 0.10(10 \times 10 \times 10) = 1100$ cubic units

One has to know what the wording means. This wording usually means that the net increase in the volume of fluid contained is 0.8%. This is not what it says, strictly speaking, but that is what it means, according to the informal conventions in use. Now the solution would be

$$x + 0.10x = 40.00 + (0.008 \times 40.00)$$
$$1.10x = 1.008 \,(40.00)$$
$$x = 36.65 \text{ liters}$$

EXAMPLE 10-11

When 90% full of a certain liquid, a container with a capacity of exactly 2500 gal contained exactly 2000 lb of the liquid. During given temperature changes the container expanded insignificantly but the liquid expanded 15%. What weight was actually in the container after expansion? Presume container volume measured to nearest gallon.

original volume of liquid = 0.90 × 2500 gal = 2250 gal
volume of liquid after expansion = 1.15(0.90 × 2500 gal) = 2588 gal
loss of volume due to overflow = 1.15(2500 gal × 0.90) − 2500 gal = 88 gal

The 2588 gal weighs 2000 lb. The 2500 gal left in the tank weighs

$$\frac{2500 \text{ gal} \times 2000 \text{ lb}}{2588 \text{ gal}} = 1932 \text{ lb}$$

Done in one fell swoop, this is

$$\frac{2500 \text{ gal}}{1.15(0.90 \times 2500 \text{ gal})} \times 2000 \text{ lb} = 1932 \text{ lb}$$

Be careful not to think that the liquid must overflow just because its percent expansion is greater than the 10% emptiness of the tank. With the tank 10% empty, the liquid could have expanded 11% without filling the tank.

$1.11(0.90 \times 2500 \text{ gal}) = 2498 \text{ gal}$

Thus there would have been no overflow and there would still have been 2000 lb of liquid in the tank.

PROBLEMS

Give setups only unless specifically directed to find answers.

1. In a certain process 89 g of platinum was put into a reaction chamber. At the end of the process 87 g of Pt was recovered. What is the percentage loss of platinum?
2. If 44 g of 90%-pure copper was used in a reaction, how much copper was actually used in the reaction?
3. Carbon dioxide is 27.3% carbon. Find the weight of carbon in 82 g of carbon dioxide.
4. Compound R is 31.9% Y. What weight of Y must be used to prepare 825 g of compound R?
5. In a certain process 5 tons of 85%-pure sulfuric acid was produced. What weight of pure sulfuric acid was in the 5 tons?
6. What weight of the sulfuric acid produced in problem 5 must be taken to obtain 35 lb of pure sulfuric acid?
7. In a certain reaction 138 g of starting material should yield 161 g of product. In a given case 138 g of starting material gave 150 g of product. Find the percent yield of product based on theoretical yield.
8. The city of A in the state of B was subjected to a fictitious population study.

	1900	1964
number of people over 40 years of age	409	617
number of people between 21 and 40	227	127
number of children under 6 years of age	184	62

What was the percent increase or decrease for the 1964 population in each category? Presuming the percent rate of population change for successive 64-year periods to be constant, find the population in the 21—40 and under-6 categories for 1836 and 2028.

9. A given tanker truck lost 3.8% of its liquid cargo by evaporation and

2.7% through spillage. If 8500 gal was delivered (at the same temperature at which the truck was filled), what volume must have originally been put in the truck?

10. What volume of air (21% oxygen by volume) would be needed to supply 70 liters of oxygen?

11. A stock increased its value by 0.9%. If its value at time of purchase was $1100, what would its value after the increase be?

12. What weight of 33%-pure HNO_3 must be used in a reaction that calls for 191 g of HNO_3?

13. What volume of fluid must be put into a tanker to allow for 8% loss by evaporation, 2% loss through spillage, and 1% loss for other causes in order to deliver 10,000 gal?

14. A certain type of mushroom increases its weight two-fold every 3 weeks. A certain ship can carry 55 tons of cargo. What weight of mushroom could be put aboard this ship (with no other cargo) in order to arrive at its destination 3 weeks later just at the moment of sinking? (What assumptions must be made to solve this problem?)

15. Given the following data on abundance of elements in the dry atmosphere (to an altitude of about 60 km):

Component	Percent by volume	Percent by weight
N_2 (nitrogen)	78.09	75.53
O_2 (oxygen)	20.95	23.14
Kr (krypton)	1×10^{-5}	2.9×10^{-4}
Ne (neon)	1.8×10^{-3}	1.3×10^{-3}
O_3 (ozone)	6.0×10^{-5}	1.0×10^{-4}

a. How many cubic centimeters would there be of Kr in 100 liters of dry air at sea level?

b. What weight of dry air would theoretically contain 40 g of O_3?

c. What volume of air would be needed to furnish 75 liters of Ne?

d. What weight of N_2 could be obtained from a sample of air that contained 5000 liters of O_2? (22.4 liters of O_2 weighs 32 g when the volume is measured at standard temperature and pressure. The same volume of N_2 under the same conditions weighs 28 g.)

11

DENSITY AND SPECIFIC GRAVITY PROBLEMS; IMMERSION PROBLEMS

DENSITY

Density by definition is the mass of a unit volume of a substance at a given temperature. A distinction should immediately be drawn here. Most definitions of density use the phrase "weight per unit volume." One might think that mass and weight were synonymous terms. Nothing could be further from the truth. Mass is a measure of the quantity of matter; it is also a measure of inertia.* Mass is supposedly fixed and invariable. A given quantity of matter has a definite number of atoms no matter where the measurement is made. However, the weight of this same quantity of matter can vary greatly with the site of measurement, since weight is a measure of the force of gravitational attraction. Decrease in weight because of "loss of gravity" is surely not unheard of by anyone likely to be reading this.

On Earth the units chosen for measurement of mass and the units for weight can be used almost interchangeably if one remembers the distinction between mass and weight. We will hereafter use the phrase weight per unit volume for density. The actual units for weight and volume are immaterial. Chemists use grams per milliliter (or cubic centimeter) for solids and liquids and grams per liter for gases and vapors. Engineers generally use pounds per cubic foot. Thus, for example, one can say that the density of water is 1 g/ml or 62.4 lb/ft^3 meaning that 1 ml of

---

*Many students find this last statement meaningless. We will try to make it clearer in Chapter 14.

water weighs 1 g or that 1 ft^3 of water weighs 62.4 lb.

You have no doubt noticed that temperature was specified as part of the definition. This is necessary because volume varies with temperature and thus density would necessarily vary with temperature also. Unless a specific temperature is mentioned, ordinary room temperature is presumed to be the temperature. For water, however, the density is 1 g/ml only at 3.97°C. At any other temperature the density of water is less than 1 g/ml, since water expands above and below this temperature.

EXAMPLE 11–1

At 20.0°C, 46.9 g of furfuran occupied 50.0 ml of space. Find the density of furfuran.

$$\text{density} = \frac{46.9 \text{ g}}{50.0 \text{ ml}} = 0.938 \frac{\text{g}}{\text{ml}}$$

Would the density be more or less than 0.938 g/ml at 40.0°C? Less. The volume would expand as temperature increases, while the weight remains constant, thereby causing each milliliter to weigh less.

EXAMPLE 11–2

What would be the volume of 50.0 g of silver? The density of silver at 20.0°C is 10.5 g/ml.

$$\text{volume} = \frac{50.0 \text{ g}}{10.5 \frac{\text{g}}{\text{ml}}} = 4.76 \text{ ml} \quad (\text{volume at } 20.0°\text{C})$$

EXAMPLE 11–3

What would be the weight of 25.0 ml of dimethyl itaconate ($d_{18.0°C}$ = 1.125 g/ml)?

$$\frac{25.0 \text{ ml} \times 1.125 \text{ g}}{\text{ml}} = 28.1 \text{ g}$$

Note that one more figure than is significant is included in the setup and used in the calculation, but the answer is presented with only three significant figures.

Can you now write the formulas for finding density (symbol: d), weight (symbol: W), and volume (symbol: V) from the appropriate data? Beware of using formulas alone. Reason out each problem and then remember formulas for quick use in the future. You get

$$d = \frac{W}{V} \quad W = dV \quad V = \frac{W}{d}$$

EXAMPLE 11-4

Concentrated HNO_3 (nitric acid) is 69.5% HNO_3 by weight. The density of concentrated HNO_3 is 1.42 g/ml. (This means that a solution whose density is 1.42 g/ml contains 69.5% HNO_3 by weight.)

a. Find the weight of 525 ml of concentrated HNO_3 solution.

$$\frac{1.42 \text{ g} \times 525 \text{ ml}}{\text{ml}} = 746 \text{ g}$$

b. Find the weight of HNO_3 in 525 ml of concentrated HNO_3 solution.

$$\frac{1.42 \text{ g} \times 0.695 \times 525 \text{ ml}}{\text{ml}} = 518 \text{ g}$$

c. What volume of concentrated HNO_3 is needed to supply 150 g of pure HNO_3?

$$\frac{150 \text{ g}}{1.42 \frac{\text{g}}{\text{ml}} \times 0.695} = 152 \text{ ml}$$

SPECIFIC GRAVITY

Specific gravity is the ratio of the weight of a given volume of a substance to the weight of an equal volume of water (at the same temperature, naturally). For gases the ratio is to the weight of an equal volume of air (at the same temperature and pressure) for practical reasons. Since specific gravity is a ratio, it is necessarily dimensionless. Anyone who can solve density problems would be hard put to be really unable to solve specific gravity problems, but perhaps a few examples would not be out of order.

Facts: 1 ml of water weighs 1 g (at 3.97°C); 1 ft³ of water weighs 62.4 lb.

Specific gravity and density are necessarily numerically the same in the metric system (since 1 ml of water weighs 1 g), but they are naturally numerically different in the English system.

EXAMPLE 11-5

The specific gravity of ellagic acid is 1.667.

a. Find the weight of 25 ft^3 of ellagic acid.

Ellagic acid is 1.667 times heavier than water, and a cubic foot of water weighs 62.4 lb. Therefore

$$\frac{62.4 \text{ lb} \times 25 \text{ ft}^3 \times 1.667}{\text{ft}^3} = 2.6 \times 10^3 \text{ lb}$$

b. Find the weight of 25 liters of ellagic acid.

Ellagic acid is 1.667 times heavier than water no matter what unit system is used; therefore

$$\frac{25 \text{ liters} \times 1000 \text{ g} \times 1.667}{\text{liter}} = 4.2 \times 10^4 \text{ g}$$

Many variations of this problem exist. They just involve cumbersome transformations from one unit system to another in many cases.

EXAMPLE 11-6

What is the volume of 35 lb of solid crystalline α arsenic? The specific gravity of α arsenic is 5.73.

Remember that specific gravity is the ratio of the weight of a substance to the weight of an equal volume of water. Since 1 ft^3 of water weighs 62.4 lb, 1 ft^3 of α arsenic weighs

$$\frac{62.4 \text{ lb} \times 5.73}{\text{ft}^3}$$

Therefore $\dfrac{35 \text{ lb}}{62.4 \dfrac{\text{lb}}{\text{ft}^3} \times 5.73} = 0.098 \text{ ft}^3$ of α arsenic

IMMERSION PROBLEMS

Immersion problems, though seemingly not chemistry problems, do involve the concept of density. Moreover, they provide a simple means of developing something quite complex, problem-solving skill—a major purpose of this book.

Imagine a 150-lb man. What weight must a chair on which he is to sit be able to bear? What weight must a hammock in which he is to rest be able to bear? Visualize this 150-lb man being held in air by a stream of compressed air from a hose. What upward force counter to the downward force of the man's weight must the stream of compressed air exert in order to hold this man in air? Your answer was 150 lb in all cases.

Now, what upward force must be exerted to hold this man up in (a) water, (b) molten iron, and (c) mercury? Again, 150 lb. In other words, before any object can float in any medium, the medium must exert a buoyant force equal to the weight of the object that is to float in it. This particular man was buoyed up by 150 lb of *counterforce,* to use the common terminology.

Now let's imagine this 150-lb man has a volume of 2.67 ft^3. To float in a liquid he must displace less than 2.67 ft^3 and at the same time displace 150 lb of the liquid. This 150 lb of liquid would exert a counterforce of 150 lb to buoy him up in the liquid. If 150 lb of a liquid had a volume greater than 2.67 ft^3, then the man would sink in the liquid; if it had a volume less than 2.67 ft^3 he would float. Alone and unaided this man could not displace more than either 150 lb of 2.67 ft^3 of any liquid.

Now let's consider two different liquids, water and ethyl ether, which have specific gravities 1.00 and 0.708, respectively. Their densities are 62.4 and 44.2 lb/ft^3, respectively. The weight of 2.67 ft^3 of water is 166 lb, that of 2.67 ft^3 of ethyl ether is 118 lb. It would obviously take 166 lb to push 2.67 ft^3 of water out of the way and only 118 lb to push 2.67 ft^3 of ethyl ether out of the way. On stepping into the water, the 150-lb, 2.67-ft^3 man could not push 166 lb of water out of the way. He would sink until he had pushed 150 lb of water away. At this point there would be a balance of forces, as it were. Thereafter he would float with what could for all practical purposes be considered zero weight. To submerge him, 16 lb would have to be put on top of him.

On the other hand, the same man could easily push 118 lb of ether out of the way on stepping into ether. He would sink to the bottom of a pool of ether with 32 lb to spare. In effect, he would weigh 32 lb when submerged in ether. His weight is greater than the weight of ether he can displace. There could not be a balance of forces, as there was when he was floating in the water, until he reached the bottom of the pool. Then the floor of the pool would supply the necessary counterforce of 32 lb for his remaining 32 lb of weight.

Let's put some of this in general terms and work some problems.

EXAMPLE 11-8

Given the following information:

Material	Physical state	Density, lb/ft³
A	solid	50
B	liquid	30
C	liquid	200
D	liquid	150
E	solid	20

a. Would A float in B?

No; 1 ft³ of A weighs more than 1 ft³ of B.

b. By how much would A have to be lightened or buoyed up to float in B?

$$50 \frac{lb}{ft^3} - 30 \frac{lb}{ft^3} = 20 \frac{lb}{ft^3}$$

c. Would A float in C?

Yes; 1 ft³ of A weighs far less than 1 ft³ of C.

d. What maximum weight could 1 ft³ of A push out of the way?

50 lb

e. Could A carry any extra weight in C without sinking?

Before 1 ft³ of A would sink in C, it would have to push 1 ft³ of C out of the way. That would require a total force of 200 lb. Since 1 ft³ of A weighs only 50 lb, it can carry more weight.

f. What weight could 1 ft³ of A carry in C?

$$1 \text{ ft}^3 \times \left(200 \frac{lb}{ft^3} - 50 \frac{lb}{ft^3}\right) = 150 \text{ lb}$$

We did ask for weight, but this information would have been more useful in terms of weight per cubic foot, so,

$$200 \frac{lb}{ft^3} - 50 \frac{lb}{ft^3} = 150 \frac{lb}{ft^3} \text{ carrying or buoying capacity}$$
(really infinitesimally less)

g. What fraction of the cubic foot of A would be below the surface in C?

One cubic foot of A displaces 50 lb of C, which occupies 0.25 ft³.

$$\frac{50 \text{ lb}}{200 \frac{lb}{ft^3}} = 0.25 \text{ ft}^3$$

Then 0.25 ft³ of A must do the displacing, and 0.25 ft³ of A is below the surface. Since

$$\frac{0.25 \text{ ft}^3}{1 \text{ ft}^3} = 0.25$$

one-fourth of the cube would be in the liquid, three-fourths would be out. Obviously, the height of the cube is 1 ft, so 0.25 ft on each side would be in the fluid, 0.75 ft out.

h. If A somehow had been fastened to the bottom of a pool of C, what would happen when it was unfastened?

A would rise to the surface.

i. Could A, in rising to the surface, bring any extra weight with it?

Obviously, yes.

j. What is the buoying capacity of A in C? (In other words, what weight could A bring to the surface with it after having been forcibly sunk or tied down in C, or what weight could it carry in C?)

$$200 \frac{\text{lb}}{\text{ft}^3} - 50 \frac{\text{lb}}{\text{ft}^3} = 150 \frac{\text{lb}}{\text{ft}^3} \quad \text{(just a trifle less really)}$$

k. Will A float or sink in D? Float. Now what weight could a solid block of A measuring 4 ft × 5 ft × 10 ft bear in a pool of D without sinking?

$$4 \text{ ft} \times 5 \text{ ft} \times 10 \text{ ft} \left(150 \frac{\text{lb}}{\text{ft}^3} - 50 \frac{\text{lb}}{\text{ft}^3}\right) = 2 \times 10^4 \text{ lb} \quad \text{(infinitesimally less)}$$

l. What weight could a forcibly sunk block of solid A 4 × 5 × 10 ft buoy up in a pool of D?

This is just the same as (k).

m. By what amount would a block of A 4 × 5 × 10 ft have to be lightened to float in B?

$$5 \text{ ft} \times 4 \text{ ft} \times 10 \text{ ft} \left(50 \frac{\text{lb}}{\text{ft}^3} - 30 \frac{\text{lb}}{\text{ft}^3}\right) = 4 \times 10^3 \text{ lb} \quad \text{(infinitesimally more)}$$

n. Will E float in B? Yes. Each cubic foot of E is lighter than one of B. Could E carry extra weight or buoy up extra weight in B? Yes. How much?

$$30 \frac{\text{lb}}{\text{ft}^3} - 20 \frac{\text{lb}}{\text{ft}^3} = 10 \frac{\text{lb}}{\text{ft}^3}$$

o. How many cubic feet of E would be needed to buoy up 1 ft³ of A in B?

From (b) you know that each cubic foot of A needs 20 lb of buoying force. You know that each cubic foot of E can supply 10 lb of buoying force. You know then that you need 2 ft^3 of E to buoy up 1 ft^3 of A in B.

$$\frac{1 \text{ ft}^3 \times (50 - 30) \text{ lb/ft}^3}{(30 - 20) \text{ lb/ft}^3} = 2 \text{ ft}^3$$

Be sure you see why this is reasonable. Had we not used the "1 ft^3," we would have had a dimensionless ratio instead of cubic feet as an answer. Be sure you see why this was done and that it was valid.

p. What volume of E would be needed to buoy up a $4 \times 5 \times 10$ ft block of solid A in B?

$$\frac{4 \text{ ft} \times 5 \text{ ft} \times 10 \text{ ft} \times (50 - 30) \text{ lb/ft}^3}{(30 - 20) \text{ lb/ft}^3} = 4 \times 10^2 \text{ ft}^3$$

q. What thickness of E must be fastened to the largest face of the block of A described in (p) to prevent it from sinking in B?

You know you need a total of 400 ft^3 of E. If the weight is uniformly distributed and the container of B suitably large, then the thickness of E to be fastened to the 10 by 5 ft face of A is

$$\frac{400 \text{ ft}^3}{10 \text{ ft} \times 5 \text{ ft}} = 8 \text{ ft}$$

r. What weight of E would be needed to buoy up the block of A as described in (p)?

You have the volume of E from (p). You know the density of E, so

$$\frac{400 \text{ ft}^3 \times 20 \text{ lb}}{\text{ft}^3} = 8 \times 10^3 \text{ lb}$$

s. What volume of E would be needed to buoy up 5×10^3 lb of A in B?

You know how to do this if you have the volume of A. You can easily get that volume, so

$$\frac{5 \times 10^3 \text{ lb} \times (50 - 30) \text{ lb/ft}^3}{50 \dfrac{\text{lb}}{\text{ft}^3} \times (30 - 20) \text{ lb/ft}^3} = 2 \times 10^2 \text{ ft}^3$$

t. What weight of E would be needed to buoy up 5×10^3 lb of A in B?

You would just turn the answer to the preceding problem into pounds by means of the density, would you not? Done in one step this gives the following setup, a combination of the ideas in (r) and (s):

$$\frac{5 \times 10^3 \text{ lb } \times (50 - 30) \text{ lb/ft}^3 \times 20 \text{ lb}}{50 \underline{\text{lb}} \times (30 - 20) \text{ lb/ft}^3 \quad \text{ft}^3} = 4 \times 10^3 \text{ lb}$$
$$\frac{}{\text{ft}^3}$$

We hope you're now wondering why we have done some of these problems in such a complicated fashion. We want to get the ideas across. You should probably be thinking of more direct ways to do these problems. Let's take a few more examples,

EXAMPLE 11–9

What weight of E would be needed to buoy 5×10^3 lb of A in B?

First ask yourself some questions:

1. What buoying does 1 lb of A need in B? Each cubic foot of A needs to be lightened by 20 lb in order to float in B, and 1 ft^3 of A weighs 50 lb, so

$$\frac{20 \text{ lb lightening needed}}{50 \text{ lb of A}} = \frac{0.4 \text{ lb lightening needed}}{\text{lb of A}}$$

2. What buoying capacity does 1 lb of E have in B? Each cubic foot of E has 10 lb of buoying force in B. Each cubic foot of E weighs 20 lb. So

$$\frac{10 \text{ lb buoying power for E}}{20 \text{ lb of E}} = \frac{0.5 \text{ lb buoying power for E}}{\text{lb of E}}$$

Now all we have to do is find the total weight to be buoyed and the weight needed to do the buoying.

$$\frac{5 \times 10^3 \text{ lb A} \times 0.4 \text{ lb b. p. needed}}{\text{lb A} \qquad \times 0.5 \text{ lb b. p. available}} = 4 \times 10^3 \text{ lb E}$$
$$\frac{}{\text{lb E}}$$

All of these examples involve English units. Had you been given metric density (grams per milliliter), or even specific gravity (from which you could get density in either English or metric units), you would solve problems in exactly the same fashion. Consider this example.

EXAMPLE 11-10

What minimum weight of maple (density 0.49 g/ml) would be needed to prevent 50.0 g of silver from sinking in carbon tetrachloride (density 1.84 g/ml)? The density of silver is 10.5 g/ml.

$$\frac{50.0 \text{ g}}{10.5 \dfrac{\text{g}}{\text{ml}}} \times (10.5 - 1.84) \frac{\text{g}}{\text{ml} \times (1.84 - 0.49) \dfrac{\text{g}}{\text{ml}}} \times 0.49 \frac{\text{g}}{\text{ml}} = 15 \text{ g}$$

| I | II | III | IV |

Step I gives volume of the silver. Step II gives the buoying or lightening needed for each milliliter of silver; multiplication of the volume of silver by this factor gives the total buoying that the silver needs. Step III gives the buoying capacity of the maple in carbon tetrachloride, in grams per milliliter of maple; division by this factor gives the volume of maple needed. In step IV, multiplication by density gives the weight of maple needed.

Table 11-1   Densities in Grams Per Milliliter at 20°C

acetone	0.791
air	0.00129
carbon tetrachloride	1.84
copper	8.93
cypress	0.53
ethanol	0.79
gold	19.3
ironwood, Tasmanian	1.05
lead	11.3
mercury	13.6
oak	0.77
redwood, medium hard	0.38
silver	10.5
sulfuric acid, concentrated	1.84
tin	5.75
water	1.00 (or 62.4 lb/ft^3)
zinc	7.14

Table 11-2 Specific Gravities at 20°C

benzene	0.88
cerussite	6.6
iron	7.86
nickel	8.90
water	1.0

PROBLEMS

Show setup only unless specifically directed to find a numerical answer.

1. 25.00 ml of water weighed 24.93 g at 21.0°C. Find the density of the water.
2. If 557 g of glycol occupy 500 cm^3 at 19.0°C, find the density of glycol.
3. 40.5 g of aluminum was dropped into a graduated cylinder filled with water to the 23.8-ml mark. After the aluminum had sunk to the bottom, the water level was at the 48.9-ml mark. Find the density of the aluminum.
4. A piece of iron 2 in. by 3 in. by 10 in. weighed 7700 g. Find the density of iron in grams per milliliter. In pounds per cubic foot.
5. What is the volume of 500 g of mercury?
6. To what level would the addition of 150 g of gold raise the water in a graduated cylinder from an initial level of 14.3 ml?
7. What volume of concentrated sulfuric acid (96% pure) must be used to obtain 250 g of pure sulfuric acid?
8. What is the weight of 30 ml of acetone?
9. What is the weight of a piece of lead 20 cm × 20 cm × 90 cm?
10. What weight of silver at 20°C must be used to have it completely fill a sphere with a capacity of 200 cm^3 at 961°C? The density of silver is 10.5 g/ml at 20.0°C and 9.3 g/ml at 961°C.
11. How thick would a piece of zinc 10 in. by 7 in. be if it weighed 59.1 g?
12. What is the edge length of a cube of tin weighing 150 g?
13. What is the specific gravity of a rock 2 ft × 6 ft × 10 ft that weighs 40,000 lb?

14. What weight of benzene would fill a box 12 in. by 12 in. by 7 ft?
15. Find the volume of 8500 lb of cerussite.
16. At 0°C and 760 torr, 300 cm³ of carbon dioxide weighed 0.595 g. What is the density of the carbon dioxide gas? (See Chapter 15 on gas problems if 760 torr is unfamiliar to you.)
17. A 100-ml glass bulb filled with air weighed 14.019 g. Filled with SO_2 gas, the same bulb weighed 14.183 g. Find the density of SO_2 gas.
18. A piece of gold weighs 5 g in air. What would it weigh suspended in water?
19. What would 50 g of silver weigh in water? In carbon tetrachloride? In mercury?
20. What weight could a solid piece of cypress measuring 10 × 10 × 100 ft carry in ethanol?
21. What volume of lead could the cypress in problem 20 carry?
22. What volume of cypress would be needed to raise 7000 m³ of solid tin from the bottom of a lake?
23. What weight of cypress would be needed to raise 5000 kg of silver (dry land weight) from the bottom of a pond of water?
24. It took four pieces of cypress 5 × 10 × 10 m to prevent a certain piece of metal with a volume of 300 m³ from sinking in water. Find the density of this metal.
25. What is the weight of a piece of oak 175 × 10 × 10 cm? What volume of water would this piece of oak displace? Would the oak sink or float? What length of oak would remain above water if this particular piece of oak were put into a cylinder 2 m high and 15 cm in diameter filled to the brim with water? Volume of cylinder is $\pi r^2 h$.
26. What weight of lead must be put on one end of an evenly sawed redwood log 100 ft long with a fairly uniform diameter of 1 ft to make the log just sink in a well filled with water? Assume depth of well is adequate. Volume of cylinder: $\pi r^2 h$.
27. How thick a piece of oak must be attached to a piece of Tasmanian ironwood 10 × 10 × 3 cm in order to have the two pieces of wood just float? Presume that you can fasten the pieces of wood together with some sort of weightless and volumeless fasteners for simplicity here.
28. A rectangular barge 150 ft by 40 ft rode in fresh water with the water level 5 ft above the bottom of the barge. When 10 pieces of metal 4 ft by 9 ft by 1 ft were placed on top of the barge, it sank another 3 ft into the water. When the empty barge entered salt water, it rode 1/16 in. higher than in fresh water. What was the weight of the unloaded barge? The specific gravity of the metal cargo? The specific gravity of the salt water?
29. The surface displacement of a certain modern submarine is 2000 tons

of fresh water. Its submerged displacement is 3000 tons of fresh water. What is the weight of the submarine? What is its total volume in cubic feet? How many cubic feet of iron, put into the surfaced submarine, would cause it to sink just below the surface?

30. A certain alloy of iron and nickel had a specific gravity of 8.53. Find the percentage of iron in the alloy.

31. What would be the weight in air, weight in water, and weight in liquid mercury of a cube of solid gold 1 in. on every edge? Presume there would be no appreciable interaction between the gold and the mercury.

*32. To raise a certain sunken ship 25 empty 75-ft^3 barrels weighing 100 lb each were lashed to the ship. What is the weight of the ship *in water?* Presume the ship is in quite shallow water and that the lashings are both weightless and volumeless.

*33. Calculate the volume of an object that weighs 1 g less in ethanol than in air.

*34. A mass of copper was suspected of being hollow. It weighed 105 g in air and 89.5 g in water. Was it hollow? If it was hollow, what was the volume of the cavity?

---

*Ideas for problems 32—34 borrowed from Dr. M. M. Mueller, City College of San Francisco.

12
GRAPHING

Properly drawn graphs can give one a tremendous amount of information rather easily. A graph of experimental data often can be used to find other information, to discover relationships, etc. Students are probably familiar with graphs made for mathematics classes. There the scales on the two axes are usually equal, the independent variable is plotted on the x axis and the dependent variable on the y axis, and both axes usually start at zero.

In experimental work there is often quite a difference in magnitude of the two factors being plotted, so that a one-to-one plot would make the graph either long and narrow or short and wide. Consequently, different scales are quite often used on the two axes. In addition, there are seldom values near zero in experimental work, so the axes do not generally start at zero. In order to have the graph show the relationship between the factors as clearly as possible, experimentalists usually want to give as much space as possible to the actual data. In graphing experimental data, then, it is customary to use the longer axis on rectangular paper for the factor with the greater range of values. This would be the y axis on $8\frac{1}{2} \times 11$ inch paper, the axis mathematicians reserve for the dependent variable. If the factor with the greater range of values happens to be the independent variable, it is a simple matter to turn the paper 90 degrees in the same plane so that the long axis is the x axis, although chemists (if not other experimentalists) are somewhat casual about keeping the independent variable on the x axis. But they are quite particular about planning the graph so that the data cover as much of the graph paper as possible, because they want the graph to show the data as clearly as possible and to be useful for finding information.

INTRODUCTION TO GRAPHICAL CONSTRUCTION

Graphs can take all sorts of forms, but the rectangular coordinate form is perhaps the most useful. This system employs two lines perpendicular to one another in the same plane (see Figure 12-1). The horizontal line (*x* axis) is the abscissa, the vertical line (*y* axis) the ordinate. The origin, 0, is the point of intersection of the two perpendicular lines (the axes). Negative values of *x* are customarily left of the origin, positive to the right. Negative values of *y* are below the origin, positive above.

In general, in constructing a graph, one would do the following:

1. Find the range of values for each variable.
2. Reserve the long axis for the variable with the greater range of values.
3. Reserve the *x* axis for the independent variable, turning the paper if necessary.
4. Choose the scales for each axis so that as much of the paper as possible can be used for plotting the data. However, a convenient, easy-to-plot, easy-to-read scale is better than an awkward, hard-to-plot, hard-to-read scale, if the convenient scale allows the data to fill most of the paper.
5. Number the major divisions on each axis.
6. Label the axes. If the graph paper does not have a margin, space must be reserved for labels.
7. Title the graph. Space under the *x*-axis label or in the upper right corner of the graph is commonly used for the title.
8. Plot the data, using a dot, a circle, a cross, or anything else that will be easily understood.
9. Draw a smooth curve that goes through as many points as possible without producing "zigzags."

These are not hard and fast rules; the only requirement in graphing is clarity. Graph paper comes in quite a variety of rulings and sizes. Anyone who did quite a lot of work involving graphing would probably have an assortment of papers. For student use 8½ × 11 inch paper with 4, 5, or 10 rulings to an inch would probably be most useful. Paper with more divisions per inch is quite commonly used to plot precise experimental work. Most graphs in this chapter were drawn on 8½ × 11 inch paper with 5 lines per inch, since this is perhaps the best size for reproduction on pages this size. Such paper has 50 divisions on one axis and 35 on the other when there is a margin on the paper. If there is no margin, there are more lines, but space for labels must then be reserved within the ruled area.

In designing a graph, one should also try to have the divisions and labels of the axes reflect the precision of the plotted measurements as closely as possible within the available space. If one measured something to three significant figures and had values such as 0.219, 0.230, and 0.289, one would not number the axis so that the major divisions were 0.20, 0.30, etc. Ideally, the major divisions would be 0.200, 0.210, etc., with 10 lines between major divisions. If the axes were divided in this fashion, then one could read three significant figures for anything on this axis and thus get values with the same number of significant figures as the plotted measurements merely by reading the graph properly. However, beware of "increasing" precision by means of graphing. A graph made by plotting values such as 0.22, 0.23, and 0.29 for this variable on a given axis could not give anything more than two significant figures despite the fact that one might be able to read the graph to what might *seem* to be greater precision. The numbering of the divisions on the axes should indicate the precision of the measurements, although one finds all too often that this is not so.

Common sense must be used in graphing as in other matters. Using the whole page for a given set of data has perhaps been overemphasized. Many beginning students plot data on a small part of a page, leaving the rest of the page blank and thereby reducing the precision to which data can be plotted or read. There must be some reasonable compromise between using the whole page and ease of plotting and also ease of extrapolation if the graph is to be used to find values near the extremes of values for the data plotted. Also, if one is visually going to compare various sets of plotted data with rather different ranges of values, the same scale must obviously be used in plotting the various sets of data.

Consider the data for the variation of the values of factor B with changes in factor A in Table 12-1. Then plot the data yourself and check your graph with Figure 12-1.

Table 12-1

Factor A	Factor B
(no units specified for A or B)	
−26.1	−46.7
−20.0	−37.0
−13.0	−25.0
− 3.8	−10.8
+ 6.3	+ 4.6
+17.1	+23.0
+25.8	+36.8

Factor A has a range of 51.9 units, factor B a range of 83.5 units. Obviously factor B should be on the longer axis, the *y* axis, the axis with 50 divisions, and A should be on the shorter axis, the one with 35 divisions. (The matter of which is the independent variable does not

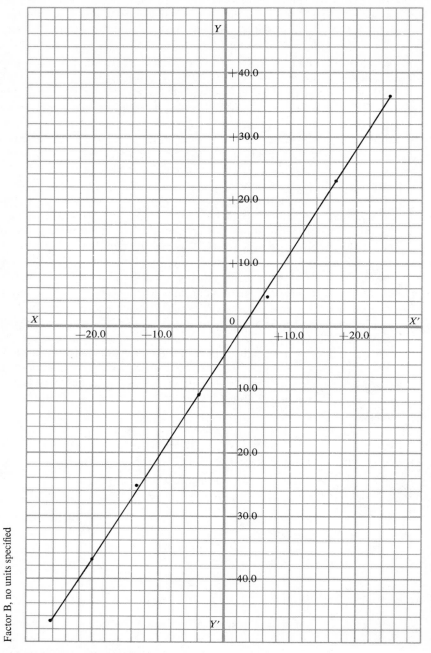

Factor B, no units specified

Factor A, no units specified

Figure 12-1

concern us here.) It is awkward to fit 51.9 units into 35 divisions but not impossible; 51.9/35 is 1.5 (approximately). If each paper division on the A axis were worth 1.5 units of A, then 52.5 units of A could easily fit on this axis, the *x* axis. The B axis must hold 83.5 units; 83.5/50 is approximately 1.67. About 1.67 units of B would fit into 1 division on the B axis. This would allow space for exactly 83.5 units of B. However, this would make the plotting somewhat awkward and inconvenient. If the axes were divided so that each graph division represented 2 units of either A or B there would be room for 70 units of A and 100 units of B. When plotted on this scale, as shown in Figure 12-1, the data almost fill the graph, and the plotting is done with greater ease and possibly with greater accuracy.

Why not check the plotting of the first set of figures on our graph. Go left on the *x* axis to −20. The lines between −20 and −30 correspond to −22, −24, −26 and −28. Find −26. You will find −27 unmarked and halfway between −26 and −28. Then −26.1 is one-tenth of the way between −26 and −27. Put a straightedge at this spot parallel to the *y* axis. Now go down along the straightedge parallel to the *y* axis until you find the −46 on the *y* axis. You see −46 and −48 there as printed lines; −47 is halfway between −46 and −48, and −46.7 is seven-tenths of the way between −46 and −47. Mark this spot with a dot, a circle, a cross, or anything that will be easily understood. Check the plotting of some of the other figures too.

All points must be clear and visible as well as accurately plotted. The points are the important things. The curve is just an aid to seeing the relationship involved. Connect the points with the smoothest curve that goes through the greatest number of points. For a curve that is essentially a straight line use a ruler or other straightedge to draw a line that goes through the greatest number of points. For a curved curve fit in the smoothest curve that goes through the greatest number of points either "by eye" or by using a French curve. Forget the zigzag graphs, graphs showing price changes or other economic trends. You were supposed to notice the ups and downs there, but such plotting obscures the issue in experimental data.

In Figure 12-1 the points corresponding to A = 6.3, B = 4.6 and to A = −13.0, B = −25.0 do not lie on the line. At these points there was either a graphing error, an error in performance of the experiment, or some unusual aberration or change in conditions. A good experimentalist would find out which it was if possible. In any event he would not make zigzag lines to include these points in the curve.

Actual experimental work seldom has negative values. Consequently the *y* axis is generally close to the extreme left of the graph and the *x* axis is very near the bottom of the graph. This system of axis placement is used on all graphs in this chapter except Figure 12-1.

SOME SIMPLE DATA IN GRAPH FORM

Graph the following data for the variation of gas volume with changing temperature (pressure constant).

Temperature, °K	33	72	100	150	197
Volume, liters	100	217	300	461	587

Here 487 volume units must be plotted against 164 temperature units. The volume would obviously go on the long axis of rectangular paper because it has the greater range of values and is in addition the dependent variable. Thus on the y axis close to 500 volume units must fit in 50 divisions, making 10 volume units per division a rather obvious choice. On the x axis, 164 temperature units must fit in 35 divisions, making about 4.67 temperature units per division. However, 6 temperature units per division is a more workable choice as well as a choice which would still allow the data essentially to fill the graph paper. Neither axis would start at zero because the lowest values are 100 liters and 33°K. Check your graph against Figure 12-2. The use and interpretation of this and a few other graphs will be discussed later in the chapter.

Now plot the following data for the variation of volume of a gas with changes in pressure (temperature constant).

Pressure, atm	0.40	0.67	1.0	1.3	1.4	1.7	3.3
Volume, liters	1250	750	500	412	350	297	150

Compare your graph with Figure 12-3. Allowing 1 division on the x axis for each 0.1 pressure unit and 1 division on the y axis for 25 volume units gives a graph that fills about 85% of the page. True, more space could have been used, but then awkward, error-producing divisions would have had to have been made. Note the discontinuity at point A. Graphing is a good way to find experimental errors or interesting variations. Interpretation of this graph will be discussed later.

Now let's try a few other things with the pressure-volume data we have just been using. Let's first plot the reciprocal of pressure against volume and then plot the pressure against the logarithm of the volume (for convenience the data have been summarized in Table 12-2).

Table 12-2

Pressure, atm	$\dfrac{1}{pressure}$	Volume, liters	Log_{10} of volume
0.40	2.5	1250	3.10
0.67	1.5	750	2.88
1.0	1.0	500	2.70
1.3	0.77	412	2.62
1.4	0.71	350	2.54
1.7	0.59	297	2.47
3.3	0.30	150	2.18

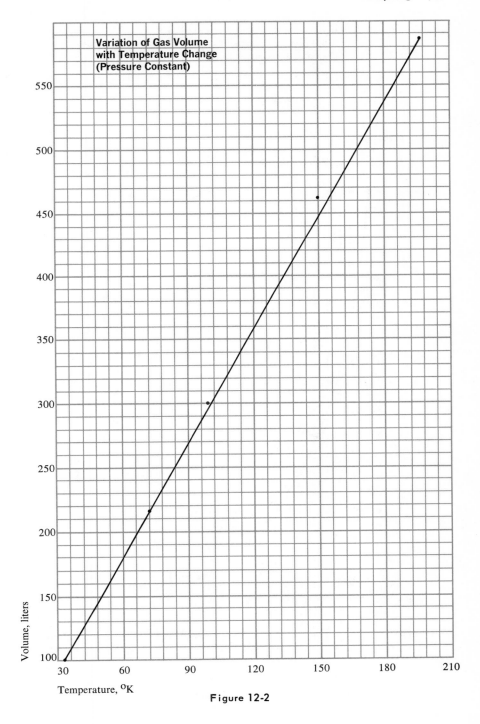

Variation of Gas Volume
with Temperature Change
(Pressure Constant)

Volume, liters

Temperature, °K

Figure 12-2

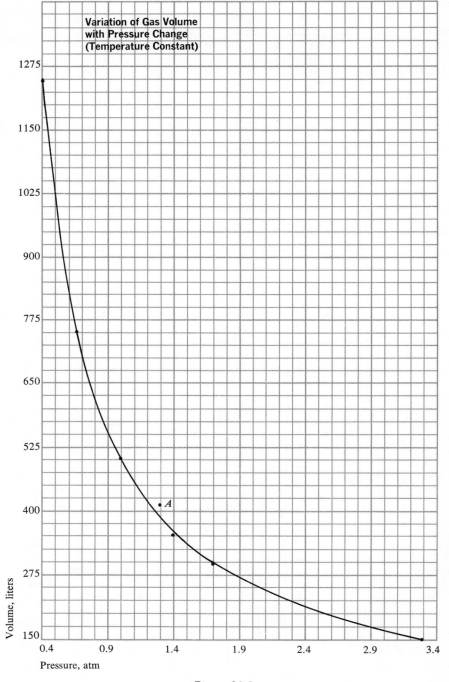

Figure 12-3

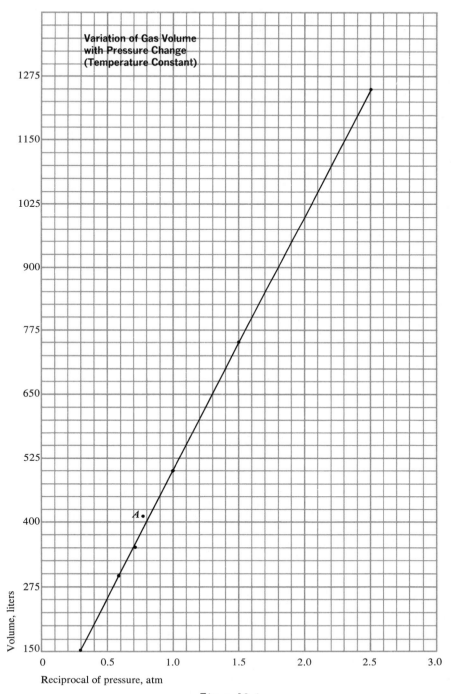

Variation of Gas Volume
with Pressure Change
(Temperature Constant)

Volume, liters

Reciprocal of pressure, atm

Figure 12-4

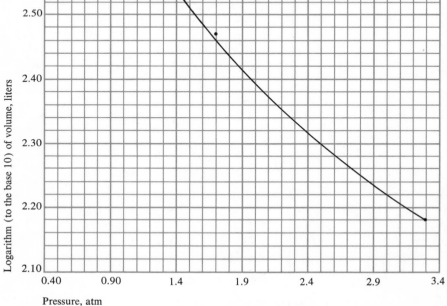

Figure 12-5

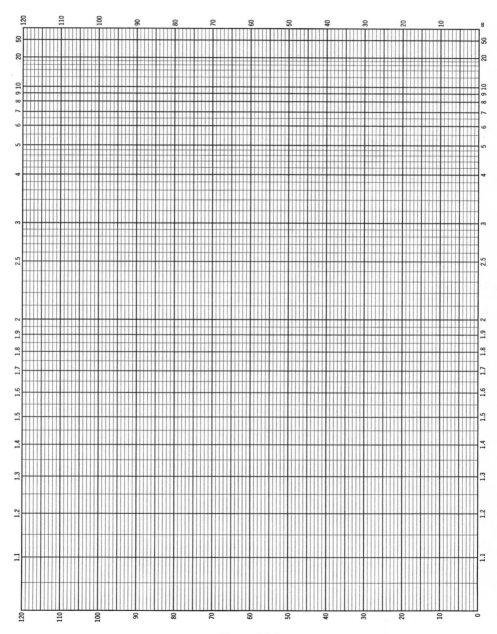

Figure 12-6

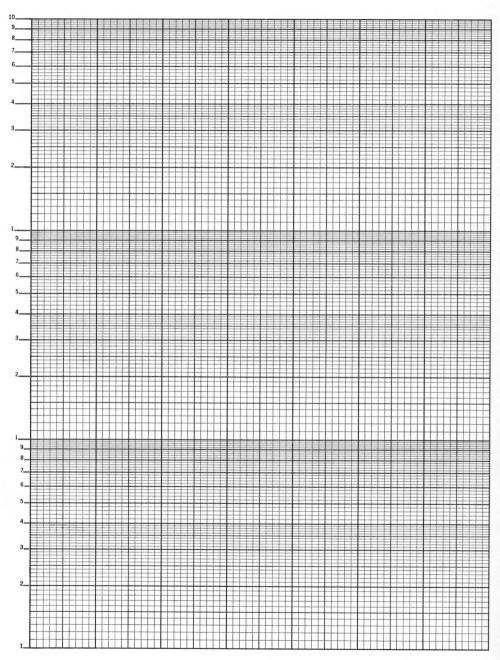

Figure 12-7

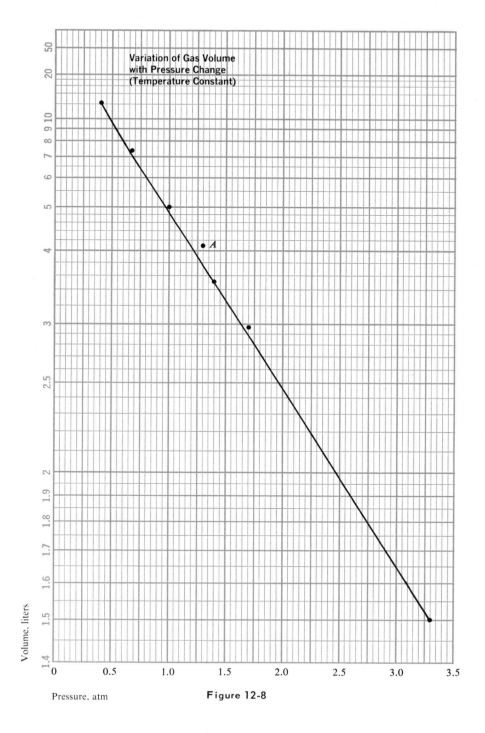

Variation of Gas Volume
with Pressure Change
(Temperature Constant)

Volume, liters

Pressure, atm

Figure 12-8

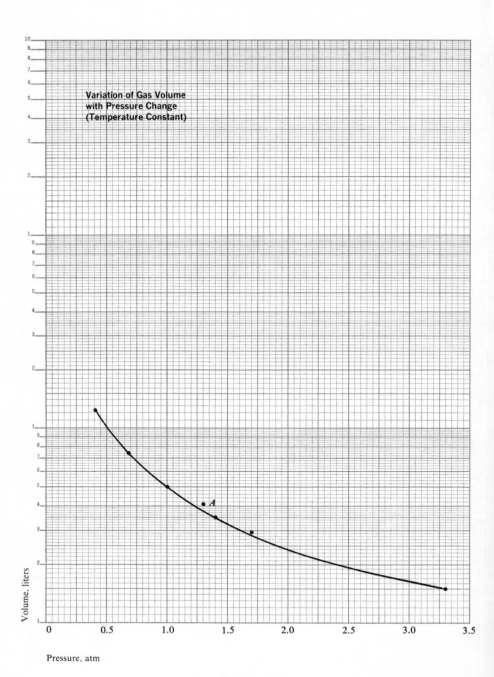

Figure 12-9

Compare your graph for the reciprocal of pressure against volume with Figure 12-4 and your graph for the pressure against the logarithm of the volume with Figure 12-5. Interpretations of these graphs will be discussed later. Notice that in each case you got the same discontinuity at point A that you had in the original graph. Changing a system of graphing can often markedly change the shape of the curve, but it cannot eliminate genuine discontinuities.

It is inconvenient to have to calculate the reciprocal or to have to find a logarithm. Use of reciprocal ruling or hyperbolic paper will eliminate the need to calculate the reciprocal, and use of semilogarithmic paper will eliminate the need to find the logarithms. Figures 12-6 and 12-7 show reciprocal ruling (hyperbolic) paper and semilogarithmic paper, respectively. With one of these papers it is possible in effect to plot the reciprocal or the logarithm of a variable directly on the paper from the actual data for the variable. Notice that each of these papers has a logarithmic scale on one axis and a uniformly ruled scale on the other axis. However, the second logarithmic cycle on the reciprocal ruled paper is "logarithmically" smaller than the first cycle, whereas the second cycle on the semilogarithmic paper is exactly the same as the first cycle. Obviously, these kinds of paper come in a variety of sizes with one, two, three, etc., cycles. Graph paper with logarithmic divisions on both axes (often called log-log paper but more properly called full logarithmic paper) is also available and commonly used. It is particularly useful for plotting wide ranges of data clearly and accurately in smaller spaces than are required on uniformly ruled paper.

How do you plot on logarithmically divided axes? Which cycle do you use? You plot the numbers the same way you would plot any others; in fact, plotting is easier because the paper has the major divisions numbered and the divisions between the major divisions are the same as those on a slide rule. The fact that the major divisions are not uniformly spaced is troublesome only at first. The only real difficulty involves knowing which cycle to use. Determining this is easier than you might think. Generally, the variable with the greater range of values is plotted on the logarithmic axis. So you first express all values of that variable in scientific notation (see Chapter 5). All numbers having the same power of ten are plotted in the same cycle. Those numbers with the lowest power of ten are plotted in the bottom cycle, those with the next highest power of ten in the next cycle, and so on. Thus, from the pressure-volume data, you would get 1.25×10^3, 7.5×10^2, 5×10^2, etc., down to 1.5×10^2 as the values for the volume in scientific notation. Obviously 150 through 750 would be plotted in the first cycle and 1250 in the second cycle. Look at Figures 12-8 and 12-9. If you have hyperbolic and/or semilogarithmic paper, plot the data yourself; if you do not have such paper, at least check the plotting on the graphs reproduced here. Interpretations of these graphs are given later.

SOME USES OF GRAPHS

Look at Figure 12-2, the graph for the temperature-volume data. You know from looking at the data that there seems to be a direct relationship between temperature (in °K) and volume. When a curve is a straight line such as that in Figure 12-2, there has to be a direct relationship between the variables plotted unless the variables have been operated on mathematically in some fashion. Note that not all points fit on the curve perfectly. All experimental data include built-in and accidental errors. Further experimentation would be needed to determine whether any discontinuities (nonfitting or poorly fitting points) are due to experimental error or to interesting fluctuations in properties. Such discontinuities are most often due to experimental error, and graphs can essentially give relationships free of experimental error because of the obvious "lack of fit" of points reflecting experimental error.

Now look at Figure 12-3 for the relationship of pressure and volume. The curve is called a hyperbola. Inverse relationships have curves of this shape, although they are not the only ones that do. You probably already suspected from the pressure-volume data that there was an inverse relationship involved, and the graph gives confirmation to the idea.

Now look at Figure 12-4. There is a straight line except for a discontinuity at point A. This is the same point that was off in Figure 12-3. Straight lines are easier to read on graphs and much easier to use to interpolate or extrapolate data. There are several techniques that can be used to obtain a straight line rather than a curved one for inverse relationships. Plotting the reciprocal of one of the variables against the other variable will give a straight line, as in Figure 12-4, where the reciprocal of pressure was plotted against volume. Another technique, illustrated by Figure 12-8, is to plot the actual values on hyperbolic or reciprocal ruled paper. Again, the curve is a straight line. Hyperbolic paper is easier to use but less commonly available than uniformly ruled paper.

Now look at Figure 12-5. Plotting the logarithm of one variable against the ordinary arithmetic value of the other variable in an inverse relationship will straighten out the curve. Whether the curve will be straighter or straight depends on whether a constant is or is not involved and is more the subject of a mathematics book. The main concern here is techniques of presenting data clearly and interpretation of graphs. Compare Figure 12-5 with Figure 12-9. Plotting of actual arithmetical values on the semilogarithmic paper is easier, but such paper may not be readily available.

Interpolation and Extrapolation

Graphs are also used to find information about conditions that one did not measure. If one uses the graph to find points that were not measured, but are within the range measured, then one is doing something called *interpolation*. If one uses the graph to find information beyond the range in which experimental measurements were made (and plotted), then one is *extrapolating* the data. One cannot be certain of information found by extrapolation, but it is often better than its only immediate alternative: nothing.

Look at Figure 12-2. If you were asked to find the temperature at which the volume would be 500 liters, you would interpolate. If you were asked to find the volume at $10°K$, you would extrapolate. To do this you must extend the curve, but there is no room on the paper. Just put an identically ruled sheet of paper along the edge, match divisions, and then extend your line. You cannot be sure of this reading. How do you even know that the substance is still a gas at this temperature? If the curve happened to be curved rather than straight, a French curve could be used to extend the curve. It is rather difficult to get decent readings in this fashion, so that if a way can be found to straighten the curve—either by mathematical operation on the data or by use of specially ruled paper—a more nearly reliable reading can be made, but the extrapolated data may or may not be reliable.

Problems that are usually solved algebraically can often be solved rather easily graphically. Let's look at the problem of Example 4-11 where we wanted to know how much 20¢/lb and 90¢/lb coffees must be mixed to produce 50¢/lb coffee. We arbitrarily decided to find the amounts needed to prepare 1 lb of this mixture. The amounts were 0.57 lb of the 20¢ coffee and 0.43 lb of the 90¢ coffee.

This kind of problem is easily solved graphically, although it might not be worth the effort for just one answer. But a graph gives more information, as you will see. First, label one of the axes for price, from 20¢ to 90¢. Then label the other axis on both sides of the graph for the amounts of 20¢ and 90¢ coffees, going from 0 to 1 lb. But do not put zero at the same end of the axis on both sides of the graph. On one side, start with zero at the bottom; on the other, zero at the top, for reasons that should be clear a little later if not now. Thus the axes are labeled as in Figure 12-10. Next, draw a diagonal from 1 lb of one of the coffees to 1 lb of the other coffee. Now we hope it is obvious why we started the coffee pound axes at opposite ends. A pound of coffee that is to sell at 20¢ must have no pounds of 90¢ coffee in it, and the opposite applies to a pound selling for 90¢. Now, let's see how this graph works.

You know that a mixture containing half a pound of each coffee would sell for 55¢/lb.

$$\frac{1}{2}(20) + \frac{1}{2}(90) = 55$$

Find the 55¢ line on the graph. Where does it intersect the diagonal? On the line that is labeled 0.5 on each side! You have half a pound of each coffee.

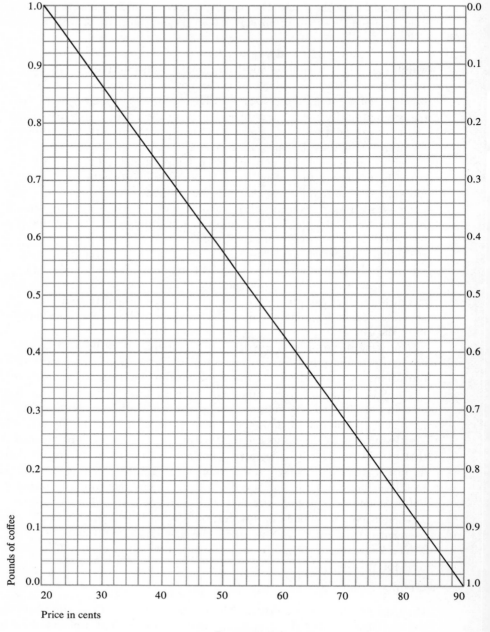

Pounds of coffee

Price in cents

Figure 12-10

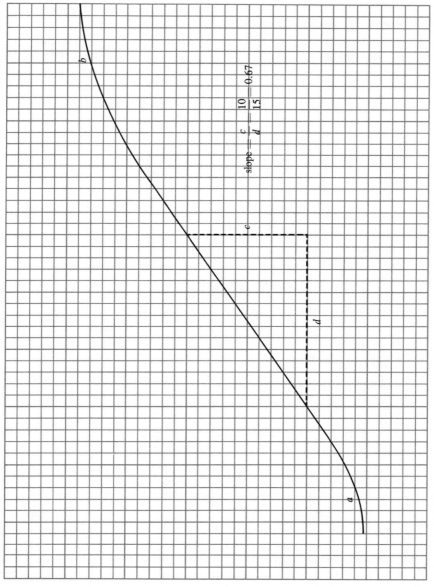

Factor I, no units specified

Factor J, no units specified

Figure 12-11

Now, if you had 1/3 lb of the 20¢ coffee and 2/3 lb of the 90¢ coffee, you would have to sell the mixture for 67¢/lb. Find the 67¢ line, and follow it up to the diagonal. This spot on the diagonal is on line with 0.67 on the 90¢ side and 0.33 on the 20¢ side.

To determine the amounts of each coffee to be put in the 50¢/lb mixture, find the 50¢ line, go up along it until you hit the diagonal, and go across from this spot to the 20¢ and 90¢ sides. You find 0.57 and 0.43 lb, respectively. This agrees with what you had already found algebraically. Your precision in reading the graph would be a function of the size of the graph and the fineness of the divisions, naturally.

Slope

The slope of a curve is the ratio of the change in the y value to the change in the x value for the distance between any two points on a curve. In other words, for a given segment of a curve

$$\text{slope} = \frac{\text{vertical distance}}{\text{horizontal distance}} \quad \text{(see Figure 12-11)}$$

For experimental work one must be sure to take the slope along a section of the curve that is behaving characteristically. Suppose we were studying a rate of reaction, and our data gave a graph like Figure 12-11. Look at the parts of the curve labeled a and b. Here the reaction would presumably be just starting and trailing off, respectively. The straighter portion of the curve would seem to be typical of the reaction itself. Thus the slope would be

$$\frac{\text{distance } c}{\text{distance } d}$$

Now let's see how slope can be used with experimental data. A certain experiment involved reaction between solution A and solution B to produce gas C. Both solution A and solution B were necessary for the reaction and affected the rate. A series of experiments were performed to find out how the concentration of A affected the rate. The rate was measured in terms of the volume of gas produced.

Consider the data in Table 12-3 for two of the trials in the series of experiments just mentioned. Plot the data and check your graph against Figure 12-12. Notice that both trials are plotted on the same set of axes. This is a common practice and makes comparison of various trials in experiments quite convenient. Notice that each trial took a little while to get going, as it were, and that each slowed down as the reagents were used up. The rate, the volume of gas produced per unit time, can be found by taking the slope of the curve. The slope is found for each curve on a typical section of the curve, not on a section representing the start-

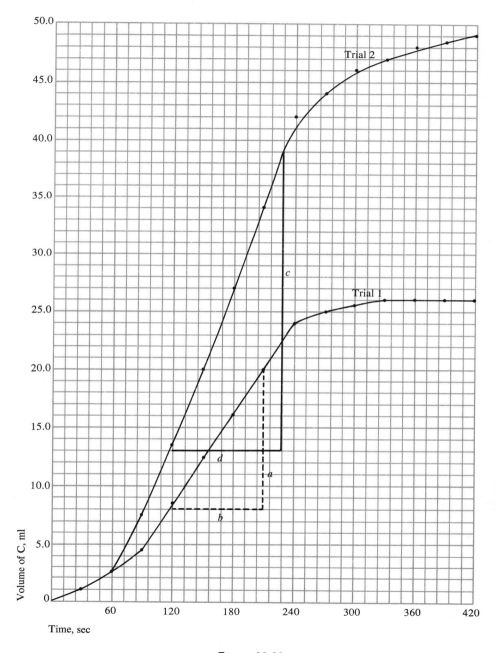

Figure 12-12

Table 12-3

Time, sec	Trial 1 10 ml of 0.4 M A 10 ml of 0.4 M B *Volume of C, ml* (*at* 20.0°C., 1 *atm*)	Trial 2 10 ml of 0.8 M A 10 ml of 0.4 M B *Volume of C, ml* (*at* 20.0°C, 1 *atm*)
30	1.0	1.0
60	2.5	2.5
90	4.5	7.5
120	8.5	13.5
150	12.5	20.0
180	16.0	27.0
210	20.0	34.0
240	24.0	42.0
270	25.0	44.0
300	25.5	46.0
330	26.0	47.0
360	26.0	48.0
390	26.0	48.5
420	26.0	49.0

ing up or running down of the reaction. The accuracy of your value for the slope will obviously depend on the accuracy with which you can read the graph. You will make about the same error in reading any given point, but if the points are separated by a longer distance the percentage error in finding the length of a line for part of a slope will be less. So always take slopes on the longest possible segment of the curve.

In Figure 12-12,

$$\frac{\text{line } a}{\text{line } b} = \frac{(20 - 8)}{(210 - 117)} \frac{\text{ml}}{\text{sec}} = 0.13 \text{ ml/sec} = \text{rate for trial 1}$$

and $$\frac{\text{line } c}{\text{line } d} = \frac{(39 - 13)}{(228 - 118)} \frac{\text{ml}}{\text{sec}} = 0.24 \text{ ml/sec} = \text{rate for trial 2}$$

The rate for trial 2 is approximately twice that for trial 1. You object. You could have gotten the information directly from the data. True in this case, but there are many cases where the data in tabular form are deceptive or difficult to interpret. Slope can be very useful. In fact, simple graphical methods can be very helpful with experimental work in general.

PROBLEMS

1. **a.** Make a suitable plot of the following data on variation in density of water with temperature.

Temperature, °C	Density, g/ml	Temperature, °C	Density, g/ml
−10.00	0.9982	4.00	1.0000
− 6.00	0.9991	6.00	1.0000
− 4.00	0.9995	8.00	0.9999
− 2.00	0.9997	10.00	0.9997
0.00	0.9999	20.00	0.9982
2.00	1.0000		

   b. It is known that only at 3.97°C is the density of water actually 1.0000 g/ml. What is the reason for listing that value at 2°C and 6°C here?
   c. From your graph find the density at 40.00°C. At −40.00°C.

2. **a.** Plot the data given in Table 15-3 (page 200) on variation of vapor pressure of water with temperature.
   b. From your graph determine the vapor pressure of water at 31°C. At 95°C.
   c. At what temperature, according to your graph, would the vapor pressure be 450 torr (mm of Hg)? 11.3 torr?

3. **a.** Plot the following data on variation in solubility with temperature.

Temperature, °C	Grams X dissolved in 100 g solvent Y	Temperature, °C	Grams X dissolved in 100 g solvent Y
10	2.8	45	27.0
15	3.9	50	29.2
20	6.1	55	30.3
25	9.4	60	30.2
30	13.8	65	30.4
35	19.3	70	30.2
40	23.7		

   b. Using your graph, find the number of grams that would dissolve in 100 g of solvent Y at 0°C? At 100°C?
   c. How many grams of X would dissolve in 1000 g of solvent Y at 60°C?

4. The data below represent other trials in the experiment from which the data in problem 3 were taken. You know there is no relationship between temperature and X or Y. What would you plot?

Temperature, $°C$	Grams X	Grams Y
10	1.4	50
20	9.2	150
30	27.6	200
40	35.6	150
50	14.6	50
60	3.0	10
70	30.2	100

5. A certain pipe leaked. When fluid under increased pressure was sent through the pipe, it not unnaturally leaked faster. (Hint: Convert to some uniform time period before plotting these data.)

Pressure, $lb/in.^2$	Time	Date	Fluid lost during time interval, $in.^3$
10	12:30–12:45 A.M.	7/1	100
12	12:30–12:35	7/2	200
15	12:30– 1:00	7/3	3000
20	12:30–12:35	7/4	1000

   a. What pressure would cause 1 ft^3 of water to leak out in 15 min? Solve graphically.

   b. What loss of water would occur in 1 hr at a pressure of 30 $lb/in.^2$?

13
DEVELOPMENT OF FORMULAS

We have been urging you to do all problems by reason. However, once one knows how to do things by reason, there is no need to commit a grand mathematical tour de force every time one does a problem. Use formulas for speed and convenience.

Table 13-1

Volume, liters	Temperature, °K (degrees absolute)
100	33
217	72
300	100
461	150
587	197

Consider the data in Table 13-1 (pressure constant). You know from Chapter 12 that there is a direct relationship between the temperature here and volume. Mathematically this could be expressed as

$V \propto T$

(Translation: volume is proportional to temperature.)

Toy with the data. Find a way in which to obtain the volume if one knows the temperature and vice versa. Do you notice that the volume is about 3 times the temperature in each case? This particular relationship, then, can be expressed as

$V = 3T$

You have eliminated the proportionality sign by means of a constant. For the given set of figures *here* the constant to convert T to V is 3. Conversely, the constant to convert V to T is 0.33 *here*; try this on the data given above.

For a single set of conditions, one can write

$$V_1 = 3T_1$$

If the same number of molecules were changed to a different temperature and volume at the same pressure, then

$$V_2 = 3T_2$$

Rearranging these equations, one would get

$$\frac{V_1}{T_1} = 3 \quad \text{and} \quad \frac{V_2}{T_2} = 3$$

Since $3 = 3$, it follows that

$$\frac{V_1}{T_1} = \frac{V_2}{T_2}$$

or $V_1 T_2 = V_2 T_1$

Here, *and only here,* 3 is a constant factor, but it is not necessary to know precisely what the constant is. For direct relationships the formula would more generally have been developed in this fashion:

$$V_1 \propto T_1 \quad \text{and} \quad V_2 \propto T_2$$

One would remove the proportionality sign by introducing a constant, k. Then

$$V_1 = kT_1 \quad \text{and} \quad V_2 = kT_2$$

$$\frac{V_1}{T_1} = k \quad \text{and} \quad \frac{V_2}{T_2} = k$$

$$\frac{V_1}{T_1} = \frac{V_2}{T_2} \quad \text{or} \quad V_1 T_2 = V_2 T_1$$

Do you see why one need not know the value of the constant to develop a formula?

Develop formulas for the following statements of relationship. Then follow our derivations.

EXAMPLE 13-1

Pressure is inversely proportional to volume (temperature constant).

$$P_1 \propto \frac{1}{V_1} \quad \text{and} \quad P_2 \propto \frac{1}{V_2}$$

$$P_1 = \frac{k}{V_1} \quad \text{and} \quad P_2 = \frac{k}{V_2}$$

$$P_1 V_1 = k \quad \text{and} \quad P_2 V_2 = k$$

Since $k = k$,

$$P_1 V_1 = P_2 V_2$$

EXAMPLE 13-2

Temperature (absolute) is directly proportional to volume and directly proportional to pressure.

$$T_1 \propto V_1 P_1 \quad \text{and} \quad T_2 \propto V_2 P_2$$

$$T_1 = k V_1 P_1 \quad \text{and} \quad T_2 = k V_2 P_2$$

$$\frac{T_1}{P_1 V_1} = k = \frac{T_2}{P_2 V_2}$$

Therefore $\dfrac{T_1}{P_1 V_1} = \dfrac{T_2}{P_2 V_2}$ or $V_1 P_1 T_2 = V_2 P_2 T_1$

You will often see this relationship in the form

$$PV = RT$$

The R is a proportionality constant (see Chapter 14).

EXAMPLE 13-3

Now let's try a moderately practical problem. Consider this reaction:

$$3A + B = 2\overline{C}$$

A, B, and C represent actual compounds. The rate of reaction was known to be proportional to the square of the concentration of B and independent of the concentration of A, although A was needed for the reaction. The reaction rate was measured by the appearance of C, a gas.

This relationship would be expressed in this fashion:

$$r \propto [B]^2 \quad \text{or} \quad r = k[B]^2$$

where r is rate and $[B]$ is concentration of B in moles per liter (symbol: M).

Calculate the value of k from the following data:

Concentration of B, M (volume = 100 ml)	Rate at which C was produced, ml/sec (standard temperature and pressure)
0.1	2
0.2	8
0.4	32

Substituting in $k = r/[B]^2$,

$$k = \frac{2 \text{ ml}}{\text{sec } (0.1 \text{ M})^2} = 200 \frac{\text{ml}}{\text{sec } M^2}$$

$$= \frac{8 \text{ ml}}{\text{sec } (0.2 \text{ M})^2} = 200 \frac{\text{ml}}{\text{sec } M^2}$$

$$= \frac{32 \text{ ml}}{\text{sec } (0.4 \text{ M})^2} = 200 \frac{\text{ml}}{\text{sec } M^2}$$

A "ml/(sec × M^2)" is a monster known neither to man nor to beast. It is a proportionality constant, something that enables one to convert a factor (or factors) into an answer in desired units. In this particular case its use in calculating rates from concentrations, and vice versa, is probably obvious.

PROBLEMS

1. Velocity of a gas is inversely proportional to the square root of the molecular weight of the gas. Develop a formula to express this.
2. Look at the following data.

Mass at T_1, g/mole	Velocity at T_1, cm/sec	Kinetic energy at T_1, ergs/mole	Mass at T_2, g/mole	Velocity at T_2, cm/sec	Kinetic energy at T_2, ergs/mole
16	10,000	9×10^8	16	100,000	8×10^{10}
2	30,000	9×10^8	12	110,000	8×10^{10}
8	15,000	9×10^8	2	280,000	8×10^{10}
4	22,000	9×10^8	4	200,000	8×10^{10}
12	12,000	9×10^8	8	140,000	8×10^{10}

Then develop a formula relating the given factors to one another. An erg, the unit in which kinetic energy is given, is equal to $gram \left(\dfrac{cm}{sec}\right)^2$. Find a proportionality constant to convert mass and velocity into kinetic energy.

3. Develop a formula to express the relationship between matter and energy indicated by the following data (a ridiculously small sample, of course) and find the proportionality constant.

Matter converted into energy, g	Energy released, ergs
2	1.8×10^{21}
4	3.6×10^{21}
8	7.2×10^{21}

4. Consider the data below for a given mass of gas at various conditions and then find the constant that will enable one to calculate the third factor if the other two are known for *one* set of conditions.

Pressure, atm	Volume, liters	Temperature, °K
1	10	122
10	1	122
5	2	122
3.3	3.0	122
3.0	3.3	122
8.0	1.3	122

14

ANOTHER APPROACH TO PROBLEM SOLVING

We're going to shock you. After making a plea for having you understand what you're doing, we're now going to ask you to work with things that cannot be rigorously proved, things that often present great difficulties in terms of understanding. If man had to work only with things he knew and understood fully, he'd be back on the threshold of the Stone Age. A fact is a fact. Once one knows it, it can be dealt with, can be used to find new information. The ideal, of course, is to understand as much as possible about various facts, to try to fit them into a general picture, to try to use them to advance knowledge and understanding, but we don't always—can't always—reach the ideal. We must use the facts at hand as best we can to advance knowledge and understanding.

Some of the following subject matter has been deliberately chosen almost at random. The goal is problem solving. Once one knows how to solve problems, it is immaterial what specific type of problem one encounters. Once one has the facts one can gather them up, whip them into shape, use them, and in using them, often find the missing piece that leads to understanding or lays a foundation for understanding.

Michael Faraday's work presents a classic example of this. Faraday was among the first to breach classical Newtonian physics. Theory there was. Facts, irrefutable facts, Faraday found. Theory and facts were at odds. The facts, used to solve numerous problems, to open so many new corridors of thought, seemed inexplicable. Nonetheless, they served as the foundation for Faraday's reconstruction of Newtonian descriptions of electricity, magnetism, gravity, light, and space and eventually for Einstein's famous General Field Theory. (It is somewhat interesting that L. Pearce Williams, in his book *Michael Faraday,* mentions that Faraday "in his twenties was a magnificent 'poetical theorist' but that his spelling was a sin and his math a calamity.")

Now let's take up some topics that may *seem* to be randomly chosen. Remember the goal is problem solving, not a balanced, logical presentation of topics normally found in science textbooks.

ENERGY

Energy has classically been defined as the ability to do work. When a body does work, its energy is decreased by an amount equal to the work done. This definition is fine for physicists but seems to leave students cold. What about the heat radiating from a hot stove or light traveling through space? What work is being done here? You know energy is involved and that the energy is functioning, as it were, but you cannot imagine that work in the ordinary sense is being done.

Students know that ther are many kinds of energy, generally classified as either potential or kinetic, and that various forms of energy can be transformed into one another. Potential energy is energy that is present and ready to function, but not functioning. Kinetic energy is energy actually being energetic as it were.

Kinetic energy of gases was long known to be proportional to the mass and velocity of the molecules. It was also known to be proportional to the temperature. These were observed facts. The exact equations for kinetic energy of an ideal gas can be derived mathematically and can be verified experimentally. The equations are:

$$KE = \frac{1 \ mv^2}{2} \quad \text{and} \quad KE = \frac{3 \ RT}{2}$$

where KE is average kinetic energy,* m is mass, v is average velocity of molecules,* R is the proportionality constant, and T is temperature in absolute degrees (°K).

Added Facts

- All gases, regardless of the mass of the gas, have the same average kinetic energy at the same temperature. (See data presented in problem 2, Chapter 13.)

- An erg is an energy unit; $erg = g\left(\frac{cm}{sec}\right)^2$.

---

*One often sees simply "kinetic energy" and "velocity"; in relation to gases these must be understood to mean "*average* kinetic energy" and "*average* velocity *of molecules.*"

- Velocity is expressed in distance per unit time, for example, 8 cm/sec.
- $R = 0.08205 \dfrac{\text{liter-atm}}{\text{mole-}^\circ\text{K}}$ (liter-atm means liters × atmospheres)

$$= \frac{8.314 \times 10^7 \text{ ergs}}{\text{mole-}^\circ\text{K}}$$

$$= \frac{1.987 \text{ cal}}{\text{mole-}^\circ\text{K}}$$

Now, looking at the facts and relationships presented, try to answer the following questions. Please don't look at the solution until you have tried the problem. To do otherwise will defeat the whole purpose of this section.

EXAMPLE 14–1

a. If the mass is in grams and the velocity in centimeters per second, what unit would kinetic energy be in?

Ergs, obviously, since the product of grams times the square of centimeters per second is the erg.

b. If you wanted kinetic energy in calories, joules, electron volts, or any other energy unit, what would you do if you had the mass in grams and velocity in centimeters per second?

Calculate the energy in ergs ($KE = \frac{1}{2}mv^2$) and then convert to the desired unit. You would look up the relationship between the erg and the unit you want. For example,

1 joule $= 10^7$ ergs
1 cal $\quad= 4.18$ joules

Since an erg is an energy unit, you would know that any unit set equal to some number of ergs would itself also be an energy unit.

c. If you knew the kinetic energy in ergs and if you knew how much gas was involved, could you find the velocity of the gas?

Yes.

$$\text{erg} = g\left(\frac{\text{cm}}{\text{sec}}\right)^2$$

Therefore $\dfrac{\text{erg}}{g} = \left(\dfrac{\text{cm}}{\text{sec}}\right)^2$

Substituting for the erg its equivalent, g (cm/sec)^2, you would get

$$\frac{g}{sec}\left(\frac{cm}{sec}\right)^2 \frac{1}{g} = \left(\frac{cm}{sec}\right)^2$$

so $\sqrt{\dfrac{erg}{g}} = \dfrac{cm}{sec}$

However, would this be the right answer? Look at the formula for kinetic energy. $KE = \frac{1}{2}mv^2$; therefore

$$v = \sqrt{\frac{2KE}{m}} = \sqrt{\frac{2 \; erg}{g}} = \sqrt{\frac{2 \; g \left(\dfrac{cm}{sec}\right)^2}{g}}$$

You had the right idea for units, but the *Actual Physical Formula* involved a factor of $\frac{1}{2}$ that you had not taken into account.

d. If you knew the kinetic energy in joules or calories or some other unit, could you find the velocity of the gas if you knew what gas it was (and thus knew its molecular weight)?

Obviously yes, but to get the velocity in centimeters per second you would have to have the kinetic energy in ergs, since the velocity component in the erg is in centimeters per second. You would have to convert the kinetic energy to ergs (conversion factors in part b).

e. Suppose you knew the temperature of a gas. Could you find its kinetic energy?

Yes. You know

$$KE = \frac{3 \; RT}{2}$$

Just substitute and solve. This is not blindly following a formula. This is what the relationship between kinetic energy and temperature is. It is a fact. Use it. Which value for R would you use? That depends on the units you want.

f. If you knew the temperature and identity (thus the molecular weight) of the gas, could you find the velocity of the molecules?

You can find the velocity if you know the kinetic energy. To find velocity in centimeters per second you need kinetic energy in ergs. You know T; therefore, you can find kinetic energy. To save unnecessary conversion of units you could use R in the form of ergs per mole-°K.

EXAMPLE 14–2

If all gases have the same kinetic energy at the same temperature, what must be the relationship between velocity and the mass of a gas?

First of all, you may wonder why all gases at the same temperature have the same kinetic energy. KE has been found to be equal to $\frac{3}{2} RT$. Certainly, $\frac{3}{2}$ is a constant value, and R is a constant; so if T is the same temperature, then the product of $\frac{3}{2} RT$ would necessarily always be the same. Now, look at the equation for kinetic energy. If the product $\frac{1}{2}mv^2$ is constant for all gases at the same temperature, heavy gases obviously must travel more slowly than light gases. What kind of relationship is this? Inverse. Succinctly stated, this is

Mass is inversely proportional to the square of the velocity at a given temperature.

or

Velocity is inversely proportional to the square root of the mass at a given temperature.

What happened to the $\frac{1}{2}$ in the formula $\frac{1}{2}mv^2$? It is not necessary here. Since $\frac{1}{2}mv^2$ for gas A $= \frac{1}{2}mv^2$ for gas B at same temperature, $\frac{1}{2}$ is on both sides of the equation and can be ignored for the present purpose. But be sure *NOT* to think mv^2 is kinetic energy. It is not.

Let's look at another formula involving mass and energy—Einstein's celebrated

$$E = mc^2$$

This says that the energy obtainable on complete conversion of matter to energy is proportional to the mass so converted. The proportionality constant needed to make the equation is the square of the speed of light. Thus E is energy, m is mass, and c is the speed of light which equals 3×10^{10} cm/sec.

EXAMPLE 14–3

a. In what units would E be if mass were in grams and velocity in centimeters per second?

You would have $g\left(\dfrac{cm}{sec}\right)^2$. Do you find this on page 172? It is the erg.

b. How much energy would be liberated if a 3-g mass were completely turned into energy? (Perhaps *produced* would be a better word here, but *liberated* is customary in problems of this sort.)

Did you get 2.7×10^{21} ergs? Could you express this energy in any unit desired, say kilocalories? Of course. Just convert after you have found ergs.

VELOCITY AND ACCELERATION

What is velocity? Velocity is often defined as the rate of change of position. If you covered 90 mi in 20 min, what would be the velocity in miles per minute?

You know it is

$$\frac{90 \text{ mi}}{20 \text{ min}} = \frac{4.5 \text{ mi}}{\text{min}}$$

In symbol form

$$v = \frac{s}{t}$$

where v is the velocity, s is distance, and t is time. At any given moment, at a constant velocity of 4.5 mi/min, you would be 4.5 mi away from where you were exactly 1 min before. Velocity is a vector; that is, it has magnitude and direction. Speed, which the layman uses synonymously with velocity, has only magnitude, no direction.

What is acceleration? Acceleration is the *rate of change* of velocity. It is always produced by a force. Suppose you were driving along a road at 25 mi/hr. At 1:15 P.M. exactly you stepped on the accelerator. At 1:17 P.M. exactly the speedometer read exactly 80 mi/hr. You have accelerated. Your rate of traveling has changed. *By how much has it changed?* That *how much* per unit of time—the rate of change in rate movement—is the acceleration.

Find the acceleration for this unusual car in feet second^{-2}. You object to feet second^{-2}? Watch the unit handling here.

What is the change in velocity?

$$80 \frac{\text{mi}}{\text{hr}} - 25 \frac{\text{mi}}{\text{hr}} = 55 \frac{\text{mi}}{\text{hr}}$$

$$\frac{55 \text{ mi} \times 5280 \text{ ft}}{\text{hr} \times 3600 \dfrac{\text{sec}}{\text{hr}} \quad \text{mi}} = 81 \frac{\text{ft}}{\text{sec}} \quad \text{(the change in velocity)}$$

In what time interval did this take place? 2 min or 120 sec. Then

$$\text{rate of change of velocity} = \frac{81 \text{ ft}}{\text{sec} \times 120 \text{ sec}} = \frac{0.68 \text{ ft}}{\text{sec}^2}$$

This means that during each second the velocity changed 0.68 ft/sec. Can you see that the unit had to be feet second^{-2} (or feet/second^2— that is, feet per second per second)? The unit is merely unfamiliar perhaps. It does not involve a square second, whatever that would be.

The general formula is

$$a = \frac{v_f - v_i}{t}$$

where a is acceleration, v_f is the final velocity, v_i is the initial velocity, and t is the time interval.

Let's do some problems to illustrate the difference between velocity and acceleration.

EXAMPLE 14-4

a. Find the distance traveled during 5 sec at a velocity of 10 ft/sec.

$$10 \frac{\text{ft}}{\text{sec}} \times 5 \text{ sec} = 50 \text{ ft}$$

In symbol form: $s = vt$ (s, distance; v, velocity; t, time)

b. Now find the distance traveled in 5 sec if the acceleration is 10 ft/sec^2. Since no speed is mentioned, we will assume that the object started from rest. Thus we have:

Time interval	Velocity at end of interval, ft/sec	Average velocity during interval, ft/sec	Distance covered during interval, ft	Total distance covered by end of interval, ft
1st sec	10	5*	5	5
2nd sec	20	15	15	20
3rd sec	30	25	25	45
4th sec	40	35	35	80
5th sec	50	45	45	125

*A common mistake involves thinking that the average velocity during the first second is 10 ft/sec. It is not. It is 10 at the end, 0 at the beginning, making the average velocity 5 ft/sec. Obviously, a wrong velocity will give a wrong total distance. Your answer would have been 150 ft instead of 125 ft if final velocity were used instead of average velocity for each second.

Now let's solve this problem in symbol form. We hope it is obvious that 125 ft would be covered in 5 sec under these conditions.

$$\text{average velocity} = \frac{v_f + v_i}{2}$$

distance = velocity × time   (velocity constant)
distance = average velocity × time   (velocity not constant)

$$s = \frac{(v_f + v_i) t}{2}$$

A check against the problem given here gives

$$s = \frac{\left(\dfrac{50 \text{ ft}}{\text{sec}} + \dfrac{0 \text{ ft}}{\text{sec}}\right) \times 5 \text{ sec}}{\times 2} = 125 \text{ ft}$$

Could we solve a problem like this without first finding the final velocity?

If $a = \dfrac{v_f - v_i}{t}$

then $at = v_f - v_i$ and $v_f = at + v_i$

Now, substituting for v_f in

$$s = \frac{(v_i + v_f) \, t}{2}$$

gives $s = \left[\dfrac{v_i + (v_i + at)}{2}\right] t$

$$= (\tfrac{1}{2} v_i + \tfrac{1}{2} v_i + \tfrac{1}{2} at) t$$

$$= v_i t + \tfrac{1}{2} at^2$$

Now let's check Example 14–4b. There we had $v_i = 0$, so

$$s = 0 + \frac{1}{2}\left[\frac{10 \text{ ft}}{\text{sec}^2} \times (5 \text{ sec})^2\right] = 125 \text{ ft}$$

From suitable data, then, you can find average velocity, acceleration, distance covered, and final velocity under accelerated conditions. Now suppose you had velocities and distance, but no time. How could you find acceleration?

EXAMPLE 14–5

A train was clocked at 50 ft/sec as it passed point A and at 100 ft/sec passing point B 500 ft farther down the track. Find the acceleration.

$$a = \frac{v_f - v_i}{t}$$

You have everything but the time; you even have the distance.

$$s = \frac{(v_i + v_f) \, t}{2}$$

Rearrange this to get t.

$$t = \frac{2s}{v_i + v_f}$$

Now substitute:

$$a = \frac{v_f - v_i}{t} = \frac{v_f - v_i}{\dfrac{2s}{v_i + v_f}} = \frac{(v_f - v_i)(v_i + v_f)}{2s} = \frac{v_f v_i + v_f^2 - v_i^2 - v_f v_i}{2s}$$

$$= \frac{v_f^2 - v_i^2}{2s}$$

$$a = \frac{\left[\left(\dfrac{100 \text{ ft}}{\text{sec}}\right)^2 - \left(\dfrac{50 \text{ ft}}{\text{sec}}\right)^2\right]}{\times 2 \times 500 \text{ ft}} = 7.5 \text{ ft/sec}^2$$

There are other ways in which this could have been developed. For example, from

$$a = \frac{v_f - v_i}{t} \quad \text{and} \quad s = \frac{(v_i + v_f)t}{2}$$

you can get

$$as = \frac{(v_f - v_i)}{t} \frac{(v_i + v_f)t}{2}$$

(Multiplication of equality by equality gives an equality.)

$$\text{Then} \quad as = \frac{(v_f v_i + v_f^2 - v_i^2 - v_f v_i)}{2} = \frac{v_f^2 - v_i^2}{2}$$

$$a = \frac{v_f^2 - v_i^2}{2s}$$

FORCE

Just what is force? Weight is force, but is force weight? Suppose you were sitting on the second story of a building and the floor was somehow pulled out from under you. Happy landing. Suppose you were in a giant space probe that orbited the Earth and then traveled to the moon. During orbit around the Earth someone slid a portion of the second floor of the probe from under you. What happened? Nothing. You stayed right where you were, floating over the "missing" floor. When the probe landed on the moon, you weighed only 17% as much as you had on Earth. Yet, essentially, there had been no change in you; you had the same mass on Earth, during orbit, and on the moon.

Weight is a type of force. Whenever there is force, there must at least be the capacity for motion. On Earth, when the deterrent to motion (the floor) was removed, motion followed. In orbit there was a balance of forces, a balance between the force of attraction between the Earth and the probe and the force produced by the rapid orbiting of the probe around the Earth. Thus there was no motion. You had the sensation of weightlessness but were not weightless.

Weight is just one type of force. It is the force associated with gravitational attraction. On the moon the gravitational attraction is only 17% of that of the Earth, so you weighed only 17% as much as you did on Earth. There are also forces associated with magnetism, electricity, etc. You have surely seen an iron nail move faster and faster toward a magnet or long hair fly out toward a comb that has been run through it. Remember the capacity of motion as being inherent in force.

The motion is an accelerated motion, a fact that is often hard to accept. The average person is probably sensibly convinced of the acceleration of the motion associated with force only in the case of the magnet. Nonetheless, all motion caused by the forces due to gravitational attraction, electrical attraction, etc., is accelerated. There are easily obtained experimental figures to demonstrate this.

On Earth the acceleration in the case of weight force (a redundant expression, obviously) is 980 cm/sec^2 (English equivalent: 32 ft/sec^2). This value is roughly constant, but it does depend on altitude and location on the globe and varies inversely with the square root of the distance between the objects attracting one another. It is slightly less on Pike's Peak than in Death Valley, much less at a great distance from the Earth. It is also slightly larger at the North Pole than at the Equator and in New York than in New Orleans because of the shape of the Earth.

Now let's take Newton's Classical Laws of Motion. They involve force among other things. At the time of their development these laws represented a fantastic creative breakthrough. They may seem commonplace and ordinary to you now, since you have known them for years. However, they are capable of experimental verification only. One cannot deduce them by even the most glorious mathematical or theoretical means. That does not prevent their use, fortunately.

1. *A body at rest or moving with a uniform velocity continues "as is" forever unless a force acts upon it.* The modern student familiar with space probes traveling fuel-less in space finds this not at all unusual.

2. *If an unbalanced force is applied to a body, the body acquires an acceleration in the direction in which the force acts and in proportion to the magnitude of the force.* This should also seem totally reasonable. Push a body at rest sufficiently vigorously and it will move. There certainly is an acceleration in the direction of the "push" because it was initially at rest and is now moving. That surely is a

change in velocity. If one pushes a moving body it will move faster
(presuming one pushes in the direction the body was moving). Certainly, if an object is moving faster (or more slowly) at time B than
at time A, there has been a change in the velocity, in other words an
acceleration (or deceleration).

3. *To every force there is an equal and opposite reaction force.* Consider the recoil of firearms. A man sitting on a chair exerts a force
   on the chair. The chair exerts equal but opposite force on the man,
   otherwise the man would run the risk of finding himself in the midst
   of kindling wood.

The first law deals with inertia. What is inertia? It is a measure of
the quantity of matter. You have already heard that weight and mass are
different. Weight varies and is dependent on gravitational attraction,
but mass is constant (except at the extraordinary condition of speeds approaching the speed of light). Mass is a measure of the quantity of matter. Mass is totally independent of gravity. So must inertia be.

This would be so easy to prove if only you could do the same experiment here and some place like Mars. Weigh object A here. Find the
force needed to move it with an acceleration of 10 cm/sec^2. Find the
force needed to stop it in a given time when it is moving with some known
acceleration. Then make the same measurements on Mars. You would
find the weights quite different, as expected. (The mass and diameter
of Mars are so different from those of the Earth; see the later section,
"Law of Universal Gravitation.") But the force needed to overcome inertia and start object A going, or to stop it, is the same as on Earth.
The object must have the same inertia on Earth and on Mars. It must
have the same resistance to change in condition or motion. We know
that the object would have the same mass on Earth and on Mars. Inertia
must indeed be a measure of mass.

Now let's consider *force*. Expressed in equation form, Newton's second law is

$F = kma$

where F is force, k is a constant, m is mass, and a is acceleration. But
one usually sees

$F = ma$

in physics books. Why? Because the units have been designed to in-
corporate whatever the constant would have been into the unit system.
This is a rather common technique.

Consider these equations:

$$F = ma \quad \text{and} \quad m = \frac{F}{a}$$

If weight is the force, the symbol W is used in place of F. The acceleration when the force is weight is the acceleration due to gravity (symbol: g) which is 980 cm/sec^2 or 32 ft/sec^2. Now, by analogy to the equations above,

$W = mg$ just as $F = ma$

$$m = \frac{W}{g}$$

$$F = \frac{W}{g} a$$

The units in force sometimes cause confusion. The words *pound* and *gram* each have two different meanings. In the absolute system they are units of mass, whereas in the gravitational system they are units of force. The absolute system is a system wherein values are defined in terms of fundamental quantities. They do not depend on acceleration due to gravity, etc. Obviously in the gravitational system there would be a dependence on acceleration due to gravity.

In the English system the absolute unit of force is the poundal, the force required to give a 1-lb mass an acceleration of 1 ft/sec^2.

1 lb $\times$ 1 ft sec^{-2} = 1 ft-lb sec^{-2} = 1 poundal

In the metric system the absolute unit of force is the dyne, the force required to give a 1-g mass an acceleration of 1 cm/sec^2.

1 g $\times$ 1 cm sec^{-2} = 1 g-cm sec^{-2} = 1 dyne

In the English system the gravitational unit of force is the pound. The pound is the force exerted by the Earth on a 1-lb mass. Naturally this 1-lb mass feels the pull of the Earth, the acceleration toward the center of the Earth, 32 ft/sec^2.

1 lb force = 1 lb mass $\times$ 32 ft sec^{-2}
$\qquad\qquad$ = 32 ft-lb sec^{-2} = 32 poundals

In the metric system the gravitational unit of force is the gram. It is the force exerted by the Earth on a 1-g mass. This same 1-g mass feels the acceleration due to gravity, 980 cm/sec^2, so

1 g force = 1 g mass $\times$ 980 cm sec^{-2} = 980 g-cm sec^{-2} = 980 dynes

In doing many problems it does not matter which system you use—the absolute or the gravitational—so long as you keep track of which you are using. For example, a milliliter of mercury has a mass of 13.65 g and a weight of 13.65 g of force.

EXAMPLE 14-6

...lute system:

In the force needed to give a 196-g body an acceleration of 10 cm/sec^2, a smooth flat surface.

$$96 \text{ g} \times 10 \frac{cm}{sec^2} = 1960 \text{ dynes}$$

Here the 196 grams was taken to be mass.

Find the acceleration accompanying a force of 640 poundals exerted on a 100-lb body along a smooth flat surface.

Here we will consider the 100 lb to be mass.

$$a = \frac{F}{m} = \frac{640 \text{ poundals}}{100 \text{ lb}} = \frac{640 \text{ ft-lb}}{sec^2 \times 100 \text{ lb}} = 6.4 \frac{ft}{sec^2}$$

EXAMPLE 14-7

In the gravitational system:

Look again at Example 14-6.

Now we're taking the 196 g to be force. This is the force between the object and the Earth. We want to find the other force needed to push this object along a smooth flat surface. Here the 196 is the W in $m = W/g$.

$$F = ma = \frac{Wa}{g}$$

so $$F = \frac{196 \text{ g}}{980 \frac{cm}{sec^2}} \times 10 \frac{cm}{sec^2} = 2 \text{ g force}$$

Proof: $$2 \text{ g force} = \frac{2 \text{ g force} \times 980 \text{ dynes}}{\text{g force}} = 1960 \text{ dynes}.$$

Find the acceleration accompanying a force of 20 lb acting on a 100-lb body along a smooth horizontal surface. Here 100 lb is force, the W in $a = (F/W)g$. So

$$a = \frac{20 \text{ lb} \times 32 \frac{ft}{sec^2}}{100 \text{ lb}} = 6.4 \frac{ft}{sec^2}$$

Do not confuse the dyne with the erg.

$$1 \text{ dyne} = g \frac{cm}{\sec^2}$$

$$1 \text{ erg} = g\left(\frac{cm}{\sec}\right)^2 \quad \text{or} \quad \text{dyne-cm}$$

The dyne is a unit of force, the erg one of energy. When one moves a force through a distance (for example, 1 dyne through 1 cm), one has done work; this is energy. Thus one can see the relationship between force and energy ... and perhaps the difference between an erg and a dyne.

PRESSURE

Pressure is force per unit area. If a force of 10^6 dynes is exerted on a floor 100 cm $\times$ 10 cm, the pressure is

$$\frac{10^6 \text{ dynes}}{10^3 \text{ cm}^2} \quad \text{or} \quad \frac{10^3 \text{ dynes}}{cm^2}$$

Pressure and solids seem to cause no one any problems, but pressure in fluids seems to be the bane of students' existence. Gases and liquids are considered fluids. Anyone who knows the force and the area upon which the force is exerted really must be able to calculate the force per unit area, the pressure.

Fluids do not exert pressure just on the container. If one could somehow get a plane surface (a flat surface) into a fluid one would find that pressure would be exerted on the surface, in fact that the pressure would be uniform in all directions if the fluid was at rest. Naturally if the fluid were "running" somewhere or were being pushed somewhere this would not be true. Pressure at a point in a fluid is that force which would be exerted on a small unit plane (that is, a flat surface of unit area) introduced at that point.

Pressure is sometimes measured in what may seem to be an unusual fashion. One could give one's weight in wildcats instead of pounds. If one considered a wildcat equivalent to 75 lb, then a 150-lb man could quite properly be considered to weigh 2 wildcats. One could do similar things in measuring pressure, but there would be no sense to it unless it made measurement easier. However, it often is easier to give the height of a mercury, water, or other liquid column that has the same pressure at the bottom of the column as the pressure under consideration.

Standard pressure is the pressure of the atmosphere at sea level. This is 14.7 lb/in.^{2} or 10^6 dynes/cm^2. This pressure is the same as the pressure at the bottom of a column of mercury 760 mm (29.9 in.) in height or at the bottom of a 34-ft column of water.

Let's look at that mercury column 760 mm tall. If one found its weight and the area on which the weight rested, one could find the weight/area or force/area, that is, the pressure. Suppose the column of mercury measures $10 \times 10 \times 760$ mm. How could you find its weight? You know the density of mercury is 13.65 g/ml. Would you get weight by multiplying density $\times$ volume? No! Remember that density is mass per unit volume. Weight (force) is mass $\times$ acceleration due to gravity, so mass must be converted to force:

$$\frac{1 \text{ g} \times 980 \text{ cm}}{\sec^2} = 980 \text{ dynes} \quad \text{(force per gram of mass)}$$

Then the weight of the column is

$$\frac{76 \text{ cm} \times 1 \text{ cm} \times 1 \text{ cm} \times 13.65 \text{ g}}{\text{cm}^3} \quad \frac{\times 980 \text{ cm}}{\sec^2} = \text{dynes}$$

The area on which the force is exerted is $1 \text{ cm} \times 1 \text{ cm}$, or 1 cm^2. The force per unit area, or pressure, is dynes per square centimeter. The complete equation is

$$\frac{76 \text{ cm} \times 1 \text{ cm} \times 1 \text{ cm} \times 13.65 \text{ g}}{\text{cm}^3} \quad \frac{\times 980 \text{ cm}}{\sec^2 \times 1 \text{ cm} \times 1 \text{ cm}}$$

$$= 10^6 \frac{\text{dynes}}{\text{cm}^2} \text{ (pressure)}$$

LAW OF UNIVERSAL GRAVITATION

Each particle of matter affects every other particle with a force that is directly proportional to the product of their masses and inversely proportional to the square of the distance between them (actually the distance between their centers, but radius can be ignored if the particle is very small relative to distance between particles). In equation form:

$$F \propto \frac{m_1 m_2}{d^2} \quad \text{or} \quad F = \frac{k m_1 m_2}{d^2}$$

where F is force of attraction, m is mass, and d is distance.

In the metric system you want the force in dynes, that is, g-cm/sec^2. The unit for force of attraction here would be g^2/cm^2, hardly dynes. Could you change this into dynes if the constant had an appropriate unit? In other words, could you multiply it by something to get dynes?

$$\frac{g^2}{\text{cm}^2} \times \text{what?} = \frac{g \times \text{cm}}{\sec^2} = \text{dynes}$$

If the "what?" (the unit for the proportionality constant) is dyne-cm^2/g^2, you have

$$\frac{g^2 \times \text{dynes} \times \text{cm}^2}{\text{cm}^2} \times \frac{1}{g^2} = \text{dynes}$$

The actual constant, the gravitation constant (symbol: G), has the value 6.67×10^{-8} dyne-cm^2/g^2.

Do not confuse G, g, and g. G is the gravitational constant, g is the symbol for acceleration due to gravity, and g is the abbreviation for grams. Also the gravitational constant and the acceleration due to gravity are two entirely different constants and are used in quite dissimilar situations.

EXAMPLE 14–8

Find the force of attraction between a 2.00-g (mass) sphere of 0.80-cm diameter and a 14.00-g (mass) sphere of 1.30-cm diameter when they are exactly 20.00 cm apart.

Have you noticed that there is a catch in this problem? Is the distance 20.00 cm? No. Why not? Does the attraction stop at the surface, or does the matter below the surface also exert a force of attraction on other matter? Naturally, the latter is the case. So the distance is 20.00 cm plus the distances between the surface and the center of each sphere, the radii. Now

$$\frac{6.67 \times 10^{-8} \text{ dyne cm}^2 \times 14.0 \text{ g} \times 2.00 \text{ g}}{g^2 \times (20.00 + 0.40 + 0.65 \text{ cm})^2} = 4.18 \times 10^{-9} \text{ dyne}$$

EXAMPLE 14–9

Knowing that the diameter of the Earth is 12.74×10^8 cm, find the mass of the Earth.

Yes, we are serious. You can find this. It just takes a little thought. You know the basic relationships. Where possible, work with unit quantities. If you had a 1-g mass on the surface of the Earth, it would be attracted by 980 dynes. Now you know the force of attraction, and you know one of the masses. You also know the diameter of the Earth, so you can find the radius of the Earth. Why do you want the radius? It is the effective distance between the two attracting bodies (the radius of the 1-g mass is insignificant). Be sure you know why the mass of 1 g on the surface is attracted by a force of 980 dynes. This is the heart of the problem.

$$980 \text{ dynes} = \frac{6.67 \times 10^{-8} \text{ dyne cm}^2 \times 1 \text{ g} \times \text{mass of Earth}}{g^2 \times (6.37 \times 10^8 \text{ cm})^2}$$

$$\text{mass of Earth} = \frac{980 \text{ dynes} \times (6.37 \times 10^8 \text{ cm})^2}{6.67 \times 10^{-8} \text{ dyne } \dfrac{\text{cm}^2 \times 1 \text{ g}}{\text{g}^2}} = 5.97 \times 10^{27} \text{ g}$$

EXAMPLE 14-10

The diameter of the moon is 0.273 that of the Earth. Find the weight of a 1-g mass on the moon. Mass of the moon is 0.0128 that of the Earth.

In this problem one would want to ask oneself some questions.

1. What is the relationship between force and mass? Direct. Consequently the less massive moon would have less weight (less force).
2. What is the relationship between force and distance separating attracting bodies? Inverse. Therefore on the smaller moon there would be more force, more weight.
3. What is the distance involved? It is the distance between the object attracted and the center of the attracting body. On the moon, for all practical purposes, it is just the radius of the moon, since the radius of the 1-g mass would be infinitesimally small with respect to that of the moon. (Obviously, both the moon and the 1-g mass would attract one another; we gave the traditional wording here.)
4. But what about on the Earth? You don't have the diameter and mass of the Earth. You do, in effect. If you take both the mass of the Earth and the radius of the Earth as 1, then 0.0128 is the mass of the moon and 0.273 its radius (diameter and radius are directly proportional to one another).

On moon: less mass, therefore less force; less diameter, less radius, therefore more force; so

$$\frac{1 \text{ g} \times 980 \text{ cm} \times 1^2 \times 0.0128}{\sec^2 \times (0.273)^2 \times 1} = 168 \text{ dynes}$$

(1 g mass weighs 980 dynes on Earth.)

You object. We didn't use the formula we have in this section. No. We didn't need to use it, and had we used it we would have had to have actual values for mass and radius, which we did not have, although we could obviously have found them by search of readily obtainable reference materials if by no other means.

EXAMPLE 14-11

Suppose a 1-g mass on the surface of a planet had a weight of 4000 dynes. Find the density of the planet. Volume of a sphere is $1.33\pi r^3$. Mass of the planet is 8×10^{20} g.

This is simpler than it may appear. You have the force, both masses, and the gravitational constant. You need only find the distance separating the two masses. This distance will be the radius of the planet, since the radius of the 1-g mass would be insignificant. From the radius you could find the volume. Then density is easily found.

EXAMPLE 14–12

The mass of the Earth is 6×10^{24} kg. The mass of the sun is about 1.8×10^{30} kg. The distance between the earth and the sun is 1.5×10^8 km. Find the attraction between the Earth and the sun in dynes and in grams of weight (grams of force).

This is really the same as the foregoing problems, only perhaps simpler. You had to convert units so that the answer was dynes. Did you use 1 g weight = 980 dynes weight?

EXAMPLE 14–13

How much would a 150-lb man weigh on the moon? Mass of the moon is 0.0128 that of the Earth, and the diameter of the moon is 0.273 that of the Earth.

Did you get about $1/6$ as much?

EXAMPLE 14–14

What would be the attractive force between two 10-g (mass) spheres when their centers are 3 cm apart? What acceleration would this force produce on *one* of the spheres? What distance could this sphere cover in 1 min if the acceleration thus produced continued to act (actually a physical impossibility, but that is not our concern here)?

You found the force. Force also equals mass times acceleration. Each sphere has a 10-g mass, so the acceleration of one sphere presents no problem.

$$a = \frac{F}{m}$$

In what units must acceleration be? We are not using acceleration due to gravity here. Be sure you see why not. Your acceleration (if force is in dynes) would have to be centimeters second^{-2}. Review the previous discussion of acceleration if you are stopped now.

EXAMPLE 14–15

Suppose you had two spheres of 10.00-cm diameter suspended from the same arm of a balance. The spheres are exactly 2 cm apart. The top one has a mass of 8.00 g and the bottom one has a mass of 95.00 g. What would be the weight of the 8.00-g mass if weighed alone? Express this weight in dynes. What would be the weight of the 8.00-g mass (again weight in dynes) if weighed on Earth in the fashion described in the first sentence of this example?

You have no difficulty finding the weight of the 8.00-g mass weighed alone:

$$\frac{8.00 \text{ g} \times 980 \text{ cm}}{\sec^2} = 7.84 \times 10^3 \text{ dynes}$$

The 8.00-g mass weighed in the fashion described would have two forces of attraction acting on it: that of gravity and that from the other sphere. The total force acting on the sphere (its weight) then is the sum of these two forces. Each is calculated in the standard fashion used in most of the preceding problems.

$$\left[\frac{8.00 \text{ g} \times 980 \text{ cm}}{\sec^2}\right] + 6.67 \times 10^{-8} \frac{\text{dyne cm}^2}{\text{g}^2} \times \frac{8.00 \text{ g} \times 95.00 \text{ g}}{(5 + 5 + 2 \text{ cm})^2}.$$
$$= 7.84 \times 10^3 \text{ dynes}$$

Obviously, only the force of gravitational attraction was significant here. This would be true except for quite massive objects.

Many other relationships similar to those illustrated here exist in problems involving illumination, magnetic attraction, etc. Facts and specific relationships vary, but the method for solving such problems is rather similar to what we have shown.

WORK

To the physicist, work involves the exertion of a force through a distance. In this sense, a man leaning against a wall is doing no work, even though he may be preventing the wall from falling over. True, the man is exerting force on the wall and the wall is exerting force on the man. However, if this man leaned with the same force against a cart, causing it to move, he would be doing work. The physicist's precise definition would be that an agent does work on a body when it exerts a force on a body through a distance along the same direction as the force. In other words, when something performs work on an object, it uses force on that object, and this causes the object to move in the direction in which the force was pointing. Work would be proportional to the force and to the distance moved. When work is done, kinetic energy in exactly the same amount is involved.

$$W = Fs$$

where W is work, and s is distance. If the force is in dynes and the distance in centimeters, the work is in dyne-centimeters. Now

$$dyne = \frac{g\text{-}cm}{sec^2}$$

$$erg \ \ = g\left(\frac{cm}{sec}\right)^2$$

and a dyne-centimeter, the work unit we have here, would be

$$\frac{g\text{-}cm}{sec^2} \times cm \quad \text{or} \quad \frac{g\text{-}cm^2}{sec^2}$$

Thus a dyne-centimeter is clearly an erg, an energy unit. This is not surprising, since energy is defined as the ability to do work.

EXAMPLE 14–16

Find the work involved in moving a 1-g weight 800 m.

1 g weight = 980 dynes weight
800 m = 80,000 cm

$$\frac{1 \text{ g (wt)} \times 980 \text{ dynes} \times 80,000 \text{ cm}}{g \text{ (wt)}} = 8 \times 10^7 \text{ ergs}$$

EXAMPLE 14–17

How much work is done when a gas in a container fitted with a piston is released from a solid compound and expands against the piston until the gas occupies 1 liter at standard temperature and pressure? (Consider the volume of the original solid to be negligible. See Chapter 15 on gases if necessary.)

You don't know how to do this? You know that gases expanding can do work. This is the whole principle involved in conventional explosives. Rather small amounts of solids or liquids react to release vast amounts of gases that can move trees, buildings, etc., out of the way in the process of expansion. This would certainly involve work. An expanded gas at a given temperature has far less energy than the same number of molecules of gas at the same temperature at a smaller volume. (A colder gas has less energy than the same mass of a hotter gas.) In losing energy, a gas does work. However, this still does not help solve this problem. Start asking yourself questions about everything you have and about the relationships involving the factors you want.

1. What is work? It is the product of force × distance.
2. Do you have either of these? No. You have a liter of gas at 0°C and 760 mm of Hg pressure.
3. Is there anything in the problem even remotely connected with force and/or distance?

Look at the liter. It is a volume unit and volume can be the product of three linear dimensions: length, width and depth. This seems far fetched, but there may well be a relationship. Think of volume as $s \times s \times s$, where s is a linear dimension.

Look at temperature. We can't see any relationship. If you know the universal gas law, you may see a relationship, but we are looking for another method now.

Look at pressure. You have it in the problem.

$$\text{pressure} = \frac{\text{force}}{\text{area}}$$

Now you have something! From pressure you should be able to get some sort of force. What is the unit, though?

$$760 \text{ mm of Hg} = 76 \text{ cm} = 1 \text{ atm} = 14.7 \frac{\text{lb}}{\text{in.}^2}$$

The 14.7 lb/in.^{2} is the "open sesame" here. Think of this as

$$\frac{\text{force} \times s^3}{s^2} = \text{force} \times s = \text{force} \times \text{distance} = \text{work!}$$

Where did you get the s^2? The area is length × width, two linear dimensions, and we are using s to represent linear dimensions. There is a problem of units here. Convert the square inches to square feet and the liters to cubic feet. (From the liters you got the s^3.)

$$\frac{\dfrac{14.7 \text{ lb}}{\text{in.}^2}}{\left(\dfrac{12 \text{ in.}}{\text{ft}}\right)^2} \times 1 \text{ liter} \times \frac{1000 \text{ cm}^3}{\left(\dfrac{2.54 \text{ cm}}{\text{in.}}\right)^3 \left(\dfrac{12 \text{ in.}}{\text{ft}}\right)^3} = \text{approx 70 ft-lb (a work unit)}$$

Suppose that after all this you wanted to work this out using the 760 mm of Hg pressure (760 torr). After all, pressure is pressure, and if 14.7 lb/in.^{2} can be used, so can 760 mm of Hg.

A gas which has a pressure of 760 mm of Hg has the same pressure (force per unit area) as that of a column of mercury 760 mm or 76 cm high. Can you find the force that this column of mercury would exert? In other words, can you find the weight of this column? You have already done this on page 185. Choose a unit area in order to have the volume become useful.

$$\frac{76 \text{ cm} \times 1 \text{ cm} \times 1 \text{ cm} \times 13.6 \text{ g (wt)}}{\text{cm}^3} = \text{weight of column of mercury}$$

You can turn this into dynes by multiplying by 980 dynes per gram of weight. Why would you want this in dynes rather than in grams? No reason except that a dyne-centimeter is a rather common, recognizable unit of work, the erg.

You have volume:

$$1 \text{ liter} \times 1000 \frac{\text{cm}^3}{\text{liter}}$$

You made up an area, 1 cm by 1 cm. From volume/area, that is, cm^3/cm^2, you could get a linear dimension, centimeters. So

$$\frac{980 \text{ dynes} \times 1 \text{ cm} \times 1 \text{ cm} \times 76 \text{ cm} \times 13.65 \text{ g (wt)} \times 1 \text{ liter}}{\text{g (wt)}} \quad \frac{}{\text{cm}^3 \times 1 \text{ cm} \times 1 \text{ cm}} \quad \frac{\times 1000 \text{ cm}^3}{\text{liter}}$$

$$= \text{approx } 1 \times 10^9 \text{ dyne-cm} = 1 \times 10^9 \text{ ergs}$$

You'll note this setup is not in strictly logical order. We put dynes in first so that you would see dynes, rather a key unit; 980 dynes/g really should have gone after the 13.65 g/cm^3.

POWER

What is power? It is the *rate* of doing work.

$$P = \frac{W}{t}$$

where P is power, W is work, and t is time. The units of power are

$$\frac{\text{ft-lb}}{\text{sec}} \text{ , } \frac{\text{dyne-cm}}{\text{sec}} \text{ , } \frac{\text{erg}}{\text{sec}} \text{ , etc.}$$

They are all work/time.

$$1 \text{ horsepower (hp)} = 550 \frac{\text{ft-lb}}{\text{sec}}$$

$$1 \text{ watt} = 10^7 \frac{\text{ergs}}{\text{sec}} = 1 \frac{\text{joule}}{\text{sec}}$$

$$\frac{1 \text{ ft-lb}}{\text{sec}} = 1.356 \text{ watts}$$

PROBLEMS

1. Find the average kinetic energy of oxygen molecules (32 g/mole) having an average velocity of 100,000 cm/sec. What is it in ergs, joules, and calories?

2. At what speed would radon gas molecules (222 g/mole) travel if they were at the same temperature as the oxygen in problem 1?

3. Find the temperature of the gas in problem 1.

4. What temperature would be needed to triple the velocity of oxygen in problem 1?

5. Find the speed with which helium would travel at 2000°C. The mass of helium is 4 g/mole.

6. If 14 g of uranium-236 were completely converted into energy, how many kilocalories (1 kcal = 1000 cal) would be liberated? How many kilocalories would be liberated per cubic centimeter of uranium-236 (density 18.90 g/ml)?

7. If 49×10^{10} kcal were released when a given mass of matter was turned into energy, find the number of grams so converted.

8. At time zero a car was going 150 mi/hr. At time zero plus 3 min it was going 10 mi/hr. Find the deceleration.

9. What acceleration is needed to cause a car traveling 25 mi/hr to reach a speed of 110 mi/hr in 2 min?

10. What distance would a car going 80 mi/hr cover in 3 hr?

11. What distance would a vehicle moving with an acceleration of 80 mi/hr^2 cover in 3 hr?

12. What force would a column of ethanol (density 0.79 g/ml) 5 ft tall exert on the bottom of a barrel with an area of 2 ft^2?

13. What constant force would be needed to give a 68-g mass an acceleration of 40 cm sec^{-2}?

14. Find the work done when a gas from the decomposition of ammonium nitrite is released in a container fitted with a piston. It expands to 5000 liters at 150°C and 1000 torr (see Chapter 15 if necessary).

15. A 5000-ton locomotive is hoisted 40 ft from a dock to the deck of a ship. How much work is done?

16. The same locomotive mentioned in problem 15 was lowered 90 ft into the hold of a ship. How much work could it have done in descending this distance?

17. How much work is done on a 4-kg box in accelerating it upward at 7 m/sec² for 5 sec?

18. A fine horse exerted a horizontal pull (force) of 200 lb when pulling a cart. If he covered 8 mi in 1.5 hr, what was his horsepower?

19. A 2000-lb car moved 80 mi in 80 min. Find the watts, the horsepower, the foot-pounds, and the joules involved. Label each as either work or power.

20. A car weighing 4000 lb and traveling 75 mi/hr is brought to a full stop in 120 ft. Find the horsepower involved in braking this vehicle.

21. Electricity in a certain area is 7¢ per kilowatt-hour. What would have been the cost of doing the work of the horse in problem 18 by electrical means in a total time of 10 min?

15

CLASSIC GAS PROBLEMS

Simple gas problems occasionally cause needless difficulty. Let's put down some facts and observations about gases before going on.

1. Gases consist of moving molecules separated from one another by distances that are vast relative to the size of the molecules.
2. A given number of gas molecules can be crowded into a smaller space; in other words, gases can be compressed.
3. If gas molecules are crowded closely enough together, gas condenses into a liquid (or a solid) because the molecules attract one another; the force of attraction varies inversely with the square of the distance between molecules.
4. Gas molecules are in constant motion but do not lose energy because of their motion. This may seem to be an absurdity, but how else can one explain the fact that a gas kept at constant temperature in a gas-tight container does not lose its pressure?
5. Gas molecules collide with one another and with the walls of the container in perfectly elastic conditions. Thus the collisions result in no net loss of kinetic or potential energy.
6. Gas molecules move faster if the temperature is raised, more slowly if the temperature is lowered.
7. The molecules of a gas in a container will hit the walls of the container more often if the walls are moved closer together without letting any gas out. They will hit the walls of the container less often if the walls are moved farther apart without letting any gas in or out.
8. Pressure is a measure of frequency of molecular impact on a surface.
9. All gases at the same temperature have the same kinetic energy.

GAS VOLUME AND TEMPERATURE

It is probably perfectly obvious to anyone likely to be reading this that there is a direct relationship between volume and temperature of gases. Consider the data in Table 15-1. For each degree rise or fall in temperature above or below 0°C the volume changed 1/273. In theory, then, at −273°C the volume of the gas would be zero.

Table 15-1

Temperature, °C (pressure constant)	Volume, liters
+10	283
+ 2	275
+ 1	274
0	273
− 1	272
− 2	271
−10	263

$$273 \text{ liters} - \frac{273}{273} (273 \text{ liters}) = 0$$

However, long before −273°C the vast majority of gases become liquids or solids, and this relationship no longer holds.

Now let's try a problem. Given 10 liters of gas at 0°C, find the volume it would occupy when the temperature is raised to 20°C (pressure constant).

$$10 \text{ liters} + \frac{20}{273} (10 \text{ liters})$$

This is awkward, so try this:

$$\frac{273}{273} (10 \text{ liters}) + \frac{20}{273} (10 \text{ liters}) \quad \text{or} \quad \frac{(273 + 20) \, 10 \text{ liters}}{(273 + 0)}$$

By adding 273 to each temperature in degrees Celsius one can get a correcting factor. The new volume can then be calculated directly from the old volume by multiplying by this correcting factor. We have in effect created a new temperature scale, the absolute or Kelvin (K) scale.*

$$°K = °C + 273$$

---

*Lord Kelvin developed this scale and called it the absolute scale. Theoretically −273°C was to have been absolute zero, but −273.18999°C has been reached at the University of California at Berkeley.

Now we can say: *Volume of a gas is directly proportional to the absolute (or Kelvin) temperature if the pressure remains constant.*

In working with gases, obviously, it is necessary to specify temperature and pressure as well as volume. Standard temperature for gases is 0°C.

EXAMPLE 15–1

Find the volume at 29.0°C of a gas that occupies 4.0 liters at 14.0°C (pressure constant).

1. You want volume, so operate on volume.
2. Change temperature to degrees Kelvin.
3. Temperature is increasing so volume must increase.

$$\frac{4.0 \text{ liters} \times (273 + 29.0)°K}{(273 + 14.0)°K} = 4.2 \text{ liters}$$

EXAMPLE 15–2

If a gas has a volume of 15 liters at 100°C, at what temperature will it fill 45 liters (pressure constant)?

You want temperature, so operate on temperature.

$$\frac{(100 + 273)°K \times 45 \text{ liters}}{15 \text{ liters}} = 1100°K$$

To get °C, subtract 273.

EXAMPLE 15–3

A 250-ml sample of gas, measured at 21°C, was cooled to −50°C (pressure constant). Find the new volume.

$$\frac{250 \text{ ml} \times (273 - 50)°K}{(273 + 21)°K} = 190 \text{ ml}$$

GAS VOLUME AND PRESSURE

To what is pressure of a gas due? To the impact of the molecules on the surface at which pressure is measured. If the walls of a closed container of gas are moved closer together, the pressure should increase, since the molecules would hit the walls oftener. If one reduced the volume by half, the molecules should hit the surface twice as often, thus doubling the original pressure. If one moved the walls out so that there was twice the original volume, the molecules would hit the walls only half as often, producing only half the pressure. Obviously, *pressure and volume are inversely proportional to one another at constant temperature.*

Standard pressure, the pressure of the atmosphere at sea level, can be expressed in various ways:

760   torr (the International unit, the pressure exerted at the bottom of
            a column of mercury 760 mm high)
760   mm of Hg
76.0   cm of Hg
29.9   in. of Hg
34.0   ft of water
1.00   atm
14.7   lb/in.^{2}

Now let's try the following problems, using reason rather than formulas.

EXAMPLE 15-4

A certain gas had a volume of 1000 ft^3 at a pressure of 20 lb/in.^{2}. Find the pressure when the gas was allowed to expand into a container of 2500-ft^3 capacity (temperature constant).

What is the relationship here? An inverse one. The volume has increased, therefore the pressure must have decreased. You want pressure, so operate mathematically on pressure.

$$\frac{20 \text{ lb}}{\text{in.}^2} \times \frac{1000 \text{ ft}^3}{2500 \text{ ft}^3} = 8 \text{ lb/in.}^2$$

EXAMPLE 15-5

A certain gas exerted a pressure of 785 torr in a 3-liter container. The gas was then forced into a smaller container at the same temperature. What is the volume of the smaller container if the gas pressure is now 3200 torr?

$$\frac{3 \text{ liters} \times 785 \text{ torr}}{3200 \text{ torr}} = 0.7 \text{ liter}$$

It makes absolutely no difference what units are used to measure pressure and volume so long as each pair is measured in the same unit.

GAS TEMPERATURE AND PRESSURE

An increase in temperature makes gas molecules move faster, so they hit the walls of a container more often. Therefore the increase in pressure should be directly proportional to the increase in temperature. To be exact, *pressure is directly proportional to absolute temperature,* if the mass of the gas and the volume are held constant.

EXAMPLE 15–6

A gas in a given container at 91°C had a pressure of 810 torr. Find the pressure at 1500°C (volume constant).

$$\frac{810 \text{ torr} \times (1500 + 273)^{\circ}K}{(91 + 273)^{\circ}K} = 3900 \text{ torr (significant figures)}$$

DALTON'S LAW OF PARTIAL PRESSURES

It should seem reasonable that in a mixture of gases that do not react with one another each gas would exert its own individual pressure. The total pressure of such a mixture should equal the sum of the individual pressures. In more usual terminology: The total pressure of a mixture of gases is the sum of the partial pressures of the individual gases. This is Dalton's law. In equation form it is

$$P = p_1 + p_2 + p_3 + \cdots$$

where P is the total pressure, and p_1, p_2, etc., are the pressures of the individual gases.

Table 15-2

Gas	Pressure, torr
nitrogen	485
oxygen	268
carbon dioxide	4
water vapor	18
total pressure	775

Consider the mixture of gases in Table 15-2. Humidity rises with temperature. Humidity is due to water vapor in the air. This vapor is a gas. It is governed by the physical laws that govern other gases. At a given temperature the atmosphere over a body of water can contain a given amount of water vapor, and this amount of water vapor has a characteristic pressure (Table 15-3). (*Aside:* What is standard atmospheric pressure

Table 15-3

Temperature, °C	Vapor pressure of water, torr	Temperature, °C	Vapor pressure of water, torr
0	4.6	26	25.2
5	6.5	28	28.3
10	9.2	30	31.8
12	10.5	35	42.2
14	12.0	40	55.3
16	13.6	50	92.5
18	15.5	70	233.7
20	17.5	80	355.1
22	19.8	90	525.8
24	22.4	100	760.0

at sea level? What is the boiling point of pure water at sea level? Do you see a connection between temperature at which a liquid will boil and atmospheric pressure?)

A gas collected over water contains water vapor; a gas collected over mercury contains mercury vapor; etc. The amount and pressure of the vapor depend upon the temperature. When a gas is collected over water as shown in Figure 15-1, the pressure in bottle B must be equal to the

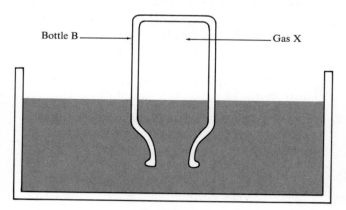

Figure 15-1

pressure of the atmosphere. In bottle B there would be gas X and water vapor. Suppose the gas was collected at 20°C and 756 torr pressure. At 20°C the vapor pressure of water is 17.5 (round to 18) torr. Therefore

$$P_{atm} = p_{gas\,X} + p_{water\,vapor}$$

$$p_{gas\,X} = P_{atm} - p_{water\,vapor}$$

$$= 756 \text{ torr} - 18 \text{ torr} = 738 \text{ torr}$$

EXAMPLE 15–7

What would be the pressure of oxygen itself if collected over a water trough at exactly 25°C when the external pressure was 0.650 atm?

$$\left(\frac{0.650 \text{ atm} \times 760 \text{ torr}}{\text{atm}} \right) - 24 \text{ torr} = 470 \text{ torr}$$

EXAMPLE 15–8

A liter of hydrogen was put into a 1.1-liter container with 0.1 liter of liquid water at 25°C. Find the total pressure. The original pressure of hydrogen was 781 torr.

$$p_{\text{hydrogen}} + p_{\text{water vapor}} = 781 \text{ torr} + 24 \text{ torr} = 805 \text{ torr}$$

MULTIPLE PRESSURE, VOLUME, AND TEMPERATURE CHANGES

In actual practice one rarely deals with temperature-pressure, temperature-volume, or pressure-volume changes. Usually there are multiple changes to be dealt with. Remember that pressure and volume are inversely proportional, pressure and temperature directly proportional, and volume and temperature directly proportional. Absolute temperature must always be used. In solving problems involving multiple changes, always find the base factor first and then consider the effect of each change on the base factor. Do not consider the effect of changes on one another: to do so causes chaos, and such chaos usually results in inability to solve the problems. *Remember that standard temperature and pressure for gases are 0°C and 760 torr, respectively.* (Standard temperature and pressure are often abbreviated as STP.)

EXAMPLE 15–9

a. At 10°C and 795 torr pressure the volume of a gas was 5.0 liters. Find the new volume after the conditions are changed to 5°C and 760 torr pressure.

You want volume, so operate on volume. Consider the effect of *each* change *on volume*, not the effect of the changes on one another. Temperature is decreasing, therefore volume should decrease. Pressure is decreasing, therefore volume should increase.

$$\frac{5.0 \text{ liters} \times 278°A \times 795 \text{ torr}}{283°A \times 760 \text{ torr}} = 5.1 \text{ liters}$$

b. If the gas in part a had been measured over water at 5°C and 760 torr, what would its volume have been?

You would do this problem in exactly the same way, but this time the new pressure is 760 minus the vapor pressure of water at 5°C, that is, (760 − 7) torr.

EXAMPLE 15–10

A 39.8-liter sample of gas measured at standard pressure and temperature was put into a 100.0-liter cylinder at 523°C. Find the pressure under the new conditions.

Old pressure and temperature were 760 torr and 0°C. The volume increases, thereby decreasing the pressure. Temperature increases, thereby increasing the pressure.

$$\frac{760 \text{ torr} \times 39.8 \text{ liters} \times (273 + 523)°\text{K}}{100.0 \text{ liters} \times (273 + 0)°\text{K}} = 882 \text{ torr}$$

EXAMPLE 15–11

What temperature is required to change the volume of a gas from 49.5 liters at 1 atm pressure and 385°C to 25.0 liters at 0.3 atm?

$$\frac{(385 + 273)°\text{K} \times 25.0 \text{ liters} \times 0.3 \text{ atm}}{49.5 \text{ liters} \times 1 \text{ atm}} = 100°\text{K} \quad (\text{or } -173°\text{C})$$

EXAMPLE 15–12

What volume was recorded for 1.0 liter of dry gas at STP when it was measured over water at 20°C and 785 torr?

volume	1.0 liter	unknown
temperature	0°C	20°C
pressure	760 torr	(785 − 18) torr

$$\frac{1.0 \text{ liter} \times (273 + 20)°\text{K} \times 760 \text{ torr}}{(273 + 0)°\text{K} \times (785 - 18) \text{ torr}} = 1.1 \text{ liters (significant figures)}$$

CONVERSION OF TEMPERATURES FROM FAHRENHEIT TO CELSIUS AND VICE VERSA

Temperature is a measure of molecular motion. Be sure not to confuse temperature and quantity of heat. A thimbleful of water at 100°C has a higher temperature than a bucket of water at 99°C, but the water in the bucket has a much greater quantity of heat.

Table 15-4

	Fahrenheit (°F)	Celsius (°C)
boiling point of water (sea level)	212	100
freezing point of water	32	0
difference:	180	100

It is obvious from Table 15-4 that 180 degrees on the Fahrenheit scale covers the same temperature range as 100 Celsius units. One degree Fahrenheit involves less difference in molecular motion than does one degree Celsius. Not only this, but the zero points on the two scales do not involve the same degree of molecular motion for a given substance.

In any attempt to find a formula to convert one temperature scale into another, one must take into account the dissimilar starting points; 32°F corresponds to 0°C, and −17.8°C corresponds to 0°F. Fahrenheit above the freezing point of water would always be at least 32 degrees higher than Celsius, and there would be further difference because 180 Fahrenheit units correspond to 100 Celsius units, leading to another numerical increase in figures on changing from Celsius to Fahrenheit. So

$$°F = 32 + \frac{180}{100}(°C) \quad \text{or} \quad °F = 32 + 1.8\,(°C)$$

Correspondingly, in converting from Fahrenheit to Celsius wouldn't Celsius always be lower for just the opposite reasons?

$$°C = \frac{(°F - 32)\,100}{180} \quad \text{or} \quad °C = \frac{°F - 32}{1.8}$$

PROBLEMS

1. What volume of nitrogen would there be at −150°C if the volume at −85°C is 49 liters (pressure constant)?
2. Find the temperature necessary to increase by 195 liters the volume of a sample of oxygen that filled 85 liters at 10°C (pressure constant).
3. A quantity of oxygen gas that measured 99 liters at standard pressure was transferred to an empty 109-liter container. Find the new pressure (temperature constant).

4. What pressure would a gas that occupies 88 liters at 900 mm of Hg pressure (900 torr) have in a 21-liter container (temperature constant)? Assume that the gas remains in the gaseous phase.

5. A gas expanded into a chamber of unknown volume. The original volume of the gas was 45 liters, the original pressure was 756 mm of Hg, and the final pressure was 49 mm. Find the volume of the chamber. Find the percentage change in volume (temperature constant throughout).

6. If 45 liters of gas, at 780 torr, was compressed to 40 liters at the same temperature (isothermally), find the new pressure.

7. What temperature would be needed to change the pressure of 40 liters of gas at 298°K from 90 atm to 100 atm?

8. A gas occupying 30 liters at 4 atm and 95°C was cooled to 15°C at constant volume. Find the new pressure.

9. If 95 liters of gas was collected at 748 mm of Hg and 19°C over water, what would its volume be at STP?

10. What volume would a gas measuring 99 liters at 760 torr and 40°C have if it were placed in a container over water at a temperature of 35°C and a pressure of 738 torr?

11. What pressure would be needed to force a gas that fills 40 liters at 20°C and 1.5 atm pressure into a 3-liter container at 50°C?

12. What would be the temperature of a 150-liter sample of methane gas, measured at −90°C and 29.9 in. of Hg, after it had expanded into a 500-liter container if the pressure were then 785 torr?

13. At what temperature would water boil when the atmospheric pressure was 500 mm of Hg?

14. Convert 50°C to degrees Fahrenheit.

15. Convert 50°F to degrees Celsius.

16. Find the temperature at which the Fahrenheit and Celsius scales are numerically equal.

17. Convert 19 atm to torr and to pounds per square inch pressure.

18. Convert 1000 torr to inches of Hg pressure.

19. A certain barometer was filled with liquid A. Density of liquid A is 2.0 g/ml. What would the height of this barometer be when a mercury barometer read 710 mm? Density of mercury is 13.65 g/ml.

16

MOLES

The term *mole* is used by chemists to represent a certain number of individual chemical units. There are 6.023×10^{23} "things" in a mole of anything. This number is known as Avogadro's number (symbol: N). The significance and method of determination of Avogadro's number are beyond the scope of this book. However, this interesting topic is covered in most college general chemistry textbooks. To be exact, a mole is now held to be the amount of a substance that contains the same number of chemical units as there are atoms in 12 g of the carbon-12 isotope.* Obviously, there must be 6.023×10^{23} atoms in exactly 12 g of carbon-12.

Note that the definition given in the preceding paragraph uses the phrase *chemical units*. It is not restricted to atoms, molecules, or any other specific entity. It also takes the carbon-12 isotope as the standard. Chemists and physicists formerly used slightly different atomic weight scales because ordinary oxygen, a mixture of oxygen isotopes, was taken as the standard at 16.0000 by chemists, whereas the physicists took the oxygen-16 isotope as the standard. A unified scale was recently developed and adopted to eliminate the use of sometimes confusing separate systems. The new scale takes the carbon-12 isotope as the standard at 12.0000, and the atomic weights in Table 16-1 are based on this standard.

---

*Isotopes are different forms of the same element that have the same number of protons but different numbers of neutrons in the nucleus. Most elements exist as mixtures of isotopes.

Table 16-1   Selected Atomic Weights Based on Carbon-12

Aluminum	Al	26.9815	Magnesium	Mg	24.312
Antimony	Sb	121.75	Manganese	Mn	54.9380
Argon	Ar	39.948	Mercury	Hg	200.59
Arsenic	As	74.9216	Molybdenum	Mo	95.94
Barium	Ba	137.34	Neon	Ne	20.183
Beryllium	Be	9.0122	Nickel	Ni	58.71
Bismuth	Bi	208.980	Nitrogen	N	14.0067
Boron	B	10.811	Oxygen	O	15.9994
Bromine	Br	79.904	Palladium	Pd	106.4
Cadmium	Cd	112.40	Phosphorus	P	30.9738
Calcium	Ca	40.08	Platinum	Pt	195.09
Carbon	C	12.01115	Potassium	K	39.102
Cerium	Ce	140.12	Rhenium	Re	186.2
Cesium	Cs	132.905	Rubidium	Rb	85.47
Chlorine	Cl	35.453	Scandium	Sc	44.956
Chromium	Cr	51.996	Selenium	Se	78.96
Cobalt	Co	58.9332	Silicon	Si	28.086
Copper	Cu	63.546	Silver	Ag	107.868
Fluorine	F	18.9984	Sodium	Na	22.9898
Gallium	Ga	69.72	Strontium	Sr	87.62
Germanium	Ge	72.59	Sulfur	S	32.064
Gold	Au	196.967	Tantalum	Ta	180.948
Hafnium	Hf	178.49	Tellurium	Te	127.60
Helium	He	4.0026	Thallium	Tl	204.37
Hydrogen	H	1.00797	Thorium	Th	232.038
Indium	In	114.82	Tin	Sn	118.69
Iodine	I	126.9044	Titanium	Ti	47.90
Iron	Fe	55.847	Tungsten	W	183.85
Krypton	Kr	83.80	Uranium	U	238.03
Lanthanum	La	138.91	Vanadium	V	50.942
Lead	Pb	207.19	Zinc	Zn	65.37
Lithium	Li	6.939	Zirconium	Zr	91.22

The weight in grams of 6.023×10^{23} atoms—that is, one mole—of an element is numerically equal to the atomic weight of the element. Similarly, the molecular weight expressed in grams of an element has 6.023×10^{23} molecules in it. For most elements the atom and the molecule are *taken* to be the same thing. For example, the atom and the molecule of calcium (Ca) are taken to be the same thing. Thus the atomic weight and the molecular weight are both 40.08. There are 6.023×10^{23} molecules in 40.08 g of Ca and 6.023×10^{23} atoms in 40.08 g of Ca. Some elements, however, do have more than one atom in a molecule. Oxygen is a good example of this. A mole of oxygen atoms weighs 15.9994 g;

there are 6.023×10^{23} atoms in 15.9994 g of oxygen. However, a mole of oxygen molecules, O_2, the normal form in which oxygen occurs, has 6.023×10^{23} molecules in it and weighs 31.9988 g. This same mole of oxygen gas, O_2, has 12.046×10^{23} atoms of oxygen, since each molecule of O_2 has 2 atoms.

This may have confused you. Let's look at some chemical formulas. In formulas, by convention, the subscript refers to the preceding element. For example, $C_5H_{10}O$ has five carbon atoms, ten hydrogen atoms, and one oxygen atom in it. So the molecular weight of this compound, in whole numbers, would be:

$$C = 5 \times 12 = 60$$
$$H = 10 \times 1 = 10$$
$$O = 1 \times 16 = \underline{16}$$
$$86 \, \frac{amu}{molecule} \quad \text{or} \quad 86 \, \frac{g}{mole}$$

(amu is atomic mass unit.)

Subscripts following parentheses refer to everything inside the parentheses. $(NH_4)_3Co(NO_2)_6$ has three nitrogen atoms and twelve hydrogen atoms in the three NH_4 groups, plus one cobalt atom, plus six nitrogen atoms and twelve oxygen atoms in the six NO_2 groups. The molecular weight of the compound is

$$N \ = 9 \times 14 = 126$$
$$H \ = 12 \times 1 = \ 12$$
$$Co = 1 \times 59 = \ 59$$
$$O \ = 12 \times 16 = \underline{192}$$
$$389 \, \frac{amu}{molecule} \quad \text{or} \quad 389 \, \frac{g}{mole}$$

We have rounded atomic weights here. In calculations for actual experiments the number of digits to be used depends upon the number of significant figures in the measured quantities.

The atomic weights given in Table 16-1 really represent atomic mass units (amu). An atomic mass unit is 1/12 of the mass of an atom of the carbon-12 isotope. An atomic mass unit actually weighs 1.66×10^{-24} g. To find the weight in grams of a mole of carbon-12 atoms one would do the following:

$$\frac{12 \ \text{amu}}{\text{atom}} \times \frac{1.66 \times 10^{-24} \ \text{g}}{\text{amu}} \times \frac{6.023 \times 10^{23} \ \text{atoms}}{\text{mole}} = 12.0 \, \frac{g}{mole}$$

Thus *numerically* the atomic weight is the *same*, whether it is given in atomic mass units per atom or in grams per mole of atoms.

By convention the atoms and molecules of elements such as Cu, Ag, and Na are the same entity. No one knows where crystalline copper the atom and crystalline copper the molecule begin or end. As a consequence, the simplest structure is *said* to be the molecule. That simplest structure is the atom. This convention holds true for most elements you'll encounter. N_2, H_2, O_2, F_2, Cl_2, Br_2, and I_2 are genuinely diatomic; that is, they have two atoms per molecule. One can find interesting and simple proofs of this in most general chemistry books. A number of elements are written monatomically even though it is well known that they are polyatomic. S_8 and P_4 are quite common, but they are generally written as plain S or P in the free state. One must consult suitable references and/or perform various experiments in order to find out whether an element is mono-, di-, tri-, ..., atomic.

Let's do some problems involving moles.* You will find the solutions to these problems on page 210. You will do yourself a disservice if you do not do each problem before looking at the solution.

16—1. How many men would there be in a mole of men?
16—2. How many elephants would there be in a mole of elephants?
16—3. How many trunks would there be in a mole of elephants?
16—4. How many legs would there be in a mole of elephants?
16—5. How many eyes would there be in a mole of elephants?
16—6. How many atoms are there in a mole of atoms?
16—7. How many molecules are there in a mole of molecules?
16—8. How many atoms are there in a mole of molecules?
16—9. How many atoms are there in a mole of sodium?
16—10. How many molecules are there in a mole of sodium?
16—11. How many molecules are there in a mole of ammonia (NH_3)?
16—12. How many atoms of nitrogen (N) are there in a mole of ammonia (NH_3)?
16—13. How many hydrogen (H) atoms are there in a mole of ammonia (NH_3)?
16—14. How many molecules are there in 0.5 mole of ammonia (NH_3)?
16—15. How many nitrogen (N_2) molecules are there in 0.5 mole of ammonia (NH_3)?
16—16. How many atoms of nitrogen (N) are there in 0.5 mole of NH_3?
16—17. How many moles are there in 3.012×10^{23} molecules of carbon dioxide (CO_2)?
16—18. How many moles are there in 1.20×10^{24} molecules of CO_2?

---

*Moles are considered integral numbers—that is, numbers with an infinite number of significant digits—when they are used in conjunction with chemical equations. Since this material is being developed for use with chemical equations, we will consider a number of moles to be an integer.

16—19. How many molecules are there in 20 moles of O_2?

16—20. How many atoms of oxygen are there in 20 moles of O_2?

16—21. What is the weight of 1 mole of Na?

16—22. What is the atomic weight of Na?

16—23. What is the molecular weight of Na?

16—24. What is the weight of 1 mole of NH_3?

16—25. What is the atomic weight of NH_3?

16—26. What is the molecular weight of NH_3?

16—27. What is the weight of 0.5 mole of NH_3?

16—28. What is the weight of 20 moles of NH_3?

16—29. What is the atomic weight of hydrogen?

16—30. What is the molecular weight of hydrogen?

16—31. How many moles are there in 34 g of NH_3?

16—32. How many moles are there in 8.5 g of ammonia (NH_3)?

16—33. How many molecules are there in 34 g of NH_3?

16—34. How many molecules are there in 8.5 g of NH_3?

16—35. How many atoms of hydrogen are there in 34 g of NH_3?

16—36. What is the weight of hydrogen in 34 g of NH_3?

16—37. What is the weight of 4×10^{20} molecules of copper (Cu)?

16—38. How many molecules are there in 126 g of nitric acid (HNO_3)?

Let's temporarily interrupt this process to give some facts about gases. One mole of *any* gas occupies 22.4 liters at STP—that is, standard temperature (0°C) and pressure (760 torr)—has 6.023×10^{23} molecules in it, and has a weight in grams numerically equal to its molecular weight. Actually the 22.4 liters applies only to ideal gases for which all sorts of values and constants have been calculated, but it is close enough to being true for real gases for us to use it. An ideal gas, by the way, is a gas that *exactly* obeys the gas laws, and there is no such gas.

16—39. What is the volume of 1 mole of acetylene (C_2H_2) gas measured at STP?

16—40. How many moles of C_2H_2 gas are there in 22.4 liters measured under standard conditions (that is, STP)?

16—41. How many moles of C_2H_2 gas are there in 11.2 liters (STP)?

16—42. What is the number of moles of C_2H_2 gas in 44.8 liters of C_2H_2 gas (STP)?

16—43. What is the weight of 22.4 liters of C_2H_2 gas (STP)?

16—44. What is the weight of 11.2 liters of C_2H_2 gas (STP)?

16—45. What is the weight of 44.8 liters of C_2H_2 gas (STP)?

16—46. What is the number of molecules in 22.4 liters of C_2H_2 gas (STP)?

16—47. What is the number of molecules in 11.2 liters of acetylene gas (STP)?

16—48. How many molecules are there in 44.8 liters of C_2H_2 (STP)?

16—49. How many atoms of hydrogen are there in 44.8 liters (STP) of NH_3 gas?

16—50. What would be the volume (STP) of 3.012×10^{23} molecules of NH_3 gas?

16—51. What would be the volume (STP) of 1.20×10^{24} molecules of NH_3 gas?

16—52. Develop a formula for each of the following conversions:
    a. Number of molecules to number of moles.
    b. Number of moles to number of molecules.
    c. Actual weight to number of moles.
    d. Number of moles to actual weight.
    e. Actual weight to number of molecules.
    f. Number of molecules to actual weight.
    g. Volume of a gas at STP to number of moles.
    h. Number of moles to volume at STP.
    i. Volume at STP to number of molecules.
    j. Number of molecules to volume at STP.
    k. Volume of a gas at STP to actual weight.
    l. Actual weight of a gas to volume at STP.

Remember that a formula is only a quick help for solution of problems. Unless one understands what one is doing in a problem, one is wasting time.

ANSWERS/SOLUTIONS

16—1. 6.023×10^{23} | 16—2. 6.023×10^{23}

16—3. $\dfrac{1 \text{ mole of elephants} \times 6.023 \times 10^{23} \text{ elephants}}{\text{mole of elephants}} \times \dfrac{1 \text{ trunk}}{\text{elephant}}$

    $= 6.023 \times 10^{23}$ trunks

16—4. $\dfrac{1 \text{ mole ele} \times 6.023 \times 10^{23} \text{ ele}}{\text{mole of ele}} \times \dfrac{4 \text{ legs}}{\text{ele}} = 2.409 \times 10^{24}$ legs

16—5. $\dfrac{1 \text{ mole ele} \times 6.023 \times 10^{23} \text{ ele}}{\text{mole of ele}} \times \dfrac{2 \text{ eyes}}{\text{ele}}$

16—6. 6.023×10^{23} | 16—7. 6.023×10^{23}

16—8.   Cannot be answered unless one knows the number of atoms per molecule.

16—9. 6.023×10^{23} | 16—10. 6.023×10^{23}

16—11. 6.023×10^{23}

16—12. $\dfrac{1 \text{ mole NH}_3 \times 6.023 \times 10^{23} \text{ molecules NH}_3 \times 1 \text{ atom N}}{\text{mole NH}_3 \qquad\qquad \text{molecule NH}_3}$

$= 6.023 \times 10^{23}$ atoms N

16—13. $\dfrac{1 \text{ mole NH}_3 \times 6.023 \times 10^{23} \text{ molecules NH}_3 \times 3 \text{ atoms H}}{\text{mole NH}_3 \qquad\qquad \text{molecule NH}_3}$

16—14. $\dfrac{0.5 \text{ mole} \times 6.023 \times 10^{23} \text{ molecules}}{\text{mole}} = 3.012 \times 10^{23}$ molecules

16—15. None; there are no N_2 *molecules* present in NH_3.

16—16. $\dfrac{0.5 \text{ mole NH}_3 \times 6.023 \times 10^{23} \text{ molecules NH}_3 \times 1 \text{ atom N}}{\text{mole NH}_3 \qquad\qquad \text{molecule NH}_3}$

16—17. $\dfrac{3.012 \times 10^{23} \text{ molecules}}{\dfrac{6.023 \times 10^{23} \text{ molecules}}{\text{mole}}}$ or $\dfrac{3.012 \times 10^{23} \text{ molecules}}{6.023 \times 10^{23} \text{ molecules mole}^{-1}}$

$= 0.5$ mole

16—18. $\dfrac{1.20 \ \times 10^{24} \text{ molecules}}{6.023 \times 10^{23} \text{ molecules mole}^{-1}} = 1.99$ moles

16—19. $\dfrac{20 \text{ moles} \times 6.023 \times 10^{23} \text{ molecules}}{\text{mole}}$

16—20. $\dfrac{20 \text{ moles} \times 6.023 \times 10^{23} \text{ molecules} \times 2 \text{ atoms}}{\text{mole} \qquad\qquad \text{molecule}}$

16—21. 22.9898 g | 16—22. 22.9898 amu atom^{-1} or 22.9898 g (mole of atoms)$^{-1}$ | 16—23. Same as 16—22; molecule and atom indistinguishable here. | 16—24. 17.031 g | 16—25. It has no atomic weight because it is a molecule composed of several atoms. |
16—26. 17.031 g mole^{-1} | 16—27. 0.5 mole $\times$ 17.031 g mole^{-1} = 8.516 g | 16—28. 20 moles $\times$ 17.031 g mole^{-1} | 16—29. 1.00797 amu atom^{-1} or 1.00797 g (mole of atoms)$^{-1}$ |
16—30. 2.01594 amu molecule^{-1} or 2.01594 g mole^{-1}

16—31. $\dfrac{34 \text{ g}}{17 \text{ g mole}^{-1}} = 2.0$ moles* | 16—32. $\dfrac{8.5 \text{ g}}{17 \text{ g mole}^{-1}}$

---

*Number of significant figures used in atomic and molecular weights depends on number of significant figures in measured quantities.

16–33. $\dfrac{34 \text{ g}}{17 \text{ g mole}^{-1}} \times \dfrac{6.023 \times 10^{23} \text{ molecules}}{\text{mole}} = 1.2 \times 10^{24} \text{ molecules}$

16–34. $\dfrac{8.5 \text{ g}}{17 \text{ g mole}^{-1}} \times \dfrac{6.023 \times 10^{23} \text{ molecules}}{\text{mole}}$

16–35. $\dfrac{34 \text{ g}}{17 \text{ g mole}^{-1}} \times \dfrac{6.023 \times 10^{23} \text{ molecules}}{\text{mole}} \times \dfrac{3 \text{ atoms H}}{\text{molecule NH}_3}$
$= 3.6 \times 10^{24} \text{ atoms H}$

16–36. $\dfrac{34 \text{ g}}{17 \text{ g mole}^{-1}} \times \dfrac{3 \text{ moles H atoms}}{\text{mole NH}_3} \times \dfrac{1.0 \text{ g}}{\text{mole H atoms}} = 6.0 \text{ g}$

16–37. $\dfrac{4 \times 10^{20} \text{ molecules}}{6.023 \times 10^{23} \text{ molecules mole}^{-1}} \times \dfrac{64 \text{ g}}{\text{mole}} = 0.04 \text{ g}$

16–38. $\dfrac{126 \text{ g}}{63.0 \text{ g mole}^{-1}} \times \dfrac{6.023 \times 10^{23} \text{ molecules}}{\text{mole}} = 1.20 \times 10^{24} \text{ molecules}$

16–39. 22.4 liters | 16–40. $\dfrac{22.4 \text{ liters}}{\dfrac{22.4 \text{ liters}}{\text{mole}}} = 1.00 \text{ mole.}$

16–41. $\dfrac{11.2 \text{ liters}}{22.4 \text{ liters mole}^{-1}} = 0.500 \text{ mole.}$

16–42. $\dfrac{44.8 \text{ liters}}{22.4 \text{ liters mole}^{-1}} = 2.00 \text{ moles.}$

16–43. $\dfrac{22.4 \text{ liters}}{\dfrac{22.4 \text{ liters}}{\text{mole}}} \times \dfrac{26.0 \text{ g}}{\text{mole}} = 26.0 \text{ g}$

16–44. $\dfrac{11.2 \text{ liters}}{22.4 \text{ liters mole}^{-1}} \times 26.0 \text{ g mole}^{-1}$

16–45. $\dfrac{44.8 \text{ liters}}{22.4 \text{ liters mole}^{-1}} \times 26.0 \text{ g mole}^{-1}$

16–46. $\dfrac{22.4 \text{ liters}}{\dfrac{22.4 \text{ liters}}{\text{mole}}} \times \dfrac{6.023 \times 10^{23} \text{ molecules}}{\text{mole}} = 6.02 \times 10^{23} \text{ molecules}$

16–47. $\dfrac{11.2 \text{ liters}}{22.4 \text{ liters mole}^{-1}} \times 6.023 \times 10^{23} \text{ molecules mole}^{-1}$

16–48. Same setup as 16–47, with 44.8 in place of 11.2

16—49. $\dfrac{44.8 \text{ liters}}{22.4 \text{ liters mole}^{-1}} \times 6.023 \times 10^{23} \text{ molecules mole}^{-1} \times \dfrac{3 \text{ atoms H}}{\text{molecule NH}_3}$

16—50. $\dfrac{3.012 \times 10^{23} \text{ molecules}}{6.023 \times 10^{23} \text{ molecules mole}^{-1}} \times 22.4 \text{ liters mole}^{-1} = 11.2 \text{ liters}$

16—51. Same setup as 16—50, with 1.20×10^{24} in place of 3.012×10^{23}

16—52. Liters for volume and grams for weight assumed in all cases.

a. $\dfrac{\text{number of molecules}}{6.023 \times 10^{23} \text{ molecules mole}^{-1}}$

b. number of moles $\times\ 6.023 \times 10^{23} \text{ molecules mole}^{-1}$

c. $\dfrac{\text{actual weight in grams}}{\text{molecular weight in grams mole}^{-1}}$

d. number of moles $\times$ molecular weight in grams mole^{-1}

e. $\dfrac{\text{actual weight, g}}{\text{molecular weight, g mole}^{-1}} \times 6.023 \times 10^{23} \text{ molecules mole}^{-1}$

f. $\dfrac{\text{number of molecules}}{6.023 \times 10^{23} \text{ molecules mole}^{-1}} \times \text{molecular weight, g mole}^{-1}$

g. $\dfrac{\text{volume of gas at STP in liters}}{22.4 \text{ liters mole}^{-1}}$

h. number of moles $\times\ 22.4 \text{ liters mole}^{-1}$

i. $\dfrac{\text{volume at STP, liters} \times 6.023 \text{ molecules mole}^{-1}}{22.4 \text{ liters mole}^{-1}}$

j. $\dfrac{\text{number of molecules}}{6.023 \times 10^{23} \text{ molecules mole}^{-1}} \times 22.4 \text{ liters mole}^{-1}$

k. $\dfrac{\text{volume at STP, liters} \times \text{molecular weight, g mole}^{-1}}{22.4 \text{ liters mole}^{-1}}$

l. $\dfrac{\text{actual weight, g} \times 22.4 \text{ liters mole}^{-1}}{\text{molecular weight}}$

PROBLEMS

1. Find the molecular weights of N_2O_5, $(NH_4)_2SO_4$, and $CuSO_4 \cdot 5H_2O$ (read as "copper sulfate *with* five waters").
2. How many moles are there in 5.0×10^4 molecules?
3. How many atoms of K are there in 49 g of K_2SO_4?
4. What is the volume of 4×10^{25} molecules of radon gas at STP?
5. How many moles of argon gas (Ar) are there in 1.65×10^5 atoms of Ar?
6. How many molecules are there in 3 g of P_2O_5?
7. How many molecules are there in 0.035 mole of PCl_5?
8. What is the weight of 25 liters (STP) of C_3H_6 gas?
9. How many oxygen atoms are there in 475 ml (cm^3) of CO_2 (STP)?
10. How many N_2O molecules are there in 150 ml of the gas at STP?
11. What is the weight of 10 million molecules of gold?
12. What is the weight of 0.0008 mole of Na_3PO_4?
13. How many moles are there in 6.7 liters (STP) of carbon monoxide (CO) gas?
14. Find the volume of 1.8 moles of H_2 gas (STP understood).
15. Find the molecular weight of a gas from this: 0.480 g occupied 175 ml at STP.

17

FINDING VOLUMES, WEIGHTS, AND
MOLECULAR WEIGHTS OF GASES

A mole of any gas occupies 22.4 liters at standard contitions (0°C and 760 torr). In other words, the weight in grams of 22.4 liters of any gas at standard conditions is numerically equal to the molecular weight of that gas. Now let's do some problems using these facts.

EXAMPLE 17–1

At standard temperature and pressure, 19 g of gas occupied 14.8 liters. Find the molecular weight of this gas.

You want grams per mole. Merely divide the number of grams by the number of moles.

$$\frac{\dfrac{19 \text{ g}}{14.8 \text{ liters}}}{\dfrac{22.4 \text{ liters}}{\text{mole}}} = 29 \frac{\text{g}}{\text{mole}}$$

You could also have thought of this in this fashion: You really want the weight of 22.4 liters at standard temperature and pressure. This would be the molecular weight in grams. You want weight, so operate on weight. Obviously, 22.4 liters would weigh more than 14.8 liters.

$$\frac{19 \text{ g} \times 22.4 \text{ liters}}{\text{mole} \times 14.8 \text{ liters}} = 29 \frac{\text{g}}{\text{mole}}$$

EXAMPLE 17–2

If 19 g of a gas at 21°C and 760 torr occupied 14.8 liters of space, find the molecular weight.

You know that a mole occupies 22.4 liters at STP. You must first convert to standard temperature (you have standard pressure already) and then solve just the way you solved Example 17–1.

$$\frac{\dfrac{19 \ \ g}{14.8 \ \text{liters} \times 273°\text{K}}}{294°\text{K} \times 22.4 \ \dfrac{\text{liters}}{\text{mole}}} = 31 \ \frac{g}{\text{mole}}$$

or, less awkwardly,

$$\frac{19 \ \ g}{14.8 \ \text{liters} \times 273°\text{K}} \times \frac{294°\text{K} \times 22.4 \ \text{liters}}{\text{mole}}$$

EXAMPLE 17–3

Find the molecular weight of this gas: 2.04 g of gas X occupied exactly 750 ml at 20.0°C and 748 mm of Hg pressure.

Find the volume of gas at STP:

$$\frac{750 \ \text{ml} \times 273°\text{K} \times 748 \ \text{mm}}{293°\text{K} \times 760 \ \text{mm}} = 688 \ \text{ml}$$

Now find the weight of this gas that would occupy 22.4 liters. You want weight, so operate on weight.

$$\frac{2.04 \ g}{688 \ \text{ml} \times 0.001 \ \dfrac{\text{liter}}{\text{ml}}} \times \frac{22.4 \ \text{liters}}{\text{mole}} = 66.4 \ g \ \text{mole}^{-1}$$

Done by the more logical mole method:

$$\frac{2.04 \ \ g}{\dfrac{0.750 \ \text{liter} \times 273°\text{K} \times 748 \ \text{mm}}{293°\text{K} \times 760 \ \text{mm} \times 22.4 \ \text{liters mole}^{-1}}}$$

or more simply

$$\frac{2.04 \ \ g}{0.750 \ \text{liter} \times 273°\text{K} \times 748 \ \text{mm}} \times \frac{293°\text{K} \times 760 \ \text{mm} \times 22.4 \ \text{liters}}{\text{mole}}$$

EXAMPLE 17–4

What would be the volume at standard temperature and pressure of 8.0 g of O_2 gas? (Molecular weight of O_2 is 32 g mole^{-1}.)

You have 1/4 mole; therefore it should occupy 1/4 of the molal volume, 22.4 liters.

$$\frac{8.0 \text{ g}}{32 \quad \text{g mole}^{-1}} \times 22.4 \text{ liters mole}^{-1} = 5.6 \text{ liters}$$

EXAMPLE 17–5

What would be the volume of 8.0 g of oxygen gas (O_2) at 200°C and 450 torr?

You can find the volume of 8.0 g of O_2 at STP. Just correct this volume to the nonstandard conditions. Here you know the volume would have to be greater than the volume under standard conditions because of increased temperature and decreased pressure. It is important to remember that any volume obtained by using 22.4 liters mole^{-1} is necessarily at standard conditions and would have to be corrected to any other conditions.

$$\frac{8.0 \text{ g}}{32 \quad \text{g mole}^{-1}} \times \frac{22.4 \text{ liters mole}^{-1} \times 760 \text{ torr} \times (273 + 200)°K}{\times 450 \text{ torr} \times (273 + \quad 0)°K} = 16 \text{ liters}$$

EXAMPLE 17–6

Find the weight of 30.0 liters of nitrogen (N_2) gas at STP.

One mole of any gas occupies 22.4 liters at STP. One mole of N_2 gas is 28.0 g. Therefore 28.0 g of N_2 should occupy 22.4 liters at STP, and 30.0 liters at STP should certainly be heavier than 22.4 liters at STP.

$$\frac{30.0 \text{ liters}}{22.4 \text{ liters mole}^{-1}} \times 28.0 \text{ g mole}^{-1} = 37.5 \text{ g}$$

EXAMPLE 17–7

Find the weight of 30 liters of N_2 measured at 40°C and 756 torr.

Correct to standard conditions. You know you need moles before you can get weight. Anything you divide by 22.4 liters mole^{-1} to get moles must be at standard conditions.

$$\frac{30 \text{ liters} \times 273°K \times 756 \text{ torr}}{313°K \times 760 \text{ torr} \times 22.4 \text{ liters mole}^{-1}} \times 28 \text{ g mole}^{-1} = 30 \text{ g}$$

EXAMPLE 17-8

Find the weight of 30 liters of N_2 collected at 40°C and 756 torr over water.

Solve just the way you solved Example 17–7 with this exception: the pressure of the N_2 is 756 minus the vapor pressure of water at 40°C, that is, 756 torr − 55 torr = 701 torr. Use 701 in place of 756 in this setup.

EXAMPLE 17-9

What would be the pressure of 16 g of methane (CH_4) gas at 0°C in a container of 22.4-liter capacity?

This is one mole of methane gas, since the molecular weight of methane is 16 g mole^{-1}. You have 22.4 liters, one mole, at standard temperature, so the pressure must be standard too.

EXAMPLE 17-10

What would be the pressure of 16 g of CH_4 at 0°C if the volume were 44.8 liters.

You know that 16 g is one mole. At 0°C it should occupy 22.4 liters at standard pressure. However, at standard temperature and some pressure it is occupying 44.8 liters. So the question is: If a certain amount of gas (standard temperature) had a volume of 22.4 liters at standard pressure (760 torr), what pressure would it have if the volume were changed to 44.8 liters?

$$\frac{760 \text{ torr} \times 22.4 \text{ liters}}{44.8 \text{ liters}} = 380 \text{ torr}$$

EXAMPLE 17-11

At what pressure would 8.0 g of CH_4 occupy 5.6 liters of space at 0°C?

You know that 8.0 g of methane is 0.5 mole and that 0.5 mole of *any* gas should occupy 11.2 liters at STP. This 0.5 mole is occupying only half that volume at standard temperature and some nonstandard pressure. It is occupying half the volume it should occupy; it must have double standard pressure. Done in one swoop:

$$\frac{760 \text{ mm} \times 8.0 \text{ g} \times 22.4 \text{ liters mole}^{-1}}{16 \text{ g mole}^{-1} \times 5.6 \text{ liters}} = 1.5 \times 10^{3} \text{ mm}$$

EXAMPLE 17-12

Find the temperature that 8 g of O_2 would have in a 7-liter box at 200 mm of Hg pressure.

Find the volume of 8 g of O_2 at STP. Then convert your STP temperature to the temperature needed to produce another volume and another pressure.

$$\frac{8 \text{ g} \times 22.4 \text{ liters mole}^{-1}}{32 \text{ g mole}^{-1}} = 5.6 \text{ liters (at STP)}$$

Now you want the temperature to cause this quantity of gas to occupy a larger volume (therefore a higher temperature needed) at a lower pressure (therefore a lower temperature needed). You want temperature, so operate on temperature.

$$\frac{(0 + 273)^{\circ}\text{K} \times 7 \text{ liters} \times 200 \text{ mm}}{5.6 \text{ liters} \times 760 \text{ mm}} = 90^{\circ}\text{K}$$

Done in one step:

$$\frac{(0 + 273)^{\circ}\text{K} \times 7 \text{ liters} \times 200 \text{ mm}}{\dfrac{8 \text{ g}}{32 \text{ g mole}^{-1}} \times 22.4 \text{ liters} \times 760 \text{ mm}}$$

EXAMPLE 17-13

Find the pressure that 1.00×10^2 g of CH_4 gas would exert at $100 \pm 1^{\circ}$C in a 1.00×10^2 liter container.

You want pressure. Your entry to this problem is through the 100 g.

$$\frac{100 \text{ g} \times 22.4 \text{ liters mole}^{-1}}{16 \text{ g mole}^{-1}}$$

will give the volume of the gas at standard conditions. You would have volume, temperature, and pressure. Now just find out whether the volume mentioned in the problem is more or less than the volume at standard temperature and pressure. If it is more, then *considering only the pressure and volume,* the pressure must be less than standard and vice versa. However, you know that the temperature in the problem is more than standard, so, *considering only temperature and volume* the pressure must be greater than standard. The final setup would be

$$\frac{760 \text{ torr} \times 1.00 \times 10^2 \text{ g} \qquad \times 22.4 \qquad \text{liters mole}^{-1} \times 373°K}{16 \text{ g mole}^{-1} \times \ 1.00 \times 10^2 \text{ liters} \qquad \times 273°K}$$

$= 1.45 \times 10^3 \text{ torr}$

All of these problems can be done rather easily by formula. However, since problem solving was the goal, we preferred to do these in rather complicated ways involving reasoning first. Now let's do them by formula, first developing the formula.

Pressure is directly related to absolute temperature, inversely related to volume:

$$P \propto \frac{T}{V} \qquad \text{So} \quad PV = kT$$

R is customarily used for k here. When pressure is in atmospheres and volume in liters, $R = 0.08205$ liter-atm mole^{-1} °K^{-1}. So we could say

$$PV = nRT$$

where n is the number of moles. This is the so-called universal gas law.

You could have solved any of the problems in this chapter by means of this formula. Let's try Example 17–12, where you want the temperature of 8.0 g of O_2 when the volume is 7.0 liters and the pressure is 200 mm of Hg. You must have the pressure in atmospheres. That is the only complication.

1 atm = 760 mm of Hg

You want T, so

$$T = \frac{PV}{nR}$$

$$= \frac{200 \text{ mm} \qquad \times 7.0 \quad \text{liters}}{760 \text{ mm} \times \ 8.0 \text{ g} \quad \times 0.082 \text{ liter-atm}} = 90°K$$

$$\underbrace{\text{atm} \quad 32 \quad \text{g}}_{\text{this is } P} \qquad \text{mole-°K}$$

$$\underbrace{\qquad \qquad \text{mole}}_{\text{this is } n}$$

Be sure not to use pairs of temperatures, pairs of pressures, etc., when working with the universal gas law. You can readily see that one can just plug in figures in this formula without knowing what is involved. This is obviously something to be avoided!

PROBLEMS

1. If 1.409 g of a gas occupied 1.581 liters at standard temperature and pressure, what is the molecular weight of this gas?
2. Find the molecular weight of the gas 2.08 g of which occupied 3.91 liters at standard temperature and a pressure of 756 mm of Hg.
3. What would be the volume of 4 g of ammonia (NH_3) gas measured at standard temperature and pressure?
4. What would be the volume of 4 g of NH_3 measured at 1500 torr and standard temperature?
5. What would be the volume of 4 g of NH_3 measured at 30°C and 760 torr?
6. What would be the volume of 4 g of NH_3 at 1500 mm of Hg and 30°C?
7. Find the weight of 10 liters of CO_2 gas.
8. Find weight of 10 liters of CO_2 collected over water at 40°C and 743 torr.
9. Find weight of 350 ml of O_2 collected over water at 19°C and 756 torr.
10. Find the weight of 350 ml of O_2 collected over mercury at 19°C and 756 torr. (Does mercury have an appreciable vapor pressure at 19°C? If you do not have access to a chemical handbook with vapor pressure values, look up the boiling point of mercury and make an estimate of the vapor pressure at 19°C.)
11. Find the volume of 10 g of O_2. (Any assumptions necessary here?)
12. Find the volume of 10 g of O_2 at 1500°C and 1000 torr.
13. Find the volume of 0.38 g of O_2 measured at 45°C and 1800 torr over water.
14. What is the molecular weight of this gas, if 0.856 g occupied 1.405 liters at 145°C and 781 mm of Hg?
15. A certain gas had a pressure of 40 atm at 500°C. What temperature increase would be necessary to cause the pressure to rise to 100 atm without causing any change in volume?
16. Find the temperature at which 17.8 g of C_2H_4 will fill a 40-liter box at 1000 torr.
17. What volume container would be needed to hold 1000 g of N_2 at 4100 torr and 450°C?
18. What would be the pressure of 91 g of CO_2 in a 45-liter container at 10°C?

18

MOLARITY

A great deal of the actual work of a chemist, biologist, etc., involves the use of measured volumes of solutions of known strength rather than the use of weighed quantities of various compounds. Among the almost infinite number of methods for expressing *concentration* (strength) of a solution, percentage, normality, and molarity are perhaps the most widely used. Percentage can present difficulties. For example, suppose one had a 3% solution of the liquid hydrogen peroxide (H_2O_2). Is this percentage by weight or by volume? It is a nuisance to have to specify. In addition, percentage is not related to any particular "chemical entity" such as the mole. Normality is still used, but its use is rapidly declining because of ambiguities involving normalities of solutions of oxidizing and reducing agents. Again, the ambiguities can be obviated by proper clarifying statements, but it is a nuisance to have to make these statements. Molarity seems to be clearest and is certainly the easiest method to use.

What is molarity? Molarity (symbol: *M*) is the name for a mathematical way of expressing the number of moles per liter of solution.* For example, a molar (1 *M*) solution of any compound has 1 mole of that compound dissolved in water and diluted *to* 1 liter with water.

---

*In calculating number of moles in a solution, be sure not to confuse liters of solution with the 22.4 liters that a mole of gas occupies at standard temperature and pressure.

$$\text{molarity} = \frac{\text{number of moles}}{\text{liters}}$$

You already know that

$$\text{number of moles} = \frac{\text{actual weight in grams}}{\text{molecular weight in grams mole}^{-1}}$$

Therefore you would expect that

$$\text{molarity} = \frac{\text{actual weight in grams}}{\text{molecular weight in grams mole}^{-1} \times \text{liters}}$$

and number of moles = molarity × liters

Formality (symbol: F) is being used more and more often now. A student who can cope with molar solutions will have no difficulty with formal-solution calculations. The distinction between molar and formal solutions involves the distinction between apparent and actual formulas. One knows only the apparent formula; hence one can have only the formula weight.

Normality calculations are made in the same way as molarity calculations, but normality expresses the number of equivalents per liter rather than moles per liter.

$$\text{normality } (N) = \frac{\text{number of equivalents}}{\text{liters}}$$

$$\text{number of equivalents} = \frac{\text{actual weight}}{\text{equivalent weight}}$$

$$\text{Therefore normality} = \frac{\text{actual weight}}{\text{equivalent weight} \times \text{liters}}$$

Definitions of equivalent weight and equivalents belong in a general chemistry book. Since molarity is more commonly used today than normality, we will concentrate on molarity problems.

EXAMPLE 18–1

Find the molarity of each of these solutions.

a. Two moles of sodium hydroxide (NaOH) dissolved in water and diluted to 1 liter in water.

$$\frac{2 \text{ moles}}{1 \text{ liter}} = \frac{2 \text{ moles}}{\text{liter}} = 2 \; M$$

b. A solution containing 80 g of NaOH in 1 liter of solution.

$$\frac{80 \text{ g}}{\frac{40 \text{ g}}{\text{mole}} \times 1 \text{ liter}} = \frac{2 \text{ moles}}{\text{liter}} = 2 \text{ } M$$

c. A solution containing 80 g of NaOH dissolved in water to form 500 ml of solution.

$$\frac{80 \text{ g}}{\frac{40 \text{ g}}{\text{mole}} \times 0.5 \text{ liter}} = \frac{4 \text{ moles}}{\text{liter}} = 4 \text{ } M$$

EXAMPLE 18-2

To what volume must 3 moles of hydrogen chloride (HCl) be diluted to make a 6 M solution?

If $M = \dfrac{\text{mole}}{\text{liter}}$, then liter $= \dfrac{\text{mole}}{M}$

So $\dfrac{3 \text{ moles}}{\dfrac{6 \text{ moles}}{\text{liter}}} = 0.5 \text{ liter}$

Note that M is not used in the setup. It is merely an abbreviation.

EXAMPLE 18-3

To what volume must 80 g of NaOH be diluted to make a 4 M solution?

$$\frac{80 \text{ g}}{\frac{40 \text{ g}}{\text{mole}} \times \frac{4 \text{ moles}}{\text{liter}}} = 0.5 \text{ liter}$$

EXAMPLE 18-4

What weight of sulfuric acid (H_2SO_4) is in 3 liters of 6 M H_2SO_4?

$$\frac{3 \text{ liters} \times \frac{6 \text{ moles}}{\text{liter}} \times \frac{98 \text{ g}}{\text{mole}}}{} = 2 \times 10^3 \text{ g}$$

Neither dilution nor evaporation can change the number of moles of material that is in a solution providing the dissolved material is non-volatile and no chemical changes occur on dilution or evaporation. Heating a solution of a volatile substance such as ethyl alcohol (boiling point 78.4°C) causes molecules of ethyl alcohol to escape. Obviously, evaporation reduces the number of moles of ethyl alcohol in solution. However, heating solutions of nonvolatile substances such as sodium chloride (boiling point 1413°C) does not cause evaporation of sodium chloride; consequently the number of moles of sodium chloride is the same before and after evaporation.

EXAMPLE 18–5

How many moles are there in 17 liters of 18 M sulfuric acid?

$$\frac{17 \text{ liters} \times 18 \text{ moles}}{\text{liter}} = 3.1 \times 10^2 \text{ moles}$$

EXAMPLE 18–6

a. Find the molarity, that is, the moles per liter, if 17 liters of 18 M sulfuric acid were diluted to a total volume of 150 liters.

$$\frac{17 \text{ liters} \times 18 \text{ moles}}{\text{liter} \times 150 \text{ liters}} = 2.0 \frac{\text{moles}}{\text{liter}} = 2.0 \ M$$

Remember that number of moles of sulfuric acid would have to be the same before and after dilution.

b. Now suppose that 17 liters of 18 M sulfuric acid were put into 133 liters of water. Find the molarity of the resulting solution.

Again, the number of moles of sulfuric acid before and after dilution is the same. However, the definition of molarity involves the total volume of solution, here 17 liters plus 133 liters or 150 liters. The solution of this problem is the same as in part a.

EXAMPLE 18–7

To what volume must 81 moles of NaOH be diluted to make a 2 M solution?

$$\frac{81 \text{ moles}}{2 \ \dfrac{\text{moles}}{\text{liter}}} = 40 \text{ liters (in significant figures)}$$

Can you see why a more precise statement of molarity should have been given? You know you need 40.5 liters, but you can use this only if you also know more significant figures for the molarity.

EXAMPLE 18-8

To what volume must 500 liters of 12 M HCl be diluted to make a 2 M solution?

The number of moles is not changed, so

$$\frac{500 \text{ liters} \times 12 \text{ moles}}{\text{liter} \times 2 \dfrac{\text{moles}}{\text{liter}}} = 3000 \text{ liters}$$

PROBLEMS

1. Find the molarity of:
   a. A solution of 75 g of silver nitrate ($AgNO_3$) dissolved in water and diluted to 3 liters.
   b. A solution of 17 g of potassium phosphate (K_3PO_4) in 395 ml of water. (In what respect is this description vague?)
   c. A solution of 150 g of 37%-pure NaOH in 500 ml of water.
   d. 50 liters of a 6 M HCl solution diluted to 100 liters.
   e. 50 liters of a 7.5 M NaOH solution plus 100 liters of water.
   f. 85 liters of a 0.001 M potassium nitrate (KNO_3) solution concentrated down to 500 ml.

2. To what volume must 5 g of $CuSO_4$ be diluted to make a 0.001 M solution?

3. What volume of water must be added to 175 ml of 2 M $CaCl_2$ to make a 0.05 M solution?

4. What weight of KCl is in 500 ml of 0.2 M KCl solution?

5. How many moles of NaBr would there be in 10 liters of 1.5 M NaBr?

6. How many molecules of $HgCl_2$ are there in 100 ml of 0.008 M $HgCl_2$?

7. If 100 liters of NH_3 gas measured at STP is dissolved in 21 liters of water, what is the molarity of the resulting solution.

8. What volume of ethanol (C_2H_5OH, density 0.79 g/ml) must be used to prepare 3 liters of 0.01 M ethanol solution in water?

9. What weight of silver could be reclaimed from 5 liters of 0.01 M silver diammine complex $[Ag(NH_3)_2]^+$?

10. A bottle containing 6 liters of 15 M NH_4OH solution (this is really $NH_3 \cdot H_2O$) lost 8 liters of NH_3 gas (STP) as a result of being opened and closed too frequently. What is the strength of the NH_4OH now?

11. If 4 liters of 0.2 M $Ca(NO_3)_2$ and 6 liters of 0.8 M $CaCl_2$ were mixed, what do you think the concentration of calcium ion in the resulting solution would be?

19

MOLALITY

Molality (symbol: m) is a means of expressing concentration in terms of number of moles of solute dissolved in 1000 *grams of solvent*. This is obviously different from molarity. Molarity represents the number of moles per *liter of solution*. Molarity is a much more common means of expressing concentration, but molality is widely used in calculations involving colligative properties—that is, properties dependent on the number rather than the kind of particles in solution. Consequently, molality is often defined in this fashion:

Molality (m) of a component of a solution is the number of moles of the component dissolved in 1 kg (1000 g) of the solvent.

Molality also has the advantage of being independent of temperature since all measurements are weight measurements.

EXAMPLE 19-1

Find the molality of a solution made by dissolving 50 g of potassium nitrate (KNO_3) in 1000 g of water. The molecular weight (mw) of KNO_3 is 101.

$$\frac{50 \text{ g}}{101 \text{ g mole}^{-1}} = 0.5 \text{ mole}$$

A solution of 0.5 mole dissolved in 1000 g of solvent (here water) is 0.5 molal.

EXAMPLE 19-2

Find the molality of 50 g of KNO_3 (mw 101) dissolved in 250 g of water.

Molality is based on solution in 1000 g of solvent. Convert the weight of solute (KNO_3) to the weight that would have been dissolved in 1000 g of solvent and find the number of moles. You have made no real change in the solution itself here. For example, wouldn't 1 cup of coffee with a teaspoon of sugar dissolved in it taste as sweet as 4 cups of coffee with 4 teaspoons of sugar?

So $\dfrac{50 \text{ g} \times 1000 \text{ g}}{250 \text{ g}} = 200 \text{ g}$

One would have to dissolve 200 g in 1000 g of solvent to make the solution of the same strength at the larger volume.

$\dfrac{200 \text{ g}}{101 \text{ g mole}^{-1}} = 2 \text{ moles}$

There are 2 moles in 1000 g of solvent. Therefore, *by definition*, the solution is 2 molal (2 *m*).

EXAMPLE 19-3

What is the molality of a solution of 5.0 g of purine ($C_5H_4N_4$; mw 120) dissolved in 200 ml of glycol?

First of all you need *weight* of solvent. A handbook gives 1.113 g/ml as the density of glycol. You can now find weight of glycol.

$\dfrac{5.0 \text{ g}}{120 \text{ g mole}^{-1}} \dfrac{\times 1000 \text{ g}}{200 \text{ ml} \times 1.113 \text{ g ml}^{-1}} = 0.19 \text{ mole in 1000 g of solvent}$
$\text{or } 0.19 \text{ molal } (0.19 \text{ } m)$

EXAMPLE 19-4

What weight of solvent is needed to make a 0.020 molal solution from 50.0 g of $MgCl_2$ (mw 95.2) and a supply of distilled water?

Let y = weight of solvent.

Then $\dfrac{50.0 \text{ g}}{95.2 \text{ g mole}^{-1} \times y} \times 1000 \text{ g} = 0.0200 \text{ } m$

$y = \dfrac{50.0 \text{ g}}{95.2 \text{ g mole}^{-1} \times 0.0200 \text{ mole}} \times 1000 \text{ g} = 2.63 \times 10^4 \text{ g water}$

EXAMPLE 19–5

What weight of KNO_3 (mw 101) must be added to 75 g of water to make a 0.030 molal solution?

Let z = weight of KNO_3.

$$\frac{z \times 1000 \text{ g}}{101 \text{ g mole}^{-1} \times 75 \text{ g}} = 0.030 \ m$$

$$z = \frac{0.030 \text{ mole} \times 101 \text{ g mole}^{-1} \times 75 \text{ g}}{1000 \text{ g}} = 0.23 \text{ g}$$

EXAMPLE 19–6

What weight of purine would be needed to make 85 ml of 0.01 molal solution of purine in glycol? (Molecular weight of purine is 120; density for this particular glycol is 1.113 g/ml.)

No one can get an answer to this without more information. What weight of solvent is involved? To know this one would have to know how much of the final volume (85 ml) is glycol. That is, what was the volume before purine was added? The volume might have been increased or decreased or not measurably changed. More facts are needed. The literature, or experimentation if necessary, would supply the facts.

PROBLEMS

1. Find the molality of:
   a. A solution of 5.5 g of sodium chloride (mw 58.5) dissolved in 175 g of water.
   b. A solution of 4.2 g of compound R (mw 59.5) in 159 ml of carbon tetrachloride (density 1.84 g/ml).
2. What weight of potassium hydroxide (mw 56) must be added to 210 g of water to make a 0.95 m solution?
3. What weight of water must be added to 61.3 g of potassium nitrate (mw 101) to make a 0.092 m solution?

20

COLLIGATIVE PROPERTIES: MOLAL FREEZING AND BOILING POINT EFFECTS

Colligative properties are properties that depend on the number of particles present in solution, irrespective of whether the individual particle is a molecule, an atom, or an ion. Among colligative properties one finds boiling-point elevation, freezing-point depression, osmotic pressure, refractive index, etc.

We'll use problems involving elevation of the boiling point and depression of the freezing point (ebullioscopic and cryoscopic problems) to represent problems involving colligative properties. There is no particular reason for doing this; other types of problems could just as easily have been chosen. Other problems involving colligative properties would naturally differ in specific items, but the principles would be the same.

A mole of dissolved particles will lower the freezing point of 1000 g of a solvent by a specific number of degrees, the molal depression constant, K_f, of the solvent. A better way of saying this is that the depression of the freezing point is proportional to the number of moles of particles in solution and that the proportionality constant for each solvent is called its molal depression constant, K_f. However, the proportionality constants were experimentally determined on the basis of 1000 g of solvent in the solution. Again, there is no particular reason for this other than the fact that weight is independent of temperature whereas volume is not. A mole of dissolved particles will similarly raise the boiling point of 1000 g of solvent by a characteristic number of degrees called the molal elevation constant, K_b. Of course, the dissolved substance must be nonvolatile.

A mole of *compound* dissolved in 1000 g of solvent will depress the freezing point by K_f and raise the boiling point by K_b only if the compound does not break up or dissociate into particles smaller than a molecule and if the molecules do not combine or associate to form anything larger than a molecule. Either of these things would obviously change the number of particles in solution and change the freezing-point depression or boiling-point elevation. When and why compounds dissociate or associate is a fascinating topic that belongs in a book on the theory and principles of chemistry. It is beyond the scope of this book. We will work with compounds that dissolve as molecules, neither associating nor dissociating, for all examples and problems in this chapter. However, once one knows the degree of dissociation or association, the calculations would be exactly the same as those we are going to illustrate.

Each solvent has its own characteristic K_f and K_b values. A few are listed in the Table 20-1. Remember that the freezing point and melting point of a material are numerically the same, and that the boiling point and condensation point of a liquid are the same.

Let's try some problems. All concentrations in the following problems are molal. Review Chapter 19 if necessary.

EXAMPLE 20–1

What would be the boiling point of a solution in which 1 mole of ribose $(C_5H_{10}O_5)$ was dissolved in 1000 g of water?

This is 1 mole dissolved in 1000 g of solvent; therefore the boiling point would be raised by an amount exactly equal to the molal elevation constant, K_b. The solution would boil at

$$100.000°C + 0.512°C = 100.512°C$$

Table 20-1

Solvent	Freezing point, °C	K_f, °C/mole	Boiling point, °C	K_b, °C/mole
acetic acid	16.7	3.9	118.5	3.07
benzene	5.5	5.12	80.15	2.53
camphor	178.4	37.7	208.25	5.95
water	0*	1.86	100*	0.512
phenol	42.0	7.27	182.1	3.56

*Freezing point of water is defined as exactly 0°C, and boiling point as exactly 100°C. Each, therefore, has an infinite number of significant figures.

EXAMPLE 20–2

What would be the boiling point of a solution in which 150 g of ribose $(C_5H_{10}O_5)$ was dissolved in 1000 g of water?

$$\frac{150 \text{ g}}{150 \text{ g mole}^{-1}} = 1 \text{ mole}$$

This is now the same as Example 20–1.

EXAMPLE 20–3

What would be the freezing point of a solution in which exactly 150 g of ribose was dissolved in exactly 500 g of phenol?

How many grams would there have been in 1000 g of phenol if there were the same relative numbers of solute and solvent particles as there are in a solution of 150 g of ribose dissolved in 500 g of phenol?

$$\frac{150 \text{ g} \times 1000 \text{ g}}{500 \text{ g}} = 300 \text{ g}$$

This would have corresponded to 2 moles:

$$\frac{300 \text{ g}}{150 \text{ g mole}^{-1}} = 2 \text{ moles}$$

Therefore we would have twice the K_f lowering, or $2 \times 7.27°C$. The actual freezing point would be $(42.0 - 14.5)$ or $27.5°C$. Put in one equation the setup is

$$42.0°C - \left(\frac{150 \text{ g}}{150 \text{ g mole}^{-1}} \times \frac{1000 \text{ g} \times 7.27°C \text{ mole}^{-1}}{500 \text{ g}} \right) = 27.5°C$$

EXAMPLE 20–4

What would be the freezing point of a solution in which 50.0 g of naphthasultam $(C_{10}H_7O_2NS)$ is dissolved in 8.00×10^2 g of benzene?

How many grams would there have been in 1.000×10^3 g of solvent?

$$\frac{50.0 \text{ g} \times 1000 \text{ g}}{800 \text{ g}} = 62.5 \text{ g}$$

How many moles are there in 62.5 g of naphthasultam?

$$\frac{62.5 \text{ g}}{205 \text{ g mole}^{-1}} = 0.305 \text{ mole}$$

How many degrees would 0.305 mole dissolved in 1000 g of benzene lower the freezing point?

$$0.305 \text{ mole} \times 5.12^\circ\text{C mole}^{-1} = 1.56^\circ\text{C}$$

Actual freezing point is $5.5^\circ\text{C} - 1.6^\circ\text{C} = 3.9^\circ\text{C}$.
Put in one equation:

$$5.5^\circ\text{C} - \left(\frac{50 \text{ g} \times 1000 \text{ g}}{800 \text{ g} \times 205 \text{ g mole}^{-1}} \times 5.12^\circ\text{C mole}^{-1}\right) = 3.9^\circ\text{C}$$

EXAMPLE 20–5

A mixture of 2.91 g of an unknown compound and 50.0 g of the solvent camphor melted at 151.4°C. What is the molecular weight of the compound?

Molecular weight is grams per mole. You must first put the grams on a 1000-g-of-solvent basis because of the rules of the game. You can find the number of moles from the freezing-point depression.

$$\frac{\text{freezing-point depression}}{K_f} = \text{number of moles}$$

$$\frac{\text{grams of solute in 1000 g of solvent}}{\text{number of moles}} = \text{g mole}^{-1}$$

$$\frac{2.91 \text{ g} \times 1000 \text{ g}}{\underbrace{50.0 \text{ g}}_{\substack{\text{this is grams in} \\ \text{1000 g of solvent}}} \times \underbrace{\left(\dfrac{(178.4 - 151.4)^\circ\text{C}}{37.7^\circ\text{C mole}^{-1}}\right)}_{\text{this is moles}}} = 81.3 \text{ g mole}^{-1}$$

In easier-to-calculate form the arrangement would be

$$\frac{2.91 \times 1000 \times 37.7}{50.0 \times (178.4 - 151.4)}$$

Problems involving *Raoult's law* provide an example of problems that are incredibly simple yet cause students difficulty. Here the difficulty is not so much problem solving—although it masquerades as such—as understanding what is involved in what one is dealing with.

Let's try to bring this into focus. Consider:

A. An 8-oz glass of beer at room temperature (approximately 20°C)
B. Another 8-oz glass of beer at body temperature (37°C)
C. A third 8-oz glass of beer poured into 3 ft^3 of water in a barrel (20°C)

1. Which—A, B, or C—has the greatest quantity of beer in it? None. Same 8 oz of beer in each.
2. Which—A or C—would have the stronger aroma of beer near it? You know A would. What causes the aroma? Vapor. Obviously, there is more vapor associated with beer above A than above C. The absolute quantities of beer are the same, but the relative amount in C is far less.
3. Consider A and B. Which would have the stronger aroma? Obviously, B. You know that the hotter solution would have the greater amount of vapor above it. Just think of a hot and a cold cup of coffee.

Above matter in the form of solids or liquids there are always molecules of the substances involved in the gaseous state. True, there may not be many, but they are there. Above a piece of steel there would be molecules of iron, manganese, etc., in the gaseous state. In a solution the amount of molecules above the surface depends on the interference with the escape of the molecules from the liquid. On the surface of A there are only "beer molecules" faced with air. On the surface of C there are many other molecules that interfere with the escape of the molecules responsible for the odor detected near beer. Therefore C's vapor could only equal A's vapor if one gave the molecules enough energy to overcome their forever bumping into water molecules with frequent "throwback" into the body of the solution. One can give them this extra energy by heating the solution.

Wouldn't it seem logical that the vapor pressure (that is, the pressure of the quantity of vapor above the liquid) would have something to do with temperature and with the relative number of molecules? If it has something to do with the relative number of molecules it must have something to do with the relative number of moles. This relative number of moles is known as *mole fraction*. Wouldn't it seem logical that vapor pressure would be proportional to the temperature and to the mole fraction? This is just what Raoult's law says. The vapor pressure of each component of the solution is proportional to the mole fraction of that component and to the vapor pressure of the pure component at the temperature of the solution. The vapor pressure of a solution is the sum of the partial vapor pressures of the components of the solution.

$$P_{total} = p_1 + p_2 + \cdots$$
$$p_1 = p_1{}^0 X_1$$

where P is the total vapor pressure of the solution, p_1 is the partial vapor pressure due to component 1, $p_1{}^0$ is the vapor pressure of pure component 1 at the temperature of the solution, and X_1 is the mole fraction of component 1 in the solution. Raoult's law applies only to dilute solutions.

EXAMPLE 20-6

Suppose you had 2 moles of A, 7 moles of B, and 191 moles of C. Find the mole fraction of A in the solution of this mixture.

$$\text{mole fraction of A} = \frac{\text{moles of A}}{\text{moles of A} + \text{moles of B} + \text{moles of C}}$$

$$= \frac{2}{2 + 7 + 191} = 0.01$$

EXAMPLE 20-7

Now suppose you had a solution of A, B, and C at 23.0°C in the proportions given in Example 20–6. The vapor pressures of *pure* A, B, and C at 23.0°C are 22, 200, and 681 mm, respectively. Find the vapor pressures due to A, to B, and to C in the mixture.

For A: Mole fraction of A × vapor pressure of A = actual pressure at the temperature for which you have the vapor pressure of pure A.

0.01 × 22 mm = 0.22 mm

For B: You must obviously calculate the mole fraction first

$$\frac{7}{2 + 7 + 191} \times 200 \text{ mm} = 7 \text{ mm}$$

For C: $\dfrac{191}{2 + 7 + 191} \times 681 \text{ mm} = 650 \text{ mm}$

The total pressure would be (0.22 + 7 + 650) or 657 mm. You object. This does not add up to atmospheric pressure. Why should it? Only "things" that are boiling need have a vapor pressure equal to atmospheric pressure. Mere mixing does not ordinarily produce boiling.

EXAMPLE 20-8

The vapor pressure of pure water at 50.0°C is 92.5 mm. At this temperature exactly 2604 g of sucrose will dissolve in exactly 1000 g of water. Find the vapor pressure of this sucrose—water solution at 50.0°C. The molecular weights of water and sucrose are 18.02 and 342.3, respectively. Sucrose is a nonvolatile substance that does not break into anything smaller than a molecule in solution.

$$\text{moles of water} = \frac{1000 \text{ g}}{18.02 \text{ g mole}^{-1}} = 55.50 \text{ moles}$$

$$\text{moles of sucrose} = \frac{2604 \text{ g}}{342.3 \text{ g mole}^{-1}} = 7.607 \text{ moles}$$

Since sucrose is nonvolatile, the vapor pressure of the solution is the same as the partial vapor pressure of the water. The partial vapor pressure due to sucrose is insignificant.

vapor pressure of water = vapor pressure of solution

$$= \frac{55.50 \text{ moles} \times 92.5 \text{ mm}}{(55.50 + 7.607) \text{ moles}} = 81.4 \text{ mm}$$

PROBLEMS

Almost any freshman chemistry book and surely any simple physical chemistry textbook or good organic laboratory manual will contain a formula that could be used to solve any of the following problems. Either do the problems by reason or do not do them at all; to use the formula would be a grand waste of time, since no one really cares what the answer to these problems is. Presume that molecules do not dissociate or associate unless specific information to the contrary is given. See page 234 for various constants.

1. What would be the freezing point of a solution of 25.0 g of sucrose $(C_{12}H_{22}O_{11})$ in 350 g of water?
2. 0.481 g of an unknown dissolved in 75 g of acetic acid produced a solution that boiled at $119.3°C$. Find the molecular weight of the unknown.
3. A solution of 0.891 g of an unknown compound in 75 g of water boiled at $100.092°C$. Other measurements indicated that the molecules dissociated into two ions per molecule. What is the molecular weight of the unknown compound?
4. How many moles should be added to 1000 g of acetic acid to give a solution boiling at $120.2°C$? If this compound weighed 45 g mole^{-1}, what weight of compound would be required to do this?
5. What weight of limonene $(C_{10}H_{16})$ would have to be dissolved in 50 g of benzene to make the solution boil at $83.51°C$?
6. When 0.852 g of limonene was dissolved in 45.21 g of solvent X, the solution froze at $-8.21°C$. The freezing point of pure X is $-5.31°C$. Find the molal depression constant, K_f, for solvent X. Limonene is $C_{10}H_{16}$.
7. A compound with a molecular weight of 150 g mole^{-1} was subjected

to a freezing-point depression test: 0.75 g of the compound was dissolved in 5.00 g of camphor, and the resulting mixture froze at 103.0°C. The molecular weight of the compound, as verified by a variety of other methods, really was 150. Can you offer an explanation for the extraordinary lowering of the freezing point of camphor by this compound?

8. What would be the boiling point of a solution of 80.0 ml of benzene (density 0.88 g/ml) in which 0.99 g of naphthalene ($C_{10}H_8$) was dissolved?

21

WEIGHT, VOLUME, AND WEIGHT—VOLUME PROBLEMS RELATED TO CHEMICAL EQUATIONS

The chemist often deals with problems involving chemical equations. Equations, and why and how the reactions that the equations describe occur, properly belong in a book on the theory and principles of chemistry. Consequently only a brief overview of the interpretation of equations will be taken. We will also assume that all reactions do occur as written, that they occur with 100% efficiency, and that all necessary conditions for the reaction are met. This is obviously what would happen in an ideal chemical world rather than in a real one. However, once one knows both how to solve problems involving chemical equations and the actual chemistry involved in specific circumstances, then it is very easy to solve problems in the real chemical world.

What is an equation? It is just a chemical sentence that indicates, in symbol form, what was used and what was formed. It says nothing about the rate, the ease, or the efficiency of the reaction. It doesn't even say whether the reaction occurs, since you can easily write an equation for a reaction that does not occur, that cannot occur.

Consider this equation:

$$3 \underline{Cu} + 8 HNO_3 \rightarrow 3 Cu(NO_3)_2 + 2 \overline{NO} + 4 H_2O$$

The coefficients, the 3, 8, 3, 2, and 4 preceding the individual formulas, can refer to numbers of molecules or to numbers of moles. Since molecules are so small, so totally impossible to deal with individually under anything except monstrously complex experimental conditions, these coefficients usually represent number of moles. However, for balancing equations it is usually easier to think of them as representing molecules.

These coefficients are integral numbers, that is, numbers with an infinite number of significant figures. Thus the number of significant figures in problems is unaffected by the relative number of moles in the basic chemical equation. The number of significant figures is governed by the number of significant figures in the measured quantities.

Now take another look at the equation. The left side of the equation represents the chemicals or reagents used, the *reactants*. The right side represents the *products* formed. The bar over the NO indicates that it is a gas. A bar under something indicates that it is a solid or a precipitate. A precipitate is a solid, albeit usually a very finely divided one, that is formed during the course of a reaction involving solutions.

Now, presuming the coefficients represent molecules,

1. How many atoms of Cu are there on the left?   3
                                on the right?   3
2. How many atoms of H are there on the left?   8
                                on the right?   8
3. How many atoms of N are there on the left?   8
                                on the right?   8   (6 + 2)
4. How many atoms of O are there on the left?   24
                                on the right?   24   (18 + 2 + 4)

Obviously, you cannot lose atoms in a reaction. You must have the same number of atoms of each element before and after the reaction.

Now let's get on with the problems themselves. Some of the problem-solving suggestions given previously may cause disorders here. For example, you were told that if you wanted gas pressure under new conditions you should operate mathematically on gas pressure. In many of the following problems you will want something like volume. But you will not have a volume on which to operate. Start working with what you have!

We hope to trigger your mind with these problems so that by doing them you will learn something you might not have thought of for use in a more difficult problem. Solutions appear at the ends of the examples. Do not look at the solution before seriously attempting to solve the problem.

EXAMPLE 21-1

Consider this equation:

$$3 \underline{Cu} + 8 \ HNO_3 \rightarrow 3 \ Cu(NO_3)_2 + 2 \ \overline{NO} + 4 \ H_2O$$

a. How many moles of HNO_3 will react with 3 moles of copper?

b. If 8 moles of HNO_3 react with sufficient Cu, how many moles of NO will be formed?

c. How many moles of HNO_3 would be needed to react with 6 moles of Cu?

d. How many moles of HNO_3 will react with 1.5 moles of Cu?

e. What weight of HNO_3 will react with 6 moles of Cu?

f. How many moles of H_2O would be produced if 45 moles of Cu reacted with sufficient HNO_3?

g. How many grams of H_2O would be produced if 45 moles of Cu reacted with sufficient HNO_3?

h. How many moles of HNO_3 will react with 127 g of Cu?

i. How many grams of HNO_3 would react with 127 g of Cu?

j. How many moles of $Cu(NO_3)_2$ would be produced if 14 moles of Cu reacted with sufficient HNO_3?

k. How many grams of $Cu(NO_3)_2$ would be produced if 14 moles of Cu reacted with sufficient HNO_3?

l. How many moles of NO gas would be produced if 3 moles of Cu reacted?

m. How many moles of NO gas would be produced if 9 moles of Cu reacted?

n. What weight of NO gas would be produced if 9 moles of Cu reacted?

o. What volume of NO gas would be produced if 9 moles of Cu reacted (volume at STP)?

p. If 150 g of Cu reacted with sufficient HNO_3, how many moles of NO gas would be formed?

ANSWERS/SOLUTIONS

Atomic weights are given in Table 16-1 (page 206). The number of significant figures to be used in atomic or molecular weights depends on the number of significant figures in the measured quantities in a problem. Remember that the coefficients in the equation do not affect the number of significant figures in the answer, since they represent moles or molecules and are considered absolute integers.

a. According to the equation, 8.

b. According to the equation, 2.

c. For every 3 moles of Cu one must have 8 moles of HNO_3 according to the equation. One can see that 8/3 as much HNO_3 would always be needed for any reaction corresponding to the given equation.

So $\dfrac{6 \text{ moles Cu} \times 8 \text{ moles } HNO_3}{3 \text{ moles Cu}} = 16 \text{ moles } HNO_3$

(It is not necessary to identify the species in the setup, as in "6 moles Cu," but we will do so in some cases for clarity.)

d. $\dfrac{1.5 \text{ moles} \times 8}{3} = 4 \text{ moles}$

e. From part a you know that 16 moles of HNO_3 would be needed. Each mole of HNO_3 weighs 63 g, so the solution is probably obvious.

$\dfrac{6 \text{ moles Cu} \times 8 \text{ moles } HNO_3 \times 63 \text{ g } HNO_3}{3 \text{ moles Cu} \qquad \text{mole } HNO_3} = 1000 \text{ g } HNO_3$

f. $\dfrac{45 \text{ moles} \times 4}{3} = 60 \text{ moles}$

g. $\dfrac{45 \text{ moles} \times 4 \times 18 \text{ g}}{3 \qquad \text{mole}} = 1100 \text{ g}$

h. Find the number of moles of Cu. One mole of Cu is 63.54 g.

$\dfrac{127 \text{ g} \qquad Cu \times 8 \text{ moles } HNO_3}{63.5 \text{ g mole}^{-1} \, Cu \times 3 \text{ moles Cu}} = 5.33 \text{ moles } HNO_3$

i. This now a combination of parts e and h.

$\dfrac{127 \text{ g Cu} \qquad \times 8 \text{ moles } HNO_3 \times 63.0 \text{ g } HNO_3}{63.5 \text{ g Cu} \qquad \times 3 \text{ moles Cu} \qquad \text{mole } HNO_3} = 336 \text{ g } HNO_3$
$\quad \overline{\quad\quad \text{mole Cu}}$

j. $\dfrac{14 \text{ moles} \times 3}{3} = 14 \text{ moles}$

k. $14 \text{ moles} \times \frac{3}{3} \times 188 \text{ g mole}^{-1} = 2630 \text{ g}$

l. According to the equation, 2.

m. $9 \text{ moles} \times \frac{2}{3} = 6 \text{ moles}$

n. $9 \text{ moles} \times \frac{2}{3} \times 30 \text{ g mole}^{-1} = 180 \text{ g}$

o. Now remember that 1 mole of any gas occupies 22.4 liters at STP. You know from part m that 6 moles of NO gas would be produced. You can calculate the volume of 6 moles of a gas.

$\dfrac{9 \text{ moles Cu} \times 2 \text{ moles NO} \times 22.4 \text{ liters NO}}{3 \text{ moles Cu} \qquad \text{mole NO}} = 134 \text{ liters NO}$

p. If you knew the number of moles of Cu you would do this the same way you did part l. You can find the number of moles of Cu.

$$\frac{150 \text{ g}}{64 \text{ g mole}^{-1} \times 3} \times 2 = 1.6 \text{ moles}$$

EXAMPLE 21–2

Refer back to the equation of Example 21–1.

a. If 150 g of Cu reacted with sufficient HNO_3, how many grams of NO gas would be formed?

b. If 150 g of Cu reacted with sufficient HNO_3, how many liters of NO gas would be formed?

c. If 150 g of Cu reacted with sufficient HNO_3, how many liters of NO gas collected at $39°C$ and 750 torr would there be?

d. If 150 g of copper reacted with sufficient HNO_3, what volume of NO gas could be collected over water at $39°C$ and 750 mm of Hg pressure (vapor pressure, Table 15-3, page 200).

e. What weight of HNO_3 would be required to react with sufficient Cu to produce 45 liters of NO gas at STP?

f. What weight of HNO_3 would be required to produce 45 liters of $\overline{\text{NO}}$ at $50°C$ and 1000 torr?

g. What weight of HNO_3 would be needed to react with 150 g of 93%-pure Cu?

h. What weight of 40%-pure HNO_3 would be needed to react with 150 g of Cu?

i. What weight of 40%-pure HNO_3 would be needed to react with 150 g of 93%-pure Cu?

j. What weight of NO would be produced from the reaction of 100 g of HNO_3 with 100 g of Cu (each measured to the nearest gram).

k. What weight of copper would be required to react with 5.00 liters of 12.0 M HNO_3?

l. What volume of 3.0 M HNO_3 would be required to react completely with 17 g of Cu?

m. Upon completely reacting with sufficient Cu, 4 liters of HNO_3 *solution* produced 76 liters of NO *gas* measured at STP. Find the molarity of the HNO_3 *solution*.

n. If 100.0 g of a copper-containing sample reacted completely with 50.0 ml of 15 M HNO_3, find the percentage of copper in the original sample. (One is forced to assume that nothing else in the sample reacted with the nitric acid; otherwise the problem becomes impossible to solve.)

ANSWERS/SOLUTIONS

a. $$\frac{150 \text{ g} \qquad Cu \times 2 \text{ moles NO} \times 30 \text{ g mole}^{-1} \text{ NO}}{64 \text{ g mole}^{-1} \text{ Cu} \times 3 \text{ moles Cu}} = 47 \text{ g NO}$$

b. $$\frac{150 \text{ g} \qquad Cu \times 2 \text{ moles NO} \times 22.4 \text{ liters mole}^{-1} \text{ NO}}{64 \text{ g mole}^{-1} \text{ Cu} \times 3 \text{ moles Cu}} = 35 \text{ liters NO}$$

c. Done exactly the way part b was done, but volume has to be corrected to nonstandard conditions. Remember that any volume obtained by using 22.4 liters mole^{-1} is necessarily at standard conditions.

$$\frac{150 \text{ g} \qquad \times 2 \times 22.4 \text{ liters mole}^{-1} \times 312°K \times 760 \text{ torr}}{64 \text{ g mole}^{-1} \times 3 \qquad\qquad\qquad \times 273°K \times 750 \text{ torr}} = 41 \text{ liters}$$

d. Solved exactly the same as part c *except* that the pressure of the gas is no longer 750 mm; it is 750 mm minus the vapor pressure of water at 39°C.

e. $$\frac{45 \text{ liters} \qquad NO \times 8 \text{ moles } HNO_3 \times 63 \text{ g mole}^{-1} \text{ } HNO_3}{22.4 \text{ liters mole}^{-1} \text{ NO} \times 2 \text{ moles NO}} = 510 \text{ g}$$

f. If one had the volume of gas at STP, one would solve this exactly the same as part e. Correct the volume to STP and then proceed in the classic fashion. Remember that you cannot use 22.4 liters mole^{-1} with any volume unless that volume is at STP.

$$\frac{45 \text{ liters} \times 273°K \times 1000 \text{ mm} \qquad\qquad\qquad \times 8 \times 63 \text{ g mole}^{-1}}{323°K \times \quad 760 \text{ mm} \times 22.4 \text{ liters mole}^{-1} \times 2}$$
$$= 560 \text{ g}$$

g. You do not have 150 g of Cu; you have 0.93×150 g. So

$$\frac{150 \text{ g} \qquad \times 0.93 \times 8 \times 63 \text{ g mole}^{-1}}{64 \text{ g mole}^{-1} \qquad \times 3} = 370 \text{ g}$$

h. You need 100/40 more HNO_3, since the HNO_3 is only 40% pure, so

$$\frac{150 \text{ g} \qquad \times 8 \times 63 \text{ g mole}^{-1} \times 100}{64 \text{ g mole}^{-1} \times 3 \qquad\qquad\qquad 40}$$

or $\dfrac{150 \text{ g} \qquad \times 8 \times 63 \text{ g mole}^{-1}}{64 \text{ g mole}^{-1} \times 3 \qquad\qquad \times 0.40} = 980 \text{ g}$

i. $\dfrac{150 \text{ g} \qquad \times 0.93 \times 8 \times 63 \text{ g mole}^{-1}}{64 \text{ g mole}^{-1} \qquad\quad \times 3 \qquad\qquad \times 0.40} = 920 \text{ g}$

or $\dfrac{150 \times 93 \times 8 \times 63 \times 100}{64 \times 100 \times 3 \quad\times 40}$ if you prefer

j. There are

$\dfrac{100 \text{ g}}{63.0 \text{ g mole}^{-1}} = 1.59 \text{ moles HNO}_3$ and $\dfrac{100 \text{ g}}{63.5 \text{ g mole}^{-1}} = 1.57 \text{ moles Cu}$

To use up 1.6 moles of HNO_3 only

$\dfrac{1.59 \text{ moles HNO}_3 \times 3 \text{ moles Cu}}{8 \text{ moles HNO}_3} = 0.60 \text{ mole Cu}$

would be needed. To use up 1.57 moles of Cu, $1.57 \times 8/3 = 4.2$ moles of HNO_3 would be needed. Obviously, the quantity of HNO_3 governs the amount of NO produced. Long before the copper supply was exhausted, the HNO_3 would have been used up

$\dfrac{100 \text{ g} \qquad HNO_3 \times 2 \text{ moles NO} \quad \times 30.0 \text{ g mole}^{-1} \text{ NO}}{63.0 \text{ g mole}^{-1} \text{ HNO}_3 \times 8 \text{ moles HNO}_3} = 11.9 \text{ g NO}$

k. You would have to find the number of moles of HNO_3 in 5.00 liters of 12.0 M HNO_3. After that the problem is solved in the usual way. Be sure to remember that M stands for moles per liter of solution; it has nothing to do with the 22.4-liter volume (STP) that a mole of gas occupies.

$\dfrac{5.00 \text{ liters HNO}_3 \times 12.0 \text{ moles HNO}_3 \times 3 \text{ moles Cu} \quad \times 63.5 \text{ g} \quad Cu}{\text{liter} \quad HNO_3 \times 8 \text{ moles HNO}_3 \qquad\qquad \text{mole}}$

$= 1430 \text{ g Cu}$

l. Find the moles of HNO_3 needed:

$\dfrac{17 \text{ g} \qquad \times 8}{64 \text{ g mole}^{-1} \times 3}$

Then remember molarity $= \dfrac{\text{number of moles}}{\text{liters}}$

so that liters $= \dfrac{\text{number of moles}}{\text{molarity}}$

$\dfrac{17 \text{ g} \quad \times 8}{64 \dfrac{\text{g}}{\text{mole}} \times 3 \times 3 \dfrac{\text{moles}}{\text{liter}}} = 0.24 \text{ liter}$

(Units cancel out to $\dfrac{1}{\frac{1}{liter}}$; multiply both sides of the main fraction line by

liters and cancel suitably.)

m. Find the moles of HNO_3 and then find moles per liter of HNO_3.

$$\dfrac{76 \text{ liters NO} \times 8 \text{ moles } HNO_3}{22.4 \text{ liters NO} \times 2 \text{ moles NO} \quad \times 4 \text{ liters } HNO_3} = 3 \dfrac{\text{moles}}{\text{liter}} HNO_3 \text{ or}$$

underneath: mole NO

$3 \, M \, HNO_3$

n. $\dfrac{15 \text{ moles} \times 50.0 \text{ ml} \times 0.001 \text{ liter} \times 3 \times 64 \text{ g} \qquad\qquad \times 100}{\text{liter} \qquad\qquad\qquad \text{ml} \qquad 8 \qquad \text{mole} \times 100.0 \text{ g}} = 18\% \text{ Cu}$

EXAMPLE 21-3

Consider this equation

$Cu + 2 H_2SO_4 \rightarrow CuSO_4 + \overline{SO_2} + 2 H_2O$

a. What weight of copper would be needed to react with 2 liters of 98%-pure concentrated sulfuric acid? Density of concentrated sulfuric acid is 1.84 g/ml.

The density of the solution with respect to pure H_2SO_4 is

0.98×1.84 g/ml = 1.80 g/ml

Now find the actual weight and the moles of H_2SO_4 and proceed as usual.

$$\dfrac{2 \text{ liters} \times 1000 \text{ ml} \quad \times 1.80 \text{ g} \qquad\qquad \times 1 \times 64 \text{ g}}{\text{liter} \qquad \text{ml} \times 98 \text{ g} \quad \times 2 \qquad \text{mole}} = 100,000 \text{ g}$$

underneath: mole

Done in one setup:

$$\dfrac{2 \text{ liters} \times 1000 \text{ ml} \quad \times 1.84 \text{ g} \quad \times 0.98 \qquad\qquad \times 1 \times 64 \text{ g}}{\text{liter} \qquad \text{ml} \qquad 98 \text{ g} \quad \times 2 \qquad \text{mole}}$$

underneath: mole

b. What change would have been made if the above problem had specified that the specific gravity of the sulfuric acid was 1.84?

None. The specific gravity indicates how much heavier a given volume of material is than an equal volume of water. Water weighs 1 g/ml; therefore you multiply 1.84×1 g/ml.

EXAMPLE 21–4

What weight of Al_2O_3 could be obtained from 33.5 g of $AlCl_3$ if the following reactions occurred:

$$AlCl_3 + 3\ NH_4OH \rightarrow \underline{Al(OH)_3} + 3\ NH_4Cl$$

$$2\ \underline{Al(OH)_3} \rightarrow Al_2O_3 + 3\ H_2O$$

From each mole of $AlCl_3$ one gets a mole of $Al(OH)_3$, but from each mole of $Al(OH)_3$ one can get only half a mole of Al_2O_3. Consequently one can get half a mole of Al_2O_3 from each mole of $AlCl_3$.

$$\frac{33.5\ g}{133.5\ g\ mole^{-1} \times 2} \times 1 \times 102.0\ g\ mole^{-1} = 12.8\ g$$

PROBLEMS

1. Consider this neutralization reaction:

$$NaOH + HCl \rightarrow NaCl + H_2O$$

a. How many grams of NaOH would be needed to react with 70 g of HCl?

b. How many grams of NaCl would be formed when 70 g of HCl reacted with sufficient NaOH?

c. How many grams of NaCl would be formed from the reaction of 70 g of NaOH with 70 g of HCl?

d. How many grams of NaCl would be formed from the reaction of 70 g of 68%-pure NaOH with excess HCl?

e. How many liters of 2 M HCl would be required to react with 50 g of NaOH?

f. If 450 ml of an NaOH solution was completely neutralized by 50 g of HCl, find the molarity of the NaOH solution. (By neutralized here we mean that the NaOH reacted with exactly the proper amount of the HCl.)

g. If 35.2 ml of an NaOH solution was completely neutralized by 28.9 ml of 0.18 M HCl, find the molarity of the NaOH solution.

h. A 10-g sample of impure NaOH was completely neutralized by 75 ml of 3.1 M HCl. Find the percentage of NaOH in the sample.

2. Consider this equation:

$$2\ NaOH + H_2SO_4 \rightarrow Na_2SO_4 + 2\ H_2O$$

ı. What weight of NaOH would react with 70 g of H_2SO_4 according to the equation given here?

b. How many grams of Na_2SO_4 would be formed from the reaction of 70 g of NaOH with sufficient H_2SO_4?

c. How many grams of Na_2SO_4 would be formed from the reaction of 70 g of NaOH with 70 g of H_2SO_4?

d. How many grams of Na_2SO_4 would be formed from the reaction of 70 g of 68%-pure NaOH with excess sulfuric acid (H_2SO_4)?

e. How many liters of 2 M H_2SO_4 would be required to react with 50 g of NaOH?

f. If 450 ml of an NaOH solution was completely neutralized by 50 g of H_2SO_4, find the molarity of the NaOH solution.

g. If 35.2 ml of an NaOH solution was completely neutralized by 28.9 ml of 0.18 M H_2SO_4, find the molarity of the NaOH solution.

h. A 20-g sample of impure NaOH was completely neutralized by 75 ml of 3.0 M H_2SO_4. Calculate the percentage of NaOH in the sample.

3. Consider this equation:

$$3 \ \underline{Ag_2S} + 8 \ HNO_3 \rightarrow 6 \ AgNO_3 + 3 \ \underline{S} + 2 \ \overline{NO} + 4 \ H_2O$$

a. What weight of S would be produced from the reaction of 4.08 g of Ag_2S with sufficient HNO_3?

b. What volume of NO gas (STP) would be produced from the reaction under the conditions of problem 3a? What weight of $AgNO_3$?

c. Find the molarity of the $AgNO_3$ solution produced if the final volume was 200 ml.

d. What volume of NO gas (measured at 25°C over water and at 756 torr) would be produced if the Ag_2S reacted completely with 350 ml of 6 M HNO_3?

e. A certain solution of $AgNO_3$ was treated with H_2S gas to form Ag_2S. The Ag_2S was filtered out and treated suitably with excess HNO_3 of the proper strength; 80 liters of NO gas measured at STP was produced. Find the weight of the silver in the original $AgNO_3$ solution.

f. An impure sample of silver weighing 100 g was dissolved in nitric acid (HNO_3). From this, Ag_2S was precipitated. When the Ag_2S was treated with HNO_3, 10 liters of NO gas (STP) was produced. The following was the sequence of reactions:

$$3 \ Ag + 4 \ HNO_3 \rightarrow \overline{NO} + 2 \ H_2O + 3 \ AgNO_3$$
$$2 \ AgNO_3 + H_2S \rightarrow \underline{Ag_2S} + 2 \ HNO_3$$
$$3 \ \underline{Ag_2S} + 8 \ HNO_3 \rightarrow 6 \ AgNO_3 + 2 \ \overline{NO} + 4 \ H_2O + 3 \ \underline{S}$$

Find the percentage of silver in the original sample.

4. Consider this reaction:

$$BaCl_2 + Na_2SO_4 \rightarrow 2\ NaCl + \underline{BaSO_4}$$

a. What volume of 2.2 M $BaCl_2$ solution would be needed to pre-cipitate all of the SO_4^{--} ions as $BaSO_4$ in a solution made from 50 g of Na_2SO_4?

b. All of the sulfate in an 11.3-g sample of sodium sulfate (Na_2SO_4), was precipitated by 32.5 ml of 1.80 M $BaCl_2$. What was the per-centage of Na_2SO_4 in the sample?

c. If 49.3 ml of 0.97 M $BaCl_2$ reacted completely with 37.3 ml of Na_2SO_4 solution, find the molarity of the Na_2SO_4 solution.

5. Consider the equation for the complete combustion of pentane (C_5H_{12}):

$$\overline{C_5H_{12}} + 8\ \overline{O_2} \rightarrow 5\ \overline{CO_2} + 6\ \overline{H_2O}$$

a. What volume of oxygen (O_2) would be required to burn an amount of pentane equivalent to 9 liters at STP?

b. What volume of oxygen measured at 100°C and 785 mm of Hg would be required?

c. What volume of oxygen at the conditions described in problem 5b would be required to burn 9 liters of pentane measured at 40°C and 756 torr?

d. What volume of air (20% oxygen by volume) would be required to burn 9 liters of pentane (STP)?

e. What volume of air (STP) would be required to burn 50 g of pen-tane?

f. What volume of air would be required to burn 50 g of pentane at 100°C and 1000 torr? (Assumptions?)

g. What volume of air would be required to burn 9 liters of a mixture of 85% pentane and 15% nitrogen? Percentage is by volume. Nitrogen cannot burn. Calculate at STP.

6. Consider this equation:

$$\underline{ZnS} + 2\ HCl \rightarrow ZnCl_2 + \overline{H_2S}$$

a. What volume of HCl (density 1.18 g/ml, 37% pure) must be used to react completely with 95 g of ZnS?

b. How many grams of 78%-pure ZnS would be required to produce 40 liters (STP) of H_2S gas?

c. How many grams of 78%-pure ZnS would be required to produce 40 liters of H_2S gas if it were known that 5% of the gas would be lost in the process before final "bottling"?

7. Consider this equation:

$$3\ CaCl_2 + 2\ Na_3PO_4 \rightarrow \underline{Ca_3(PO_4)_2} + 6\ NaCl$$

   a. What volume of 0.2 M Na_3PO_4 would be required to precipitate all of the calcium ions in a 40-g sample of $CaCl_2$?

   b. 40.3 ml of 0.23 M Na_3PO_4 solution was required to precipitate all of the calcium ions in a suitably dissolved sample of impure calcium chloride ($CaCl_2$). The sample weighed 2.08 g. Find the percentage of $CaCl_2$ in the sample.

   c. As a check on the value obtained in problem 7b a 2.63-g sample of $CaCl_2$ reacted with sufficient 0.19 M $AgNO_3$ solution. What weight of AgCl should have been produced if the following reaction (and no other) had occurred?

$$CaCl_2 + 2\ AgNO_3 \rightarrow \underline{2\ AgCl} + Ca(NO_3)_2$$

8. A 1.00-g sample containing a mixture of NaCl and NaBr was titrated with excess 0.100 M $AgNO_3$ solution. A precipitate weighing 2.39 g was obtained. The only possible reactions were:

$NaCl + AgNO_3 \rightarrow \underline{AgCl} + NaNO_3$
and $NaBr + AgNO_3 \rightarrow \underline{AgBr} + NaNO_3$

Thus, the precipitate consisted of AgCl and AgBr. Find the percentage of NaCl and the percentage of NaBr in the sample. You might want to use algebra to solve this problem.

9. Another 1.00-g sample containing another proportion of NaCl and NaBr reacted completely with 131.4 ml of 0.100 M $AgNO_3$. The only possible reactions, as far as anyone knew, were those given in problem 8. Find the percentage of NaCl and the percentage of NaBr in this sample.

10. A 1.00-g sample of NaCl and KCl was treated with excess $AgNO_3$ to form 2.08 g of precipitate. Find the percentage of NaCl in the sample. The only possible reactions were:

$NaCl + AgNO_3 \rightarrow \underline{AgCl} + NaNO_3$

$KCl + AgNO_3 \rightarrow \underline{AgCl} +\ KNO_3$

22

DETERMINATION OF FORMULAS OF COMPOUNDS

Formulas give the relative number of moles of each element in a mole of a given compound. For example, a mole of water, H_2O, has 2 moles of hydrogen atoms for every mole of oxygen atoms. A formula can obviously represent the relative number of atoms of each element in a molecule of compound too.

By weight water is 11.2% hydrogen and 88.8% oxygen. Since percent means parts per hundred, it is obvious that 100 g of water would have 11.2 g of hydrogen atoms and 88.8 g of oxygen atoms in it. At the same time, in this or any other quantity of water there would be twice as many atoms of hydrogen as atoms of oxygen or twice as many moles of hydrogen atoms as moles of oxygen atoms.

How would one go about converting data about the composition of a compound into a formula? Percentage by weight is directly proportional to weight; consequently it would make no difference whether one had data in terms of weight or percentage by weight for the individual elements in a given quantity of a compound. One would have to find the number of moles of each element in the compound and then convert the actual number of moles into the relative number of moles in finding the formula of a compound.

EXAMPLE 22–1

Find the formula of water from this information: Water is 11.2% hydrogen and 88.8% oxygen by weight.

$$H = \frac{11.2}{1.01} = 11.1 \quad \text{or} \quad \frac{11.2 \text{ g}}{1.01 \frac{\text{g}}{\text{mole}}} = 11.1 \text{ moles}$$

$$O = \frac{88.8}{16.0} = 5.55 \qquad \frac{88.8 \text{ g}}{16.0 \frac{\text{g}}{\text{mole}}} = 5.55 \text{ moles}$$

This begins perhaps to look like a formula, but it is still not a formula. Formulas have only whole numbers. Why not divide each quotient by the smallest quotient, here 5.55?

$$\frac{11.1}{5.55} = 2 \quad \text{and} \quad \frac{5.55}{5.55} = 1$$

The formula is H_2O.

One would want to carry out the initial division to at least three significant digits. After that one would round such numbers as 0.9, 0.8, 1.0, 1.2, since one cannot have parts of atoms.

EXAMPLE 22–2

Find the formula of this compound: 2.90 g of Na, 4.05 g of S, 3.04 g of O.

$$Na = \frac{2.90}{23.0} = 0.126 \qquad \frac{0.126}{0.126} = 1.00$$

$$S = \frac{4.05}{32.0} = 0.127 \qquad \frac{0.127}{0.126} = 1.01$$

$$O = \frac{3.04}{16.0} = 0.190 \qquad \frac{0.190}{0.126} = 1.51$$

Do not round the 1.51. This is a clear signal to double everything. The correct formula is $Na_2S_2O_3$, a well-known compound, the so-called photographer's hypo. Notice that 16.0 was used for oxygen. Oxygen atoms, not the free element O_2, were in the compound.

EXAMPLE 22–3

Find the formula of the following compound: 85.5% carbon, 14.5% hydrogen.

Did you get CH_2? This is known as the *empirical formula,* so called because it is obtained from experimental data. It may or may not be the correct formula, since CH_2, C_2H_4, C_3H_6, etc., all have the same percentage composition. If you knew the molecular weight of this compound as well as the percentage composition you could rather easily find the true formula. Suppose you knew that 1.25 g of this compound as a gas (its natural state, by the way) occupied 500 $\pm$ 1 ml at STP. From this you could find the molecular weight.

$$\frac{1.25 \text{ g}}{0.500 \text{ liter} \times} \times \frac{22.4 \text{ liters}}{\text{mole}} = 56.0 \text{ g mole}^{-1}$$

CH_2 would have an apparent molecular weight of 14. The actual compound has a molecular weight four times this (56/14 = 4). Therefore the true formula, the molecular formula, for the compound seems to be C_4H_8.

EXAMPLE 22-4

After 1.25 g of a hydrated copper sulfate sample was heated to a constant weight at a suitable temperature, the residue weighed 0.80 g. Find the empirical formula of the hydrate.

Fact: Hydrates are crystalline compounds containing water. They have a general formula of this sort: $CuSO_4 \cdot xH_2O$. In hydrates and in a number of other compounds entities that can exist as separate compounds are locked together, as it were, in a composite molecule.

Assumption: Residue was free of water, so that it was $CuSO_4$. Sample did not lose anything but H_2O.

The difference between 1.25 and 0.80 must be the weight of water lost. This naturally must be the weight of water that was in the compound originally.

$$CuSO_4 = \frac{0.80}{160} = 0.0050 \qquad \frac{0.0050}{0.0050} = 1$$

$$H_2O = \frac{0.45}{18} = 0.025 \qquad \frac{0.025}{0.0050} = 5$$

The empirical formula of the hydrate would seem to be $CuSO_4 \cdot 5H_2O$.

PROBLEMS

See Table 16-1 (page 206) for atomic weights.

1. Find the empirical formulas from the given data in each case.
   a. 92.6% mercury, 7.4% oxygen.

   b. 45.5% nickel, 54.5% chlorine.

   c. 88.9% bromine, 5.20% nitrogen, 5.94% oxygen. (This sums to more than 100%. Rarely in experimental work would the composition percentages total exactly 100%.)

   d. 86.8% palladium, 13.2% sulfur.

   e. 52.83% platinum, 16.79% phosphorus, 30.40% oxygen.

   f. 87.6% zinc, 12.5% nitrogen.

2. The empirical formula of a given compound was found to be HF. The experimentally determined molecular weight was 41. Find the molecular formula for this compound.

3. Find the molecular weight and molecular formula for a compound that is 7.5% hydrogen, 92.5% carbon, given the fact that 1.365 g occupied 168 ml at 150°C and 785 torr.

4. Under suitable experimental conditions, 2.62 g of zinc reacted with sulfur to produce 3.90 g of product. Find the formula of the compound.

5. Under suitable conditions 10.36 g of lead was allowed to react with 50.00 liters of chlorine (Cl_2) gas. After the reaction had stopped, the excess (unreacted) chlorine gas occupied 47.72 liters (STP). Find the empirical formula for the compound presumably formed.

6. If the unreacted chlorine in problem 6 had occupied 52.50 liters collected and measured at 23°C and 749 torr, find the formula of the compound.

7. Find the empirical formula for a compound containing 52.2% C, 13.1% H, 34.8% O. Then use the following information to find its molecular formula.

A vessel containing this liquid was allowed to boil. The vapors from the boiling liquid were streamed through a previously weighed receiving flask for 10 min. At the end of this time it was considered unlikely that any appreciable amount of other vapors or gases would still be in the flask. The receiving flask was sealed and weighed at room temperature. It was noted that the vapors had condensed to a liquid prior to the time of weighing.

Weight of empty receiving flask	53.210 g
(weighed in air; density of air 1.29 g/liter)	
Weight of receiving flask plus condensed vapor	53.242 g
Volume of receiving flask	130.4 ml
Temperature at which gas filled flask	90.0° C
Pressure at which gas filled flask	756 torr

(If you think that the vapor weight is 53.242 − 53.210, please reconsider.)

8. A hydrocarbon (a compound containing hydrogen and carbon exclusively) was burned completely in oxygen to produce only CO_2 and H_2O. Find the molecular formula of the hydrocarbon from the following data: 11.0 g of hydrocarbon produced a total volume of gaseous products after complete combustion and removal of excess oxygen of 56.1 liters when measured at 110°C and 745 torr. Upon being cooled to 10°C, it shrank to 17.8 liters at 745 torr. (Boiling point of H_2O is 100°C. At standard pressure CO_2 is a gas at temperatures above −78.5°C.)

23

CALORIMETRY

Temperature is a rough measure of molecular motion. The same quantity of heat will produce a different temperature change in equal weights of different substances. This is not at all odd. Engines of the same horsepower will move a Lincoln and a Comet at rather different speeds. It takes less heat to raise the temperature of a cup of milk a given number of degrees than it does a cup of water. In other words, different and characteristic amounts of heat are required to heat the same weight of different substances through the same temperature range. Be sure not to confuse temperature and quantity of heat. Which would melt more ice, a thimbleful of boiling water or a bucket of water at 90°C? Vote for the bucket.

When a given quantity of water or any other temperature-stable liquid is heated, the temperature rises rather uniformly until the boiling point is reached; then the temperature remains the same until the liquid is boiled off. As a liquid is cooled, the temperature drops rather uniformly until the material begins to freeze; then the temperature remains at the freezing point until all of the substance has frozen. At the freezing point or boiling point, heat, which causes molecules to move faster during a temperature rise in a particular phase (solid, liquid, gaseous), is used to enable the molecules to get and remain farther from one another. One of the major differences between solids, liquids, and gases is the distance between molecules.

Some fundamental definitions would seem to be in order now.

calorie (cal): quantity of heat liberated or absorbed when 1 g of water is cooled or heated 1°C. (To be exact, this is true only between 14.5°C and 15.5°C. However, the amount of heat associated with 1°C temperature change is usually so close to 1 cal that this figure is used unless very precise work is in progress.)

specific heat: The quantity of heat liberated or absorbed when the temperature of 1 g of a substance falls or rises 1°C. Specific heat is temperature- and phase-dependent. Thus one must know not only the substance but also the temperature range and whether a solid, liquid, or gas is involved.

heat of vaporization: Amount of heat required to turn 1 g of liquid at its boiling point into 1 g of vapor at the same temperature.

heat of fusion: Amount of heat liberated when 1 g of liquid is turned into 1 g of solid at the same temperature.

Obviously, each of these quantities could be expressed in terms of a mole of substance rather than a gram of substance.

The unit for specific heat is calories per gram per degree, which may be written

$$\frac{cal}{g\text{-}°C} \quad \text{or} \quad cal\ g^{-1}\ °C^{-1}$$

This unit sometimes causes difficulty. Suppose that a given Roman emperor ordered that each lion be fed 1 gladiator per day. This could have been expressed as 1 gladiator lion^{-1} day^{-1}. Obviously, 2 lions would eat 8 gladiators in 4 days.

$$\frac{1\ \text{gladiator} \times 2\ \text{lions} \times 4\ \text{days}}{\text{lion-day}} = 8\ \text{gladiators}$$

Specific heat is treated the same way.

Now let's try some problems. Table 23-1 provides some data.

Table 23-1

Substance	Specific heat, cal/g-°C	Freezing point, °C	Heat of fusion, cal/g	Boiling point, °C	Heat of vaporization, cal/g
water (liquid)	1.00	0.0	79.7	100.0	540
water (solid)	0.46				
ammonia (liquid)	1.05	−77.7	79.3	−33.4	327
ammonia (solid)	0.50				
ethanol (liquid)	0.58	−114.5		78.4	204

EXAMPLE 23-1

How much heat would be required for each of the following?

a. To heat 1.0 g of liquid ethanol from 10°C to 50°C.

$$\frac{0.58 \text{ cal}}{\text{g-}°\text{C}} \times 1.0 \text{ g} \times (50 - 10)°\text{C} = 23 \text{ cal}$$

b. To boil 1.00 g of liquid ethanol at 78.4°C.

$$\frac{204 \text{ cal} \times 1.00 \text{ g}}{\text{g}} = 204 \text{ cal}$$

c. To turn 42 g of ethanol at 78.4°C into vapor at 78.4°C.

$$204 \text{ cal g}^{-1} \times 42 \text{ g} = 8.6 \times 10^3 \text{ cal}$$

d. To take 42 g of liquid ethanol at 10.0°C to ethanol vapor at 78.4°C.

Take the liquid from 10.0°C to 78.4°C; then boil it.

$$\frac{0.58 \text{ cal}}{\text{g-}°\text{C}} \times 42 \text{ g} \times (78.4 - 10.0)°\text{C} + \frac{204 \text{ cal} \times 42 \text{ g}}{\text{g}} = 1.0 \times 10^4 \text{ cal}$$

EXAMPLE 23-2

How much heat would be liberated if 42 g of ethanol vapor at 78.4°C were condensed to liquid at 10.0°C?

This is the same as Example 23-1d. The order of events would be reversed, and the heat would be liberated rather than absorbed.

EXAMPLE 23-3

In heating 1.0 g of metal 10.0°C, 0.45 cal was supplied. This is a 10.0°C range; you do not know what the temperatures were. Find the specific heat of the metal.

$$\frac{0.45 \text{ cal}}{1.0 \text{ g} \times 10.0°\text{C}} = 0.045 \text{ cal/g-}°\text{C}$$

EXAMPLE 23-4

In heating 10 g of a metal from 31.9°C to 41.7°C, 9 cal was supplied. Find the specific heat of the metal.

$$\frac{9 \text{ cal}}{10 \text{ g} \times (41.7 - 31.9)°\text{C}} = 0.09 \text{ cal/g-}°\text{C}$$

EXAMPLE 23-5

In an experiment 100 g of metal at 80.0°C was dropped into 150 g of water at 20.0°C. The temperature of the water rose to an equilibrium temperature of 21.7°C. Find the specific heat of the metal.

You know the weight of the metal and the temperature range through which it passes. If only you knew the heat lost by the metal. You know the heat gained by the water, however, and this must be the same as the heat lost by the metal, so

$$\frac{150 \text{ g} \times 1 \text{ cal} \times (21.7 - 20.0)°C}{\text{g-}°C \times 100 \text{ g} \times (80.0 - 21.7)°C} = 4 \times 10^{-2} \text{ cal/g-}°C$$

PROBLEMS

Refer to Table 23-1 as needed.

1. Find the heat liberated when 99 g of water at 0°C becomes ice at 0°C.
2. Find the heat liberated when 99 g of water at 0°C becomes ice at −33°C.
3. Find the heat liberated when 99 g of water at 79°C becomes ice at −33°C.
4. Find the heat liberated when 99 g of water vapor at 100°C became liquid water at 100°C.
5. Find the heat required to turn 99 g of ice at −33°C into water vapor at 100°C.
6. How much heat would be required to take 50 g of solid ammonia at −100°C to ammonia gas at −33.4°C?
7. How much heat would be required to heat 40 g of tungsten (specific heat 0.034 cal g^{-1} °C^{-1}) from 40.0°C to 100.0°C (all in the solid phase)?
8. To what temperature could 75 g of nickel at 95°C heat 100 g of water at 25.0°C if the two were mixed? What do you know to be equal here? How many significant figures in answer? (Specific heat of nickel is 0.109 cal g^{-1} °C^{-1}.)
9. How much more heat would it take to heat 50 g of Ni (specific heat 0.109 cal g^{-1} °C^{-1}) than 50 g of Al (specific heat 0.217 cal g^{-1} °C^{-1}) through a 10°C range? Or does it take less heat? Examine the constants.

10. Find the specific heat of this metal: 10 g of metal caused the temperature of 100 g of mercury (specific heat 0.033 cal g^{-1} °C^{-1}) to rise 25.0°C. Initial temperature of the metal was 85.0°C. (What must have been the final temperature of the metal as far as this experiment is concerned?)

24

THERMOCHEMISTRY

The Study of Heat Changes
Related to Chemical Reactions

It is generally known that energy is associated with all sorts of chemical and physical reactions. Either energy is liberated or else it is absorbed. The energy can be manifested in all sorts of forms—heat, light, sound, electricity, etc.

Energy, usually in the form of heat, is required to melt ice, but exactly the same quantity of heat is liberated when the water so produced is reconverted into ice. Paper, wood, and coal burn, but not spontaneously at room temperature. Each burns with a different degree of readiness; in fact, each requires energy to start the burning process, but once the burning is started it continues of its own accord, always liberating the same amount of energy, no matter what the form of energy, for the same weights of the same materials.

The elements sodium and chlorine react magnificently and violently when put together, giving off heat and light in the process as well as forming sodium chloride, a very stable compound. In order to decompose sodium chloride an amount of energy equal to that given off when the compound was formed must be supplied, but it need not be supplied in the same form. Sodium chloride is usually decomposed by means of a direct electric current under suitable conditions.

Various explosives can be caused to react by supplying them with just enough energy to start decomposition; then they give off energy of their own accord. Some highly sensitive compounds need only to be shouted at sufficiently vigorously in order to have them explode. With this brief introduction, let's plunge into a more formal treatment of thermochemistry.

Enthalpy (symbol: H) is a measure of the heat content of a compound.

One can easily find how much heat is liberated or absorbed when a mole of compound is formed, but it is presently impossible to measure the actual heat content of a free element or of a compound. Elements certainly do have some form of energy, which can be manifested as heat as well as other forms of energy, but we can find only the energy liberated or absorbed when the element reacts with another element or compound. Consequently the enthalpy (heat content) of a free element is conventionally taken as zero.

The standard heat of formation of a compound (symbol: ΔH_f°; Δ is the Greek letter delta) is defined as the heat change associated with the formation of 1 mole of a compound from its elements under standard conditions, $25^\circ C$ and 1 atm.* If the symbol ΔH_f (without the superscript $^\circ$) is used, nonstandard conditions are involved. By convention $\Delta H_f^\circ = 0$ for each element.

If heat is given off during the formation of a compound from its elements, the original elements had more energy in them than does the compound so formed. The ΔH_f for such a compound is negative, the minus sign indicating that energy was liberated. The resulting compound is more stable than the original elements, since energy must be supplied to decompose it into its elements. When energy must be supplied not only to start a reaction but to keep it going, then the compound that is formed has more energy in it than the elements from which it was formed. Its ΔH_f is positive, indicating that energy was absorbed during the formation of the compound from its elements, and the compound is less stable than the elements from which it was formed.

When 1 mole of carbon dioxide (CO_2) is formed from 1 mole of carbon (C) and 1 mole of oxygen (O_2) under thermodynamic standard conditions, 94 kcal is liberated. When 1 mole of hydrazine (N_2H_4) is formed from 1 mole of nitrogen (N_2) and 2 moles of hydrogen (H_2) under thermodynamic standard conditions, 12 kcal is absorbed. The standard heats of formation, ΔH_f°, for CO_2 and N_2H_4 are -94 and $+12$ kcal/mole, respectively.

Wouldn't it seem entirely reasonable that the heat of a reaction would be equal to the difference between the heat content (enthalpy) of the products and the heat content (enthalpy) of the reactants? If the products have a greater heat content than the reactants, then some heat—or an equivalent amount of energy in another form—must be supplied or there would be no products. (We are speaking in broad general terms here; there can be exceptions to this under some conditions.) Conversely, if the products of a reaction have a lower heat content than the reactants, then heat (or some other form of energy) must have been liberated. If heat is absorbed, the reaction is said to be endothermic and the heat

---

*Thermodynamic standard conditions differ from the STP for gases in that the standard temperature is $25^\circ C$ instead of $0^\circ C$.

of reaction would have a plus sign; if heat is liberated, the reaction is said to be exothermic and the heat of reaction would have a minus sign.

It is impossible to measure the heat content (enthalpy) of a compound or an element. All that can be measured is the heat liberated or absorbed when the compound reacts or is formed. This would necessarily put determination of heats of reaction on a totally experimental basis except for one happy fact. The difference between the heats of formation of products and reactants is numerically the same as the difference between the heat contents of the products and reactants. Heats of formation for compounds must be experimentally determined, but once heats of formation have been found, then the heats of reaction can be found mathematically rather than experimentally. Thus we can say

$$\Delta H^{\circ}_{reaction} = \Sigma H_{products} - \Sigma H_{reactants}$$
and $\Delta H^{\circ}_{reaction} = \Sigma H^{\circ}_{f(products)} - \Sigma \Delta H^{\circ}_{f(reactants)}$

where ΔH° is heat of reaction, and H and ΔH°_f are enthalpy (heat content) and heat of formation, respectively. If the difference has a minus sign, then heat is liberated; if it has a plus sign, then heat is absorbed. (Sigma, Σ, is used as a sign for a sum. It is customarily used for more sophisticated summation, but its use is proper and traditional here.)

Let's take some examples.

EXAMPLE 24-1

Find the heat of reaction, ΔH°, for the reaction

$$FeI_2 + H_2S(g) \rightarrow 2 HI + FeS(s)*$$

ΔH°_f, kcal/mole	ΔH°_f products	ΔH°_f reactants
FeI_2 = -30	$2(-14) = -28$	-30
$H_2S(g)$ = -5	-23	-5
HI = -14	-51	-35
$FeS(s)$ = -23		

$$\Delta H^{\circ} = \Sigma \Delta H^{\circ}_{f(products)} - \Sigma \Delta H^{\circ}_{f(reactants)}$$
$$= -51 - (-35) = -16 \text{ kcal}$$

This means that when 1 mole of FeI_2 reacts with 1 mole of H_2S gas to form 2 moles of HI and 1 mole of solid FeS, 16 kcal of energy is liberated. Since heat (or an equivalent amount of energy in another form) is liberated, the products have less heat content than the reactants, so the sign for ΔH° is negative.

---

*(s), (l), and (g) represent solid, liquid, and gaseous states.

EXAMPLE 24-2

Find the heat of this reaction

$$3 \, PbI_2(s) + 2 \, Na_3PO_4 \rightarrow Pb_3(PO_4)_2(s) + 6 \, NaI$$

ΔH_f°, kcal/mole

PbI(s)	= − 42	$\Delta H^\circ = [(-620) + 6(-71)] - [3(-42) + 2(-475)]$
Na_3PO_4	= −475	$= [-620 \quad + (-426)] - [(-126) + \quad (-950)]$
$Pb_3(PO_4)_2(s)$ = −620		$= -1046 - (-1076)$
NaI	= − 71	$= +30 \, kcal$

The reaction (which does not occur to an appreciable extent, by the way) is endothermic; it absorbed heat.

EXAMPLE 24-3

Find the heat of reaction for $C(s) + O_2(g) \rightarrow CO_2(g)$ from this information: ΔH_f° for $CO_2(g)$ is −94 kcal/mole.

Supply yourself mentally with this information: ΔH_f° for any free element, in its standard state (25°C and 1 atm), is zero by convention. Therefore

$$\Delta H^\circ = -94 - (0 + 0) = -94 \, kcal$$

EXAMPLE 24-4

Find ΔH° for this reaction:

$$N_2(g) + 2 \, H_2(g) \rightarrow N_2H_4(l)$$

ΔH_f° for N_2H_4 is +12 kcal/mole.

$$\Delta H^\circ = +12 \, kcal - 0 + 2(0) = +12 \, kcal$$

EXAMPLE 24-5

Find the heat of this reaction:

$$2 \, C_5H_{12}(g) + 16 \, O_2(g) \rightarrow 10 \, CO_2(g) + 12 \, H_2O(l)$$

ΔH_f°, kcal/mole

$C_5H_{12}(g)$ = −35		$\Delta H^\circ = [10(-94) + 12(-68)] - [2(-35) + 16(0)]$
$CO_2(g)$	= −94	$= -1756 - (-70) = -1686 \, kcal = -1700 \, kcal$
$H_2O(l)$	= −68	

One can also use heats of reaction to find heats of formation of various compounds.

EXAMPLE 24-6

Find ΔH_f° for compound D from this information:

$$3 \text{ A} + 2 \text{ B} \rightarrow 4 \text{ C} + 2 \text{ D} \quad \Delta H^{\circ} = -49 \text{ kcal}$$

ΔH_f°, kcal/mole

$$\text{A} = -\ 3$$
$$\text{B} = -12$$
$$\text{C} = +\ 1.5$$

$$\Delta H_{\text{reaction}}^{\circ} = \Sigma \Delta H_{f(\text{products})}^{\circ} - \Sigma \Delta H_{f(\text{reactants})}^{\circ}$$
$$-49 = 4(+1.5) + 2(\Delta H_{f(D)}^{\circ}) - [3(-3) + 2(-12)]$$
$$= +6 + 2(\Delta H_{f(D)}^{\circ}) - [-9 + (-24)]$$
$$= +6 + 2(\Delta H_{f(D)}^{\circ}) + 33$$
$$-2(\Delta H_{f(D)}^{\circ}) = +88$$
$$\Delta H_{f(D)}^{\circ} = -44$$

ΔH_f° for D is -44 kcal/mole.

Naturally no one would use the complicated presentation given here. It was given lest someone make a slip somewhere and not be able to trace his error.

It should be mentioned that the method of handling heats of reaction and calculation of heats of reaction given here is an example of a method rather widely used in chemistry. Entropy and free energy are handled in exactly the same fashion. These are both fascinating topics, but unfortunately this is a book on problem solving, and a discussion of these topics is inappropriate here.

The heat of any one reaction is always the same, whether it takes place in one or several steps. This is a logical consequence of the law of conservation of energy.

EXAMPLE 24-7

$$\text{C(s)} \ + \tfrac{1}{2} O_2(g) \rightarrow CO(g) \ + 26.4 \text{ kcal}$$
$$\underline{CO(g) + \tfrac{1}{2} O_2(g) \rightarrow CO_2(g) + 67.6 \text{ kcal}}$$
$$\text{C(s)} \ + \ \ O_2(g) \rightarrow CO_2(g) + 94.0 \text{ kcal}$$

$$\text{C(s)} \ + \tfrac{1}{2} O_2(g) \rightarrow CO(g) \qquad \Delta H^{\circ} = -26.4 \text{ kcal}$$
$$\underline{CO(g) + \tfrac{1}{2} O_2(g) \rightarrow CO_2(g) \qquad \Delta H^{\circ} = -67.6 \text{ kcal}}$$
$$\text{C(s)} \ + \ \ O_2(g) \rightarrow CO_2(g) \qquad \Delta H^{\circ} = -94.0 \text{ kcal}$$

Note what happened to the $CO(g)$. It seems to be canceled out. These are chemical equations, not mathematical equations, so this is a perfectly legitimate procedure. The carbon monoxide that was produced as the product of one reaction is used up in another reaction. This accounts for its disappearance.

This technique of adding equations—and various values associated with the equations—is a common one. Chemists do this not only for heats of reaction but also for free energy, equilibrium constants, etc., with suitable but essentially simple modifications.

EXAMPLE 24-8

Find the heat of reaction for this equation:

$A + B + C \rightarrow D + F$

using this information:

(a) $A + B \rightarrow E$ $\Delta H = -21$ kcal
(b) $D + F \rightarrow C + E$ $\Delta H = -90$ kcal

If equation (b) were reversed and added to equation (a), one would have the original equation. But if one reverses the equation, one must reverse the sign. If 94,000 cal is liberated when carbon and oxygen react to form carbon dioxide, then 94,000 cal must be supplied when carbon dioxide is decomposed.

$CO_2(g) \rightarrow C(s) + O_2(g)$ $\Delta H = +94,000$ cal

So, reverse equation (b) and the sign, and add the ΔH values to get the ΔH for the new reaction.

(a)	$A + B \rightarrow E$	$\Delta H = -21$ kcal
(b)	$C + E \rightarrow D + F$	$\Delta H = +90$ kcal
reversed		

$A + B + C \rightarrow D + F$ $\Delta H = +69$ kcal

EXAMPLE 24-9

Find the heat of reaction for

$F_2(g) + 2\ HBr(g) \rightarrow Br_2(g) + 2\ HF(g)$

by any combination of appropriate thermochemical equations, using these facts:

ΔH_f° for HBr(g) $= -8.7$ kcal/mole
ΔH_f° for HF(g) $= -64.2$ kcal/mole
ΔH_f° for free elements in their standard state is zero (by convention).

We know that

$$H_2(g) + Br_2(g) \rightarrow 2\ HBr(g) \quad \Delta H^\circ = -\ 17.4\ \text{kcal}$$
$$H_2(g) + F_2(g) \rightarrow 2\ HF(g) \quad \Delta H^\circ = -128.4\ \text{kcal}$$

Now we rearrange these equations to get the equation given at the beginning of the problem.

$$F_2(g) + H_2(g) \rightarrow 2\ HF(g) \qquad\qquad \Delta H^\circ = -128.4\ \text{kcal}$$
$$\underline{2\ HBr(g) \rightarrow H_2(g) + Br_2(g) \qquad\qquad \Delta H^\circ = +\ 17.4\ \text{kcal}} \quad \begin{array}{l}\text{(note sign}\\ \text{reversal)}\end{array}$$
$$F_2(g) + 2\ HBr(g) \rightarrow 2\ HF(g) + Br_2(g) \quad \Delta H^\circ = -111.0\ \text{kcal}$$

PROBLEMS

1. ΔH_f° for HNO_3 is -49 kcal/mole. Is the enthalpy (heat content) of HNO_3 more or less than the enthalpy of the elements from which it is formed?

2. Consider this equation:

   $$AgBr(s) + \tfrac{1}{2} Cl_2 \rightarrow AgCl(s) + \tfrac{1}{2} Br_2 \quad \Delta H = -6.6\ \text{kcal}$$

   Is heat liberated or absorbed in this reaction?

3. Consider this equation:

   $$S(s) + O_2(g) \rightarrow SO_2(g) \quad \Delta H = -71\ \text{kcal}$$

   How much heat is liberated in the burning of 2 moles of sulfur? How much heat is liberated in the burning of 4 g of sulfur?

4. How much carbon must be burned to produce 10 kcal of heat energy by the reaction

   $$C(s) + O_2(g) \rightarrow CO_2(g) \quad \Delta H = -94\ \text{kcal}$$

5. The heat from the combustion of carbon was used to heat water. If 6000 gal of water was taken from $10°C$ to $95°C$, what weight of carbon must have been burned? (Specific heat of water is 1 cal/g-$°C$; density of water is 1 g/ml; 1 gal = 4 qt; 1 liter = 1.06 qt.)

6. How much heat would be required to convert 5000 liters of water at $40°C$ to water vapor at $100°C$? (See problem 5. Heat of vaporization of water is 540 cal/g.)

7. How many grams of carbon would have to be burned to produce the heat required in problem 6?

8. How many tons of coal (presumed to be 40% carbon with no other heat-producing or -absorbing reactions involved) would be required to produce the heat needed in problem 6?

9. Calculate the ΔH for this reaction:

$$H_2S(g) + MnCl_2 \rightarrow MnS(s) + 2 \ HCl$$

Heats of formation for $H_2S(g)$, $MnCl_2$, $MnS(s)$, and HCl are -4.8, -132, -48.8, and -28 kcal/mole, respectively.

10. ΔH_f° for liquid mercury is zero. ΔH_f for gaseous mercury is $+14.5$ kcal/mole. Offer several explanations and interpretations.

11. The heat of reaction for the complete combustion of acetylene (C_2H_2) is -311 kcal:

$$2 \ C_2H_2(g) + 5 \ O_2(g) \rightarrow 4 \ CO_2(g) + 2 \ H_2O(g) \quad \Delta H^\circ = -311 \ kcal$$

Find the heat of formation for acetylene. ΔH_f° for $H_2O(g)$ and $CO_2(g)$ are -58 and -94 kcal/mole, respectively.

12. Calculate the heat of formation for $PCl_5(g)$ from this information:

$$2 \ P(s) + 3 \ Cl_2(g) \rightarrow 2 \ PCl_3(l) \quad \Delta H = -162 \quad kcal$$
$$PCl_3(l) + Cl_2(g) \rightarrow PCl_5(g) \quad \Delta H = -\ 29.7 \ kcal$$

13. 1550 cal is needed to change the temperature of the water and the container for the water (in other words, a calorimeter) by $1°C$. The complete combustion of 1.40 g of ethylene (C_2H_4) caused the temperature to rise by $10.7°C$. Find the heat of combustion for 1 mole of ethylene.

14. Find the ΔH for

$$COCl_2 + 2 \ H_2S(g) \rightarrow 2 \ HCl + H_2O + CS_2$$

given: $2 \ HCl + COS \rightarrow COCl_2 + H_2S(g) \quad \Delta H = +42.9 \ kcal$
$\ COS + H_2S(g) \rightarrow H_2O + CS_2 \quad \Delta H = +\ 3.9 \ kcal$

25

ELECTROCHEMISTRY

Electrochemistry deals with the relationship between electrical energy and chemical energy. Each can be converted into the other under suitable experimental conditions. In solving electrochemistry problems one must know the number of electrons that atoms or ions lose, gain, or share in particular circumstances. Why atoms and ions do these things, and how to predict just what they are likely to do, is a major topic in chemistry. It is adequately introduced in most college level general chemistry books. Since our primary purpose here is problem solving, we will give you the specific chemical facts as needed.

Electricity is said to be a flow of electrons. This is a grossly inadequate description, but it will have to do now. One could measure a quantity of water by means other than buckets, etc. One could put a stick into a river with a uniform flow rate and see how long it took to reach a certain point a known distance away. If one knew the depth and breadth of the river and what the uniform flow rate was, one could rather easily calculate the volume of water flowing past a certain point at a given time. One doesn't actually have to measure the water itself. Something of this sort is done in electricity. Rather than count the actual number of electrons themselves, other means are found to measure quantities of electricity.

A coulomb is a quantity of electricity; it is an ampere-second. If 1 amp flows for 1 sec, if 100 amp flows for 0.01 sec, or if 0.01 amp flows for 100 sec, etc., 1 amp-sec or 1 coulomb of electricity has been involved. The charge on an electron (symbol: e^-) is 1.602×10^{-19} coulomb (or amp-sec). A mole of electrons would have a charge of 96,500 coulombs.

$$\frac{1.602 \times 10^{-19} \text{ coulomb} \times 6.023 \times 10^{23} \, e^-}{\text{mole}} = 96,500 \text{ coulombs mole}^{-1}$$

This same quantity of electricity is also known as a faraday. Obviously, 1 faraday is the electrical charge on 1 mole of electrons.

1 faraday = 96,500 coulombs
= 96,500 amp-sec
= 1 mole e^-

EXAMPLE 25-1

a. How many faradays of electricity are there in 3.0×10^{14} electrons?

$$\frac{3.0 \times 10^{14} \, e^-}{6.023 \times 10^{23} \, e^- \text{ faraday}^{-1}} = 5.0 \times 10^{-10} \text{ faraday}$$

b. How many coulombs?

1 faraday = 96,500 coulombs

so $\dfrac{5.0 \times 10^{-10} \text{ faraday} \times 96,500 \text{ coulombs}}{\text{faraday}} = 4.8 \times 10^{-5} \text{ coulomb}$

c. How many ampere-seconds?

1 coulomb = 1 amp-sec

So there would be 4.8×10^{-5} amp-sec.

EXAMPLE 25-2

a. How long would a 5.0-amp current have to flow to deliver 193,000 coulombs?

$$\frac{193,000 \text{ coulombs} \times 1 \text{ amp-sec}}{\text{coulomb} \times 5.0 \text{ amp}} = 3.9 \times 10^4 \text{ sec}$$

b. What strength current must be used to deliver 193,000 coulombs in exactly 10 hr?

$$\frac{193,000 \text{ coulombs} \times 1 \text{ amp-sec}}{\text{coulomb} \times 10 \text{ hr} \times 3600 \text{ sec hr}^{-1}} = 5.36 \text{ amp}$$

c. How long would a 5.0-amp current have to flow to deliver 2.0 faradays?

$$\frac{2.0 \text{ faradays} \times 96,500 \text{ coulombs} \times 1 \text{ amp-sec}}{\text{faraday} \qquad \text{coulomb} \times 5.0 \text{ amp}} = 3.9 \times 10^4 \text{ sec}$$

EXAMPLE 25-3

a. How many faradays would be needed to turn 1 mole of sodium ions (Na^+) into sodium atoms under suitable conditions?

Fact: Each sodium ion has to gain 1 electron to become a sodium atom.

A mole of sodium ions needs 6.023×10^{23} e^-, the number of electrons in 1 faraday.

b. How many faradays would be needed to turn 1 mole of magnesium ions (Mg^{++}) into magnesium atoms under suitable conditions?

Fact: Each magnesium ion needs 2 e^- to become an atom.

$$\frac{1 \text{ mole } Mg^{++} \times 2 \text{ moles } e^- \times 1 \text{ faraday}}{\text{mole } Mg^{++} \qquad \text{mole } e^-} = 2 \text{ faradays}$$

c. How many faradays would be needed to turn 1 mole of aluminum ions (Al^{+++}) into aluminum atoms under suitable conditions?

Fact: Each aluminum ion needs 3 e^- to become an atom.

So 1 mole of aluminum ions needs 3 moles of electrons or 3 faradays.

EXAMPLE 25-4

What weight of sodium could 1 faraday deposit from a suitable sodium-ion (Na^+) source under suitable experimental conditions? What weight of magnesium from magnesium ions (Mg^{++})? What weight of aluminum from aluminum ions (Al^{+++})? The atomic weights of sodium, magnesium, and aluminum are 23, 24, and 27, respectively.

Since 1 faraday is 1 mole of electrons, and 1 mole of sodium needs 1 mole of electrons, 1 mole of magnesium needs 2 moles of electrons, and 1 mole of aluminum needs 3 moles of electrons, 1 faraday will deposit 1 mole of sodium, 0.5 mole of magnesium, and 0.33 mole of aluminum.

$$\frac{1 \text{ faraday} \times 1 \text{ mole } e^- \times 23 \text{ g Na}}{\text{faraday} \qquad \text{mole } e^-} = 23 \text{ g Na}$$

$$\frac{1 \text{ faraday} \times 1 \text{ mole } e^- \times 24 \text{ g Mg}}{\text{faraday} \qquad 2 \text{ moles } e^-} = 12 \text{ g Mg}$$

$$\frac{1 \text{ faraday} \times 1 \text{ mole } e^- \times 27 \text{ g Al}}{\text{faraday} \qquad 3 \text{ moles } e^-} = 9 \text{ g Al}$$

In terms of quantity of electricity required to produce them under appro-

priate experimental conditions it would seem that
1 mole of sodium is equivalent to 0.5 mole of magnesium, which in turn is equivalent to 0.33 mole of aluminum, and 23 g of sodium is equivalent to 12 g of magnesium, which in turn is equivalent to 9 g of aluminum.

EXAMPLE 25-5

How many faradays would be required to plate out (deposit) 81 g of aluminum metal from a suitable aluminum-ion source under suitable conditions?

Each aluminum ion needs to gain 3 e^- to become an aluminum atom. Therefore

$$\frac{81 \text{ g}}{27 \text{ g mole}^{-1}} \times \frac{3 \text{ moles } e^-}{\text{mole Al}} \times \frac{1 \text{ faraday}}{\text{mole } e^-} = 9 \text{ faradays}$$

EXAMPLE 25-6

How many grams of aluminum could 2.0 amp flowing exactly 90 min through a suitable aluminum-ion source produce?

$$\frac{2.0 \text{ amp} \times 90 \text{ min} \times 60 \text{ sec} \times 27 \text{ g}}{96,500 \frac{\text{amp-sec}}{\text{mole } e^-} \quad \text{min} \quad 3 \text{ moles } e^-} = 1.0 \text{ g}$$

EXAMPLE 25-7

How many hours must a 2.0-amp current run through molten sodium chloride to produce 1.0×10^4 liters (STP) of Cl_2 gas?

Fact: Each chloride ion (Cl^-) must lose 1 e^- to become an atom; each molecule of Cl_2 gas consists of two Cl atoms.

$$\frac{1.0 \times 10^4 \text{ liters} \times 2 \text{ moles Cl} \times 1 \text{ mole } e^- \times 96,500 \text{ amp-sec}}{22.4 \frac{\text{liters}}{\text{mole}} \quad \text{mole } Cl_2 \quad \text{mole Cl} \quad \text{mole } e^- \times 2.0 \text{ amp} \times 3600 \frac{\text{sec}}{\text{hr}}}$$
$$= 1.2 \times 10^4 \text{ hr}$$

PROBLEMS

1. How many faradays were involved when 15 amp ran for 25 hr?

2. How many moles of calcium ions could be plated out under suitable experimental conditions by 5 amp running 4 hr? (Each calcium ion must gain 2 e^-; see Table 16-1, page 206 for atomic weights.)

3. What weight of oxygen would be produced in the electrolysis of water by a 2-amp current running 40 hr? (Each oxygen ion must give up 2 e^- to become an oxygen atom. Oxygen atoms pair to become O_2.)

4. What volume at STP would the oxygen produced in problem 3 occupy?

5. What weight of copper (from a suitable cupric-ion source under suitable conditions) could be plated out by a 5-amp current running 10 hr? (Each cupric ion must gain 2 e^-.)

6. How many faradays would be needed to produce 150 g of copper from a cupric sulfate ($CuSO_4$) solution under suitable conditions? (Each cupric ion must gain 2 e^-.)

7. How long must 2-amp current run to accomplish the plating of 150 g of copper in problem 7?

26

RATES

Everyone is familiar with the fact that different "things" occur at different rates. Some children grow slowly and others seem to grow all at once. Some plants take centuries to grow (or almost), while bamboo seems almost to grow before one's eyes. Wood burns faster in pure oxygen than in air. One can also imagine that different amounts of "things" can affect rates. Which would cook a roast sooner, an oven at 200°F or an oven at 450°F? One can also readily imagine that something could be necessary for a reaction but not involved in the rate of the reaction. Certainly children need oxygen to live and thus indirectly to grow. However, within limits, more or less oxygen would not affect the rate of growth.

How does one determine what affects the rate of a reaction or the rate at which an event occurs? The following ridiculous example is presented in an attempt to put this across. Consider the so-called data in Table 26-1. See whether you can determine which factors affected the rate and in what manner they did so. Express this in symbol form.

$r \propto$ something

where r stands for rate. Then check your rate law with the one we have given on page 281. Worry the data. Try to find some sort of relationship. Don't be discouraged if you are somewhat wrong at first. Students find difficulty with this for some reason.

Now look at lines 1 and 2 in Table 26-1. Evidently all of the necessary "things" are not present in line 1, since no children entered the building. Evidently there must be at least one little old lady in the schoolyard.

Table 26-1

	Factor A	Factor B	Factor C	"Reaction" rate
	Number of teachers on duty in schoolyard	Number of little old ladies with umbrellas on duty in schoolyard	Number of open doors	Number of children entering the building per minute
1.	40	0	1	0
2.	40	1	1	3
3.	80	1	1	3
4.	160	1	1	3
5.	40	1	2	6
6.	40	1	3	9
7.	80	1	2	6
8.	40	2	1	12
9.	40	3	1	27
10.	80	2	1	12
11.	0	1	1	0
12.	0	10	20	0

Look next at line 3 and compare it to line 2. In 3 all conditions are the same as 2 except that the number of teachers was doubled. You would automatically know that the rate was independent of the number of teachers. You might think that they were not necessary for the reaction, the reaction here being the entry of the children into the building. Look at line 11. This says they are necessary for the reaction, whereas line 3 says they do not affect the rate. Line 4 should help confirm the idea that the number of teachers, that is, factor A, does not affect the rate.

Look at line 5. Compare it to 2. Factor C was doubled and the rate doubled. This would lead you to think that there was a simple, direct relationship between the number of open doors (factor C) and the rate at which the children entered the building. Look at line 6 and compare it to line 2. A tripling of factor C caused a tripling of the rate. This tends to confirm your original idea of a simple relationship, a one-to-one proportion, as it were.

Compare lines 8 and 2. You have doubled factor B, but what has happened to the rate? What relationship is there between 3 and 12? $3 \times 4 = 12$ and $3 \times 2^2 = 12$. You have doubled factor B. Could it be that the rate would go up by 2^2? Now look at line 9 and compare it to line 2. You tripled B and the rate went up to 27. What relationship is there between 3 and 27? Well, $27 = 3 \times 9$; $9 = 3^2$. Could it be that the rate would go up by 3^2? Suppose you quadrupled B. What would the rate be? If we are to judge by what we have here, wouldn't it have to be 3×4^2 or 48? There are other ways of thinking of this. A number of books explain relationships such as those in 2 and 8 and in 2 and 9 in this fashion: 3 doubly doubled is 12; 3 triply tripled is 27. The author does not care for this approach, but many students understand it better than her approach. In any event, it would seem that the rate would be proportional to the square of the number of little old ladies with umbrellas.

Summary: rate independent of A
rate directly proportional to C
rate directly proportional to the square of B

therefore $r \propto B^2C$
and rate law is $R = kB^2C$

where r is the rate and k is a proportionality constant.

EXAMPLE 26-1

Consider the information in Table 26-2 and then find the rate law and the rate constant based on this limited set of data. ([KI] and [H_2O_2] stand for concentration of potassium iodide and concentration of hydrogen peroxide, respectively.)

Table 26-2

Trial	[KI], mole/liter	[H_2O_2], mole/liter	O_2 formed, ml/min
1	0.10	0.05	10
2	0.20	0.05	10
3	0.10	0.10	20
4	0.00	0.05	0
5	0.10	0.00	0
6	0.20	0.10	20
7	0.10	0.20	40

According to trials 4 and 5, both hydrogen peroxide and potassium iodide are necessary for the reaction, but only hydrogen peroxide (according to trials 2 and 6) affects the rate. According to trials 3, 6, and 7, hydrogen peroxide concentration affects the rate directly: doubling the concentration doubles the rate, quadrupling the concentration quadruples the rate.

Therefore rate $= k[H_2O_2]$

Now could we find k? We know that

$$k = \frac{\text{rate}}{[H_2O_2]}$$

For trial 3 this would be

$$k = \frac{20 \text{ ml}}{\text{min} \times 0.10 \dfrac{\text{mole}}{\text{liter}}}$$

or $\;k = \dfrac{200}{\text{min}} \dfrac{\text{ml}}{} \times \dfrac{\text{liters}}{\text{moles}}$

Checked by finding the rate in trial 7

rate $= k \, [\text{H}_2\text{O}_2]$

$$= \frac{200}{\text{min}} \dfrac{\text{ml}}{} \times \dfrac{\text{liters}}{\text{moles}} \times 0.20 \dfrac{\text{mole}}{\text{liter}}$$

$= 40 \text{ ml/min}$

PROBLEMS

1. Develop a rate law from the following data:

Pressure, atm		Rate at which product G is formed, ml/min
Factor E	Factor F	
1	1	200
2	1	200
1	2	400
2	3	600

2. Develop a rate law for the data below and then find the rate at which K would be produced when H = 2, I = 2, and J = 2.

Concentration, mole/liter			K produced, ml/sec
H	I	J	
1	1	1	3
2	1	1	12
1	2	1	3
1	1	2	6

3. The rate law for a certain reaction is

$r = k[\text{L}] [\text{M}]$

When [L] was 1 M and [M] was 1 M, the rate of product formation was 7 ml/sec. What would the rate of product formation be if [L] was 10 M and [M] was 0.5 M?

27

EQUILIBRIUM

Equilibrium is such an interesting, useful, and really easy subject once one understands it. In fact, many who understand it cannot see how anyone could fail to understand it when it is properly explained. Somehow or other generation after generation of bright students in chemistry fail to understand equilibrium. Something about it just fails to penetrate the mind of the student. We propose to give some rather ridiculous examples in an effort to find the right track in the mind. Bear with us.

Consider a gymnasium in which an event of some sort is to be given. Suppose the Fire Department regulations specified that the ratio of people in the gym itself to those in the lobby of the building must be 5:1. Let's disregard the fact that no reasonable fire department would make this ruling.

Suppose 2000 people converged on the building and entered it. In complying with Fire Department regulations, how many people would there have to be inside the gym and how many people would there have to be in the lobby?

Let x = the number of people in the lobby
then $2000 - x$ = number of people in the gym itself

Now by Fire Department regulations

$$\frac{\text{number of people in gym}}{\text{number of people in lobby}} = \frac{5}{1}$$

so $\dfrac{2000 - x}{x} = \dfrac{5}{1}$

$$2000 - x = 5x$$
$$x = 333$$

Therefore the number of people in the lobby is 333, and the number of people in the gymnasium is 1667. Since

$$\frac{1667}{333} = \frac{5}{1}$$

the Fire Department condition is satisfied.

You could, of course, have solved this in other ways. For example,

Let y = the number of people in the gymnasium itself
$2000 - y$ = the number of people in the lobby

therefore $\dfrac{y}{2000 - y} = \dfrac{5}{1}$

$y = 1667$ = the number of people in the gymnasium

$2000 - y = 333$ — the number of people in the lobby

The ratio is still 1667/333 or 5/1.

Now suppose that the Fire Department made a further regulation that there must be a constant interchange of people between the lobby and the gymnasium, perhaps to prevent anyone from having sufficient time to build a bonfire. But the Fire Department also insists that the previously mentioned ratio of 5:1 be maintained while this interchange of people between lobby and gymnasium is taking place.

How could this be done?

This could easily be done if the *rate* at which people left the gym to enter the lobby was *exactly equal* to the *rate* at which people left the lobby to enter the gym. What the rates were would be immaterial to anyone except the Fire Department, but the rates would have to be the *same* if the ratio dictated by the Fire Department were to be maintained.

Now suppose that 1000 people suddenly entered the lobby from the outside. There already was a total of 2000 people in the whole building. The influx of 1000 people would radically change the ratio when they enter the lobby. However, according to the Fire Department, a ratio of 5:1 must be maintained or re-established, and the constant interchange of people between lobby and gym must be maintained. What must happen? There must be a shifting of people to re-establish the ratio. *For a while* more people must enter than leave the gym until the 5:1 ratio is re-established. Once the ratio is re-established, the rates of entering and leaving the gym and entering and leaving the lobby would have to be the same.

Of the 1000 people mentioned above, how many of these at a given instant would be in the gymnasium itself? How many people altogether would be in the gym at a given instant?

Let x = number out of the new 1000 who would remain in the lobby at a
        given instant

$1000 - x$ = number of the 1000 who would be in the gym at a given instant

But remember there were originally 1667 in the gym at a given instant and 333 in the lobby.

So now

$$\frac{1667 + (1000 - x)}{333 + x} = \frac{5}{1}$$

$$2667 - x = 1665 + 5x$$

$$x = 167$$

167 more people would be in the lobby at a given instant, making a total of $(333 + 167)$ or 500 people. $(1000 - 167)$ or 833 more people would be in the gym at a given instant, making a total of $(1667 + 833)$ or 2500. Does this maintain the ratio? Yes, as you can readily see.

$$\frac{2500}{500} = \frac{5}{1}$$

You should be able to think of a number of easier ways in which this problem could have been done. We're putting in the foundation needed for later work on equilibrium problems. So, bear with a little more of this apparently roundabout approach.

Now, having happily established an equilibrium involving 2500 people in the gym and 500 in the lobby, suppose 200 people were suddenly ejected from the lobby. Again, suppose that the constant motion and the 5:1 ratio mandates of the Fire Department had to be heeded. What must happen? The ratio has been upset. Consequently, for a while more people would have to leave the gym to enter the lobby than were leaving the lobby to enter the gym. In the end, how many people at a given instant would be in the gym and how many in the lobby?

At the instant before adjustment occurred, there were 2500 people in the gym.

At the instant before adjustment occurred, there were $(500 - 200)$ people in the lobby.

You have decided that some extra people must move from the gym to the lobby, that is, some number over and above the number entering and leaving to satisfy the Fire Department antibonfire mandates.

Let x = the number of people who must leave the gym to enter the lobby

Then

$$\frac{2500 - x}{(500 - 200) + x} = \frac{5}{1}$$

$$\frac{2500 - x}{300 + x} = \frac{5}{1}$$

$$x = 167$$

Now the number at any given instant in the gym is 2500 − 167 or 2333, and the new number at any given instant in the lobby is 300 + 167 or 467.

$$\text{ratio} = \frac{2333}{467} = \frac{5}{1}$$

When you look at any of these problems you find them simple. You could really have done any of these yourself. In fact, they are so simple that you see no point in doing them. Well, problems in equilibrium are just as simple as this. In the foregoing cases you had an equilibrium, a dynamic equilibrium. Everything would *seem* to be the same. You had a certain number outside the gym in the lobby and a certain number inside the gym in a given system, but you had a constant interchange in this constant system.

Now let's apply some of this to chemical equilibrium. There are quite literally millions of equilibrium conditions involving elements and compounds. In an equilibrium there is a constant conversion of reactants to products, accompanied by a constant conversion of products back to reactants at *exactly the same rate* once equilibrium has been established.

Consequently, at equilibrium,

$$\frac{[\text{products}]}{[\text{reactants}]} = \text{a constant   (symbol: } K)$$

Both products and reactants are expressed in moles per liter. If only gases are involved, then products and reactants may be expressed in pressure units. Pressure is obviously directly related to the number of moles, thereby making the constant the same no matter whether molarity or pressure units were used.

The constants for chemical equilibria are traditionally expressed without units. This causes no confusion because everything would be expressed in the same units. Do not confuse K, the equilibrium constant (really a ratio which happens to have a constant value at a given temperature), with k, the proportionality constant that has been discussed at various times in this book. The effect of temperature on equilibrium constants will be taken later in the chapter.

Why isn't the constant just the opposite? No reason why not. However, it would be confusing in the extreme to have to specify the type of ratio to which one was referring, so [products]/[reactants] *for the equation as written* is universally used in chemistry merely to prevent confusion.

EXAMPLE 27–1

Consider this equation: $\overline{A} \rightleftharpoons \overline{B}$

⇌ is an equilibrium symbol. It means here that the rate at which A forms B is *exactly equal* to the rate at which B forms A. Here A and B stand for some gaseous elements or compounds. It is immaterial which compounds or elements are actually involved. Suppose that *at equilibrium* there were, in a liter container, 100 moles of B and 1 mole of A. Find the equilibrium constant.

$$[B] = \frac{100 \text{ moles}}{1 \text{ liter}} = 100 \, M \qquad [A] = \frac{1 \text{ mole}}{1 \text{ liter}} = 1 \, M$$

At any given instant, since the mixture would be at equilibrium, analysis of the mixture would show [B] to be 100 M and [A] to be 1 M, but at the same time A would be producing B at *exactly the same* rate at which B was regenerating A.

Now solve the problem:

$$K = \frac{[B]}{[A]} = \frac{100}{1} = 100$$

The equilibrium constant is 100. The figures 100/1 are merely the figures from which the constant was obtained. They correspond to the 5:1 ratio in the Fire Department problem.

The equilibrium expression is $\dfrac{[B]}{[A]}$

Reconsider this equilibrium:

$$\overline{A} \rightleftharpoons \overline{B} \qquad K = \frac{[B]}{[A]} = 100$$

At equilibrium the rate at which A reacts to form B is exactly the same as the rate at which B reacts to form A. Suppose more B were added to the system; the value for [B]/[A] would be greater than 100. To restore equilibrium the rate at which A was formed would temporarily have to be greater than the rate at which B was formed. As soon as the value for [B]/[A] was again 100 the rates would again be equal. In other words, the system would restore equilibrium by changing the composition of the members of the equilibrium. This change is known as *shifting* the equilibrium. Here more reactants were formed, so the equilibrium is said to have been shifted to the left.

What would happen if B were removed from the system? The equilibrium would shift to the right by forming more B to restore the equilibrium ratio of [B]/[A] = 100. Similarly, addition of A would shift the equilibrium to the right, removal would shift it to the left. In all cases, unless temperature were changed, the equilibrium constant would necessarily be the same once equilibrium was restored. The effect of temperature on equilibrium constants is discussed later in the chapter.

For the equilibrium

$$\overline{C} + \overline{D} \rightleftharpoons \overline{E} + \overline{F}$$

the equilibrium expression is

$$K = \frac{[E][F]}{[C][D]}$$

Why the constant involves $[E][F]$ and $[C][D]$ will have to be left to the chemists, much as the author hates to have students take anything of this sort "on faith." Consult the discussion of the law of mass action in chemistry textbooks for reasons for the form of the constant.

Now suppose that C and D were the same thing. The equation then would be

$$\overline{C} + \overline{C} \rightleftharpoons \overline{E} + \overline{F} \qquad K = \frac{[E][F]}{[C][C]}$$

Couldn't this be written

$$2\,\overline{C} \rightleftharpoons \overline{E} + \overline{F} \qquad K = \frac{[E][F]}{[C]^2}$$

EXAMPLE 27–2

Write equilibrium expressions for each of the following reactions.* Do not look at the solutions until you have tried your hand at these.

a. $2\,\overline{CHCl_3} + \overline{N_2O_4} \rightleftharpoons 2\,\overline{COCl_2} + 2\,\overline{HCl} + 2\,\overline{NO}$

b. $4\,\overline{CHCl_3} + \overline{N_2O_4} \rightleftharpoons 4\,\overline{COCl_2} + 4\,\overline{HCl} + \overline{N_2}$

c. $\overline{CHCl_3} + \overline{N_2O_4} \rightleftharpoons \overline{CO_2} + \overline{HCl} + 2\,\overline{NOCl}$

d. $\overline{N_2} + 3\,\overline{H_2} \rightleftharpoons 2\,\overline{NH_3}$

Did you get these?

a. $K = \dfrac{[COCl_2]^2\,[HCl]^2\,[NO_2]^2}{[CHCl_3]^2\,[N_2O_4]}$

b. $K = \dfrac{[COCl_2]^4\,[HCl]^4\,[N_2]}{[CHCl_3]^4\,[N_2O_4]}$

---

*Reactions a, b, and c are from *Chemical and Engineering News*, Dec. 21, 1964, p. 4, letter from Sidney W. Benson. These equations can, incidentally, easily represent explosions as well as equilibria, depending on conditions.

c. $K = \dfrac{[CO_2]\,[HCl]\,[NOCl]^2}{[CHCl_3]\,[N_2O_4]}$

d. $K = \dfrac{[NH_3]^2}{[N_2]\,[H_2]^3}$

EXAMPLE 27-3

Consider this equilibrium:

$$\overline{A} + \overline{B} \rightleftharpoons \overline{C} + \overline{D}$$

a. Write the equilibrium expression and then find the constant from the following data.

Trial	[A], moles/liter	[B], moles/liter	[C], moles/liter	[D], moles/liter
1	0.5	2	2	50
2	1	1	10	10
3	0.01	200	3	66.7

$$K = \dfrac{[C]\,[D]}{[A]\,[B]}$$

Trial 1: $K = \dfrac{50 \times 2}{0.5 \times 2} = 100$

Trial 2: $K = \dfrac{10 \times 10}{1 \times 1} = 100$

Trial 3: $K = \dfrac{3 \times 66.7}{0.01 \times 200} = 100$

It is probably obvious that *at equilibrium* the constant for this particular reaction must be 100, but that there can be a rather wide variety of actual concentrations.

b. Find the concentration of D if [A], [B], and [C] are each 1 M ($K = 100$).

$$100 = \dfrac{[C]\,[D]}{[A]\,[B]} = \dfrac{1 \times [D]}{1 \times 1}$$
$$[D] = 100\ M$$

Where did the M for this obviously fantastically high molarity come from? K is composed of molarities; here you had molarities for the other figures.

c. Given [B] = 3 M, [C] = 4 M, and [D] = 5 M, find [A].

Did you get 0.067 M?

EXAMPLE 27–4

Consider this equilibrium:

$\overline{E} + \overline{F} \rightleftharpoons \overline{G} + \overline{H}$

At equilibrium the partial pressures of E, F, G, and H were 0.020, 0.225, 0.250, and 0.450 atm, respectively. Find the equilibrium constant.

$$K = \frac{0.250 \times 0.450}{0.020 \times 0.225} = 25$$

EXAMPLE 27–5

Now, again using the equilibrium in Example 27–3,

$\overline{A} + \overline{B} \rightleftharpoons \overline{C} + \overline{D}$ $K = 100$

suppose that 10 moles of A and 10 moles of B were put in a 1-liter container. Suppose that they reacted to form C and D and that equilibrium was reached. Find the concentration of each member of the equilibrium —that is, [A], [B], [C], and [D] at equilibrium.

You don't know how to do this? You really do, you know. Ask yourself some questions first.

1. For every mole of A that reacted according to the equation given, how many moles of B would have to react?
2. For every mole of A that reacted, how many moles of C would be formed?
3. For every mole of A that reacted, how many moles of D would be formed?

The answer to all three questions is 1.

4. Does the equilibrium constant have to hold? Yes.
5. What is the equilibrium constant? 100.
6. What is the equilibrium expression?

$$\frac{[C]\,[D]}{[A]\,[B]}$$

It would seem, from the questions posed and answered here, that this problem could be solved if you knew how much A reacted. Try this.

Let x = the amount of A that reacted (this is really moles/liter of A)

Then x = amount of B that reacted, moles/liter
and x = amount of C that formed, moles/liter
     x = amount of D that formed, moles/liter

What would be the equilibrium concentrations under these conditions?

$[A] = 10 - x$ (10 moles per liter is 10 *M*)
$[B] = 10 - x$
$[C] = x$
$[D] = x$

So $K = \dfrac{[C]\,[D]}{[A]\,[B]}$

$100 = \dfrac{(x)(x)}{(10 - x)(10 - x)}$

Now all you would have to do would be to solve for x and then in two cases do a bit of subtraction to find the equilibrium concentrations of A, B, C, and D. We won't stop for the actual mechanics of the algebraic solution at the moment. We want setups now. Other problems will have complete solutions. See the algebra section of Chapter 4 if necessary.

Be sure you see the difference between Examples 27–3 and 27–5. In Example 27–3 you were given concentrations for existing equilibrium mixtures. In Example 27–5 you were given the concentrations of reactants that would react to form an equilibrium mixture.

EXAMPLE 27–6

Now suppose that 10 moles of C and 10 moles of D were put into a 1-liter box. The equilibrium constant and equation for the equilibrium are still the same as those given in Example 27–3. What would happen? C and D would have to form A and B, thereby decreasing the amount of C and D.

For every C that reacted, how many D would have to react? 1
                                    how many A would be produced? 1
                                    how many B would be produced? 1

Let x = the amount of C that reacted, moles/liter
     x = the amount of D that reacted, moles/liter
     x = the amount of A formed, moles/liter
     x = the amount of B formed, moles/liter

At equilibrium

$[C] = 10 - x$
$[D] = 10 - x$
$[A] = x$
$[B] = x$

So $K = \dfrac{[C]\,[D]}{[A]\,[B]}$ and $100 = \dfrac{(10-x)^2}{x^2}$

Again, after solving for x and doing a bit of subtracting, one would know [A], [B], [C], and [D] at equilibrium *for this reaction*.

EXAMPLE 27-7

Now suppose that 10 moles of A, 10 moles of B, 10 moles of C and 10 moles of D were put into a 1-liter container and allowed to come to equilibrium—again, the equilibrium given in Example 27–3. Find the concentrations of A, B, C, and D at equilibrium.

Ask yourself some questions again. Will there be any change? If so, in which direction? In other words, is there too much or too little A and B, or too much or too little C and D? To find out see how far from reaching the constant you are at present.

$$\dfrac{[C]\,[D]}{[A]\,[B]} = 100 \qquad \dfrac{(10)(10)}{(10)(10)} = 1 \quad \text{(far below 100)}$$

You need far more in the numerator and far less in the denominator to reach $K = 100$. How would you get more in the numerator and less in the denominator? Reaction of some A and B to form more C and D would do just this.

Let x = the amount of A that reacts to form C and D, moles/liter
x = the amount of B that reacts to form C and D, moles/liter
x = the amount of C newly formed, moles/liter
x = the amount of D newly formed, moles/liter

At equilibrium [A] = 10 − x (10 moles/liter is the original molarity)
[B] = 10 − x
[C] = 10 + x
[D] = 10 + x

$$K = \dfrac{[C]\,[D]}{[A]\,[B]} = 100 = \dfrac{(10+x)^2}{(10-x)^2}$$

Once x is found (see algebra section of Chapter 4 if necessary), addition and subtraction, as indicated, will give the equilibrium concentrations.

EXAMPLE 27-8

Suppose that the 10 moles of A, 10 moles of B, 10 moles of C, and 10 moles of D were put in a 2-liter container. In what way would solution of the problem differ?

In all of these problems molarities were used. When the volume of the container is 1 liter, the number of moles and the molarity are numerically the same. We chose liter containers to make problems easier. However, when a volume other than 1 liter is involved, using the number of moles will produce errors, since the number of moles and molarity would not be the same numerically. *One must use molarity.* Here one would use

$$\frac{10 \text{ moles}}{2 \text{ liters}} = 5 \ M$$

and then solve the problem in exactly the same fashion:

$$100 = \frac{(5 + x)^2}{(5 - x)^2}$$
$$\text{etc.}$$

EXAMPLE 27-9

Consider this equilibrium:

$$2 \ \overline{NO_2} \rightleftharpoons \overline{N_2O_4} \quad K = 0.04 \quad \text{(imaginary value)}$$

Find the concentrations of NO_2 and N_2O_4 at equilibrium after 4 moles of NO_2 had been injected into a 2-liter flask.

First change the moles to molarity: 4 moles/2 liters = 2 M. For every mole of NO_2 that reacted, how many moles of N_2O_4 would be formed? Half as many.

So let x = amount of NO_2 that reacted, moles per liter
   $0.5 \ x$ = amount of N_2O_4 formed, moles per liter

At equilibrium $[NO_2]$ $= 2 - x$
        $[N_2O_4] = 0.5 \ x$

So $0.04 = \dfrac{[N_2O_4]}{[NO_2]^2}$ $0.04 = \dfrac{0.5 \ x}{(2 - x)^2}$

Once one knew x here, one could easily find $(2 - x)$ and then have all the concentrations needed. This involves a quadratic equation (see page 297). We'll actually solve a few of these later. At the moment we want to focus attention on the setups.

EXAMPLE 27-10

Consider this equilibrium:

$$\overline{A} + 2 \ \overline{B} \rightleftharpoons 3 \ \overline{C} + \overline{D} \quad K = 9$$

Write the equilibrium expression.

$$K = \frac{[C]^3 \, [D]}{[A] \, [B]^2} = 9$$

Suppose 5 moles of A and 3 moles of B were put into a 4-liter container. Find the concentrations of A, B, C, and D at equilibrium.

Change to molarity. This need not be done first, but before you put anything into the equilibrium expression it must be in molarity. Both C and D would have to form, thereby decreasing the concentrations of A and B.

1. For every mole of A that reacted, how many moles of B would have to react? 2.
2. For every mole of A that reacted, how many moles of C would have to be formed? 3.
3. For every mole of A that reacted, how many moles of D would have to be formed? 1.

Let x = the amount of A that reacts, moles/liter
  $2x$ = the amount of B that reacts, moles/liter
  $3x$ = the amount of C that forms, moles/liter
  x = the amount of D that forms, moles/liter

At equilibrium

$[A] = 1.25 - x$ (5 moles/4 liters = 1.25 M)
$[B] = 0.75 - 2x$ (3 moles/4 liters = 0.75 M)
$[C] = 3x$
$[D] = x$

Therefore $9 = \dfrac{(3x)^3 \, (x)}{(1.25 - x)(0.75 - 2x)^2}$

We refuse to attempt to solve this without having a reason for wanting the answer. Solving it now is purely a mathematical exercise.

What would happen to a system in equilibrium if the temperature were changed? You don't know perhaps. Let's look at an equilibrium with which you are familiar.

a. ice + heat $\rightleftharpoons$ water

This describes an equilibrium condition in which 0°C water is in equilibrium with 0°ice. You know that if you heated this system ice would melt and water would be formed. The water has a greater enthalpy or heat content. When heat is added to the system it sends the system to the form that can absorb heat, the form with the greater heat content.

Now let's describe the equilibrium the opposite way.

b.   water $\rightleftharpoons$ ice + heat

or water $\rightleftharpoons$ ice $\Delta H = -$

Now if this mixture is heated, *considering the equation as written* in b, in what direction would the equilibrium shift? You know more water would form, so the equilibrium would go left as written. You know that the side that absorbs heat (here the water side) would be the side to which the equilibrium would be shifted.

The word *shift* as just used above causes some difficulty. We have previously used this word with reference to equilibria disturbed by the addition or removal of one or more members of the equilibrium. Here, however, no member of the equilibrium is either added or removed. The actual ratio of products to reactants is changed and cannot be restored unless the temperature is restored to its original value. The constant would be different. So *it is important to remember that the constant is constant only at constant temperature.* A change in temperature can cause a change in the constant itself. Nothing else you will encounter will change the equilibrium constant itself. It is obviously necessary to know the temperature at which equilibrium constants were determined.

Now let's do a problem to illustrate this.

EXAMPLE 27–11

Consider this equilibrium:

$\overline{A} \rightleftharpoons \overline{B} + 10,000$ cal

or $\overline{A} \rightleftharpoons \overline{B}$ $\Delta H = -10,000$ cal (-10 kcal)

What would happen to the equilibrium if the mixture were heated? Do this by analogy to the ice-water system. There is nothing unrespectable about doing this. This is exactly analogous to the condition in equation b. If the system were heated, more A would form. This could also be solved by thinking of it thermodynamically. When B is formed, heat is liberated. Obviously, when A is formed, heat is absorbed. To absorb the heat the equilibrium would shift to the left, forming more A.

EXAMPLE 27–12

Reconsider the equilibrium given in Example 27–10. The same constant holds. Suppose that 7 moles of A, 6 moles of B, 4 moles of C, and 2 moles of D were allowed to come to equilibrium in a 9-liter box. Find the concentration of each member of the equilibrium (that is, [A], [B], [C], and [D]) at equilibrium.

First, change to molarity. Did you get 0.78, 0.67, 0.44, and 0.22 M for [A], [B], [C], and [D], respectively?

Now $K = \dfrac{[C]^3[D]}{[A][B]^2} = 9$

but $\dfrac{(0.44)^3 (0.22)}{(0.78) (0.67)^2} = $ about 0.05

Therefore there must be a reaction. The numerator must increase and the denominator must decrease in approaching 9. This seems to mean that more C and D would have to form at the expense of A and B.

For every C formed one would get 1/3 as much as D. Halt! This approach becomes awkward. Let's try D. For every new D one would get 3 times as much C. That's better. So

Let x = the amount of D newly formed, moles/liter
   $3x$ = the amount of C newly formed, moles/liter

Now for every D formed 2 B must have reacted with 1 A. So

x = the amount of A used to form the products, moles/liter
$2x$ = the amount of B used to form the products, moles/liter

At equilibrium the concentrations would be

$[A] = 0.78 - x$
$[B] = 0.67 - 2x$
$[C] = 0.44 + 3x$
$[D] = 0.22 + x$

Now you would proceed just as you did in Example 27–10.

EXAMPLE 27-13

Consider this equilibrium:

$$\overline{PCl_5} \rightleftharpoons \overline{PCl_3} + \overline{Cl_2}$$

At the start of the reaction, when only pure PCl_5 was in the container, the pressure was 0.32 atm. At equilibrium the pressure was 0.40 atm. Find the equilibrium constant.

If all of the PCl_5 had been converted to PCl_3 and Cl_2, there would have been twice as many moles of gaseous material in the same volume. If the temperature had remained constant (and we must assume that this was the case or the problem becomes utterly unworkable with the present data), this would mean that the pressure would have to have doubled. For any loss in pressure due to decomposition of PCl_5 there would be a gain of exactly twice this amount due to the formation of PCl_3 and Cl_2.

Let x = pressure loss due to decomposition of PCl_5, atm
x = pressure gain due to formation of PCl_3, atm
x = pressure gain due to formation of Cl_2, atm

pressure of PCl_5 + pressure of PCl_3 + pressure of Cl_2 = 0.40 atm

$$(0.32 - x) + x + x = 0.40$$
$$x = 0.08$$

Therefore at equilibrium the actual pressures of the individual gases would be $(0.32 - 0.08)$ atm, 0.08 atm, and 0.08 atm for PCl_5, PCl_3, and Cl_2.

$$K = \frac{(0.08)\,(0.08)}{(0.32 - 0.08)} = 3 \times 10^{-2}$$

In working with equilibrium problems whose solution involves solution of a quadratic equation, one occasionally has to choose which root one will take as the value for x. This is never really a problem in chemical equilibrium problems. Let's take an example.

EXAMPLE 27-14

Consider this equilibrium:

$$\overline{R} \rightleftharpoons \overline{S} + \overline{T} \quad K = 0.008$$

Find the concentrations of R, S, and T at equilibrium after 4 moles of R had been injected into an empty 1-liter container.

Let $\quad x$ = amount of S formed, moles/liter
x = amount of T formed, moles/liter
$(4 - x)$ = amount of R at equilibrium, moles/liter

Therefore $0.008 \quad = \dfrac{x^2}{4 - x}$
$x^2 + 0.008x - 0.032 = 0$

(You may have had $x^2 = 0.032 - 0.008x$; rearrange it into traditional quadratic form. See algebra section if necessary)

The main equation is now a classic quadratic equation in one unknown. It can be solved efficiently if uninterestingly by quadratic formula. The quadratic formula is

$$x = \frac{-b \pm \sqrt{b^2 - 4ac}}{2a}$$

Here *a, b,* and *c* are 1, 0.008, and −0.032, respectively.

$$x = \frac{-0.008 \pm \sqrt{(0.008)^2 - 4(1)(-0.032)}}{2(1)}$$

$$= \frac{-0.008 \pm \sqrt{6.4 \times 10^{-5} + 0.128}}{2}$$

(Ignore the 6.4×10^{-5}; it is insignificant with respect to the other figures.)

$$= \frac{-0.008 \pm 0.358}{2}$$

$$= \frac{-0.008 + 0.358}{2} = +0.175 \quad \text{(not in significant figures)}$$

$$= \frac{-0.008 - 0.358}{2} = -0.183 \quad \text{(not in significant figures)}$$

You have found two roots for *x.* Which root would you choose? You know that the concentration of R must be less than 4. Which value for *x* will give a value less than 4?

$$(4 - 0.175) = 3.825$$
$$[4 - (-0.183)] = 4.183$$

(We really should have had a better figure than 4: 4.01 or something or other)

Obviously +0.175 was the proper *x* here.

Doubtless you found solution by quadratic formula tedious. Why not try approximating in conditions of this sort (see Chapter 28)?

PROBLEMS

1. Consider this equilibrium:

   $$\overline{A} + \overline{B} + \overline{C} \rightleftharpoons \overline{D} + \overline{E}$$

   a. Find the constant if, at equilibrium, there were 4, 3, 2, 1, and 0.9 moles of A, B, C, D, and E, respectively, in a 2-liter box.
   b. If 10 moles each of A, B, C, D, and E were put into a 10-liter box, find the concentration of each when equilibrium was reached, using the constant obtained in problem 1a.
   c. If 8 moles of D and 7 moles of E were put into a 1-liter box, what would be the concentrations of A, B, C, D, and E at equilibrium?

2. Consider this equilibrium:

$2\,\overline{F} + \overline{G} \rightleftharpoons \overline{H} + 2\,\overline{I}$ $\quad K = 1 \times 10^{-9}$

a. Write the setup for finding the concentrations of F and G in an equilibrium mixture that formed after 8 moles of H and 0.2 mole of I had been injected into a 3-liter container.

b. If 1, 2, 3, and 4 moles respectively of F, G, H, and I had been put into a 1-liter container and allowed to come to equilibrium, would it be possible to calculate the concentration of I at equilibrium? If so, write the setup.

3. Consider this equilibrium:

$\overline{A} + \overline{B} + \overline{C} \rightleftharpoons \overline{D} + 2\,\overline{E} + \overline{F}$ $\quad K = 8$

An equimolar mixture of A, B, and C was put into a container at an initial total pressure of 40 atm and allowed to come to equilibrium. Find the pressure due to E at equilibrium.

28

IONIC EQUILIBRIUM PROBLEMS

There are two general types of equilibrium problems: molecular and ionic. Molecular equilibrium involves molecular species only. The preceding chapter dealt with molecular equilibria. Ionic equilibria involve an equilibrium between some sort of molecular species or complex ion and the ions from such species. For example,

$$HCN \rightleftharpoons H^+ + CN^-$$
$$Al(OH)^{++} \rightleftharpoons Al^{+++} + OH^-$$
$$\underline{AgCl \rightleftharpoons Ag^+ + Cl^-}$$

Problems involving ionic equilibria are set up in exactly the same fashion as are the problems in Chapter 27. Anyone who understood those problems should have little difficulty with the problem-solving aspects of ionic equilibrium problems. However, there could be great difficulty with the chemistry involved in the problems, in which case a good book on general chemistry should be consulted. You will be given all necessary chemical facts in the following problems in order to focus attention on our primary goal: problem solving.

There is a bewildering variety of equilibrium constants for various ionic equilibria, but they must all be descriptions of either *dissociations*, such as

$$HCN \rightleftharpoons H^+ + CN^- \qquad K_{dissociation} = \frac{[H^+]\,[CN^-]}{[HCN]}$$

or associations, such as

$$H^+ + CN^- \rightleftharpoons HCN \quad K_{association} = \frac{[HCN]}{[H^+][CN^-]}$$

Obviously $K_{association} = \dfrac{1}{K_{dissociation}}$

We will deal only with dissociation constants here. They are probably what you will more commonly encounter, and both types of constants are treated in the same fashion mathematically.

Among dissociation constants one finds

K_i an ionization constant, frequently just another symbol for $K_{dissociation}$

K_a K_i for a weak acid

K_b K_i for a weak base

K_w the constant for the dissociation of water

K_{sp} the constant for the equilibrium involving the ions in a saturated solution of a sparingly soluble solid, known as the solubility product constant

Now let's try some problems. Remember that the equilibrium constant is temperature dependent. All constants used here are for 25°C.

PLAIN K_i PROBLEMS

If you have a problem involving only a weak acid, a weak base, or a complex ion in water, it is necessarily a plain K_i problem.

EXAMPLE 28–1

Find the H^+ concentration in 0.10 M HCN solution.

Fact: HCN dissociates or ionizes slightly to give a little H^+ and a little CN^-. Obviously, for every HCN that ionized there would be one H^+ and one CN^- ion produced. The equilibrium involved is

$$HCN \rightleftharpoons H^+ + CN^-$$

K_i for HCN is 7.2×10^{-10}. The equilibrium expression is

$$\frac{[H^+][CN^-]}{[HCN]} = K_i = 7.2 \times 10^{-10}$$

Let x = moles of HCN that dissociate in 1 liter of solution
      x = moles of H^+ in 1 liter of solution
      x = moles of CN^- in 1 liter of solution
$0.10 - x$ = moles/liter of undissociated HCN in solution

But the x in the expression $(0.10 - x)$ is so small here that it is insignificant (look at the constant; look at the setup given below), so use 0.10 for HCN's concentration here.

$$7.2 \times 10^{-10} = \frac{x^2}{0.10}$$
$$x = 8.5 \times 10^{-6} \text{ mole/liter}$$

Therefore H^+ concentration must be 8.5×10^{-6} M.

EXAMPLE 28-2

Find the H^+ concentration in a 0.1 M HNO_2 solution.

Fact: HNO_2 dissociates slightly and sets up an equilibrium with the ions from its dissociation. This is the equilibrium:

$$HNO_2 \rightleftharpoons H^+ + NO_2^- \quad K_i = 4 \times 10^{-4}$$

Let $\quad x$ = moles/liter of HNO_2 that dissociate or ionize
$\qquad x$ = moles/liter of H^+ in solution
$\qquad x$ = moles/liter of NO_2^- in solution
$0.1 - x$ = moles/liter of undissociated HNO_2 in solution

The setup is

$$4 \times 10^{-4} = \frac{x^2}{0.1 - x}$$

This time the x in $(0.1 - x)$ is significant. How does one know this? Make a quick mental calculation for the value of x using just the 0.1, not the $(0.1 - x)$. x^2 = approximately 40×10^{-6}; x = about 6×10^{-3}. This is significant with respect to 0.1 as far as this type of problem is concerned.

There are two ways to solve this: by the formula for the solution of a quadratic equation or by approximation. To use the quadratic formula, one would put the setup in this form:

$$4 \times 10^{-5} \times (4 \times 10^{-4})x = x^2$$
$$x^2 + (4 \times 10^{-4})x - 4 \times 10^{-5} = 0$$

and substitute in the quadratic formula

$$x = \frac{-b \pm \sqrt{b^2 - 4ac}}{2a}$$

This seems to be a dreadfully complicated way to do a simple little problem. It would be very easy and quite respectable to solve this problem by approximation, that is, by intelligent guessing. You have already guessed that the value of x is about 6×10^{-3}. Substitute this estimated value for x in the setup in place of the x in the expression $(0.1 - x)$ and then solve for x.

$$4 \times 10^{-4} = \frac{x^2}{0.1 - 0.006}$$
$$x = 6.1 \times 10^{-3}$$

Now reapproximate using the value 6.1×10^{-3} for x in the expression $(0.1 - x)$.

$$4 \times 10^{-4} = \frac{x^2}{0.1 - 0.0061}$$
$$x = 6.1 \times 10^{-3}$$

The number of times you will have to approximate obviously depends on the accuracy of your original intelligent guess. You would continue approximating (with adjustments to be made if you were rather wide of the mark in your original guess) until two successive values for x were the same.

SIMPLE COMMON ION PROBLEMS

These are problems in which you have a weak base, weak acid, slightly ionized soluble salt, or a complex ion. In addition to the compound or ion with the K value you have another compound. Ask yourself some questions about this compound:

1. Does it ionize appreciably?
2. Are any of the ions so produced the same as any of the ions in the equilibrium expression?
3. Do any of the ions so produced have the ability to bind any ion that is part of the equilibrium expression?

EXAMPLE 28–3

Find the H^+ concentration in a solution containing 0.10 mole of HCN dissolved in exactly 1 liter of 2.0 M NaCN.

This problem could be phrased and modified in a number of ways and yet require the same mathematical solution, for example,

a. Find the H^+ concentration of a solution that is 2.0 M with respect to NaCN and 0.10 M with respect to HCN.
b. Find the $[H^+]$ of exactly 1 liter of 1.9 M NaCN to which 0.10 mole of NaOH and 0.20 mole of HCN were added.

c. Find the $[H^+]$ of a solution made by mixing exactly 1 liter of 4.0 M NaCN and exactly 1 liter of 0.20 M HCN.

Fact: HCN ionizes slightly to set up this equilibrium system:

$$HCN \rightleftharpoons H^+ + CN^- \qquad K_i = 7.2 \times 10^{-10} = \frac{[H^+]\,[CN^-]}{[HCN]}$$

Now let's turn to the problem as posed initially. Ask yourself the three questions given just above. Ask them about the NaCN.

1. NaCN dissociates virtually 100%. With a few exceptions (for example, mercuric chloride and lead acetate), soluble salts are virtually 100% ionized.
2. Na^+ is not part of the equilibrium expression. CN^- is part of the expression.
3. Neither Na^+ nor CN^- does this, but bear in mind the fact that the CN^- is part of the equilibrium and will shift the equilibrium to the left as written in order to maintain the equilibrium constant.

Now, let x = the moles of HCN that dissociate in 1 liter of solution
$$x = [H^+], \text{ moles/liter}$$
$2.0 + x = [CN^-]$, moles/liter (you have a virtually fully ionized source of CN^- in NaCN and you have a little from the HCN)
$0.10 - x$ = the concentration of the undissociated HCN, moles/liter

Then $7.2 \times 10^{-10} = \dfrac{(x)(2.0)}{0.10}$

Here x will be very small compared to 2.0 and 0.10. Consequently x can be ignored in $(2.0 + x)$ and $(0.10 - x)$.

$x = 3.6 \times 10^{-11}$ mole/liter

Therefore $[H^+]$ here is 3.6×10^{-11} M.

K_w PROBLEMS

Water dissociates slightly to set up this equilibrium:

$$H_2O \rightleftharpoons H^+ + OH^-$$

The equilibrium expression is

$$K = \frac{[H^+]\,[OH^-]}{[H_2O]}$$

The concentration of water is rather constant. Barring significant changes in temperature, which would change the density, 1 liter of water is 1000 g, about 55.5 moles. One could therefore think of the molarity of water as 55.5 M. Since water dissociates so slightly, the concentration of undissociated molecules is taken as 55.5 M and is incorporated into the constant, called K_w.

$$K \times 55.5 = K_w = [H^+] [OH^-] = 1.0 \times 10^{-14}$$

EXAMPLE 28–4

Find the OH^- concentration in a solution having a H^+ concentration of 6.3×10^{-6} M.

$$1.0 \times 10^{-14} = [H^+] [OH^-]$$
$$[OH^-] = \frac{1.0 \times 10^{-14}}{6.3 \times 10^{-6}} = 1.6 \times 10^{-9} \ M$$

SOLUBILITY PRODUCT PROBLEMS

Even quite insoluble salts are not completely insoluble. There is always a small amount that is dissolved, and this amount dissociates into ions that are in equilibrium with the undissolved solid in a saturated solution. All equilibrium constants vary with temperature, but solubility product constants often vary quite widely with changes in temperature because of the effect of temperature on the solubility of the salt. All constants used here are for 25°C.

Consider this equilibrium:

$$AgCl \rightleftharpoons Ag^+ + Cl^-$$

AgCl is a quite insoluble material. Only a very small amount of it dissolves in water. The equilibrium expression would be:

$$K = \frac{[Ag^+] [Cl^-]}{[AgCl]}$$

The concentration of the solid AgCl is constant and is incorporated in the equilibrium constant. The product of the equilibrium constant and the constant concentration of the solid is K_{sp}, the solubility product constant. In this case

$$K_{sp} = [Ag^+] [Cl^-] = 1.6 \times 10^{-10}$$

EXAMPLE 28–5

Find the following for a saturated aqueous solution of AgCl:

a. Concentration of Ag^+ in such a solution.

Let x = moles/liter of AgCl that dissolve and dissociate
x = concentration of Ag^+ = concentration of Cl^-

1.6×10^{-10} = $[Ag^+][Cl^-]$ = x^2
$x = 1.3 \times 10^{-5}\ M$, the silver ion concentration

b. The moles/liter of AgCl that actually dissolved. You have this. Look at definition of x. It is 1.3×10^{-5} mole.

c. The grams of AgCl that dissolve in exactly 1 liter of saturated solution of AgCl (in water). You know the moles/liter that dissolve, and you can find the molecular weight of AgCl. Then

$$\frac{1.3 \times 10^{-5}\ \text{mole} \times 143.3\ \text{g}}{\text{liter} \qquad \text{mole}} = 1.9 \times 10^{-3}\ \text{g/liter}$$

d. The grams of AgCl that would dissolve in 50.0 ml of a saturated solution.

0.0500 times as much would dissolve as would dissolve in 1 liter.

$$\frac{0.0500\ \text{liter} \times 1.9 \times 10^{-3}\ \text{g}}{\text{liter}} = 9.5 \times 10^{-5}\ \text{g}$$

EXAMPLE 28–6

Find the moles per liter of dissolved AgCl and the Ag^+ concentration in a saturated solution of AgCl in 0.10 M NaCl.

Ask yourself the questions posed on page 304. You have 0.10 M Cl^- from the NaCl. It enters into the AgCl equilibrium.

Let x = moles/liter of AgCl that dissolve and dissociate
x = $[Ag^+]$ in the saturated solution, moles/liter
$0.10 + x$ = $[Cl^-]$, moles/liter (the Cl^- from the AgCl and from the fully dissociated NaCl)

The x in $(0.10 + x)$ is insignificant, so $[Cl^-]$ is taken as 0.10 M.

1.6×10^{-10} = $[Ag^+][Cl^-]$ = $x(0.10)$
$x = 1.6 \times 10^{-9}$ = $[Ag^+]$ = moles/liter of AgCl dissolved

EXAMPLE 28–7

Find the grams of Ag_2S that would be dissolved in 180 ml of a saturated solution and the Ag^+ concentration in that solution.

The equilibrium is

$Ag_2S \rightleftharpoons 2\ Ag^+ + S^{--}$ $K_{sp} = 5.5 \times 10^{-51}$

Let x = moles/liter of Ag_2S that dissolve
$$2x = [Ag^+]$$
$$x = [S^{--}]$$

$$5.5 \times 10^{-51} = [Ag^+]^2 [S^{--}] = (2x)^2(x)$$
$$4x^3 = 5.5 \times 10^{-51}$$
$$x = 1.1 \times 10^{-17}$$

Therefore

$$\frac{1.1 \times 10^{-17} \text{ mole} \times 248 \text{ g} \times 0.180 \text{ liter}}{\text{liter} \quad \text{mole}} = 4.9 \times 10^{-16} \text{ g of } Ag_2S \text{ that}$$
would dissolve in 180 ml of water

HYDROLYSIS PROBLEMS

EXAMPLE 28-8

Find the H^+ concentration in a solution of 0.10 M NaCN.

Fact: NaCN hydrolyzes in water and sets up the equilibrium

$$CN^- + H_2O \rightleftharpoons HCN + OH^-$$

This is part of two separate equilibrium systems whose constants must be kept:

$$H^+ + CN^- \rightleftharpoons HCN \quad K = \frac{1}{K_{dissociation}} = \frac{1}{7.2 \times 10^{-10}}$$
$$H_2O \rightleftharpoons H^+ + OH^- \quad K = K_w = 1.0 \times 10^{-14}$$

* $CN^- + H_2O \rightleftharpoons HCN + OH^- \quad K \text{ for reaction} = \frac{1}{7.2 \times 10^{-10}} \times 1 \times 10^{-14}$

$$K_{hyd} = 1.4 \times 10^{-5}$$

$$1.4 \times 10^{-5} = \frac{[HCN] [OH^-]}{[CN^-]} \quad ([H_2O] \text{ incorporated in } K_w)$$

Let x = moles/liter of CN^- that hydrolyzes
x = [HCN] produced as result of hydrolysis, moles/liter
x = [OH$^-$], moles/liter

$$1.4 \times 10^{-5} = \frac{x^2}{0.1}$$
$$x = 1.2 \times 10^{-3}$$

---

*See Chapter 24 for other instances of adding equations.

$[OH^-] = 1.2 \times 10^{-3}$ mole/liter. To find H^+ concentration, solve for $[H^+]$ in the equation

$$[H^+][OH^-] = 1.0 \times 10^{-14}$$

Many more complex equilibrium problems exist. However, to solve them intelligently one must know the chemistry involved. The difficulty with complex equilibrium problems is rarely mathematical; it is almost invariably chemical.

PROBLEMS

1. Find the hydrogen ion concentration in a 1 M acetic acid solution. For acetic acid the equilibrium is

$$HAc \rightleftharpoons H^+ + Ac^- \qquad K_i = 1.8 \times 10^{-5}$$

2. Find the H^+ concentration in a solution made by mixing 2 moles of sodium acetate (NaAc), a fully ionized salt, with 8 moles of HAc and diluting the mixture to 10 liters.
3. Find the OH^- concentration in problem 2 ($K_w = 1.0 \times 10^{-14}$).
4. Find the number of moles of ZnS that would dissolve in a 1.0-liter saturated water solution of ZnS. ZnS is a sparingly soluble salt with $K_{sp} = 1.2 \times 10^{-23}$.
5. Find the Zn^{++} concentration in a saturated solution of ZnS in a 0.1 M $ZnCl_2$ solution. Assume that $ZnCl_2$ is fully dissociated.
6. How many grams of ZnS would be dissolved in 1 liter of the solution in problem 5?

SELECTED SOLUTIONS
AND ANSWERS

All answers are expressed in significant figures unless otherwise indicated.

CHAPTER 2

1. a. 0.66 g/hr   **b.** 4.0 g   **c.** 0.01 mole/liter (*M*)   **2. a.** 0.0002 g/hr

b. $\dfrac{0.00009\ \text{mole} \times 0.1\ \text{g} \times 24\ \text{hr} \times \text{``365''}\ \text{days}}{\text{liter} \qquad \text{hr} \qquad \text{day} \qquad\qquad \text{yr} \quad \times 0.001\ \dfrac{\text{g}}{\text{yr}}} = 80\ \text{moles}$

3. a. 0.8 g/hr   **b.** 20 g

4. a. $\dfrac{49\ \text{tr} \times 10\ \text{men} \times 2\ \text{mo} \times \text{``30''}\ \text{days} \times 24\ \text{hr} \times 60\ \text{min}}{103\ \text{men} \qquad\qquad \text{mo} \qquad\qquad \text{day} \qquad \text{hr} \times 30\ \text{min}} = 14,000\ \text{tr}$

b. 6.0 men   **c.** 6306 min

5. a. $\dfrac{3,000,000\ \text{accts} \times 5\ \text{mach} \times 15\ \text{hr} \qquad\qquad \times 20\ \text{days}}{50\ \text{mach} \qquad \text{day} \times 8\ \dfrac{\text{hr}}{\text{day}} \times 15\ \text{days}} = 750,000\ \text{accts}$

b. $\dfrac{8\ \text{hr} \times 15\ \text{days} \times 50\ \text{mach} \times \qquad 28,000\ \text{accts}}{\text{day} \qquad\qquad 80\ \text{mach} \times 3,000,000\ \text{accts}} = 0.7\ \text{hr}$

(The "24 hr/day" has no bearing on the total time required.)

c. $\dfrac{8\ \text{hr} \times 50\ \text{mach} \times 800,000\ \text{accts} \times 15\ \text{days}}{\text{day} \quad 220\ \text{mach} \times 3,000,000\ \text{accts} \times 10\ \text{days}} = 0.73\ \text{hr/day}$

311

6.   67 friction units

7. $\dfrac{70 \text{ ft}}{\text{sec}} \times \dfrac{\sqrt{80 \text{ tu}} \times \sqrt{2 \text{ g/yd}}}{\sqrt{17 \text{ tu}} \times \sqrt{7 \text{ g/yd}}} = 80 \text{ ft/sec}$

8. a. $\dfrac{12.6 \text{ ft}^2 \times (6 \text{ ft})^2}{(2 \text{ ft})^2} = 113 \text{ ft}^2$

b. $\dfrac{2 \text{ ft} \times \sqrt{78.5 \text{ ft}^2}}{\sqrt{12.6 \text{ ft}^2}} = 5 \text{ ft}$

9. a. 93 words   **b.** 840 words

c. $\dfrac{2 \text{ hr}}{24 \dfrac{\text{hr}}{\text{day}}} \times \dfrac{140 \text{ words}}{800 \text{ words}} = 0.01 \text{ day}$ **d.** 336 min

10. a. $\dfrac{40 \text{ words}}{\text{hr}} \times \dfrac{20 \text{ yr} \times (3 \text{ hr})^2 \times 61°\text{F} \times 3 \text{ hr}}{22 \text{ yr} \times (1 \text{ hr})^2 \times 69°\text{F}} = 900 \text{ words}$

b. $\dfrac{40 \text{ words} \times 20 \text{ yr} \times 61°\text{F}}{45 \text{ yr} \times 52°\text{F}} = 21 \text{ words/hr};$ $\dfrac{75 \text{ words}}{21 \dfrac{\text{words}}{\text{hr}}} = 3.6 \text{ hr}$

c. Out of range of information

11. a. 0.3 lb; 8 lb   **b.** 900 lb   **c.** 8 lb

d. $\dfrac{120 \text{ lb} \times 2.0°\text{C} \times 19 \text{ fath} \times (3 \text{ mi/hr})^2 \times}{20.0°\text{C} \times 4 \text{ fath} \times (90 \text{ mi/hr})^2} \left(\dfrac{8 \text{ ft}}{1.5 \text{ in.}} \times \dfrac{12 \text{ in.}}{\text{ft}}\right)^7 = 3 \times 10^{11} \text{ lb}$

e. 0.09°C

12. a. $\sqrt{\dfrac{(365 \text{ days})^2 \times (2)^3}{(1)^3}} = 1033 \text{ days}$ or $365 \text{ days} \times \sqrt{\left(\dfrac{2}{1}\right)^3}$

b. $\sqrt[3]{\dfrac{(93{,}000{,}000 \text{ mi})^3 \times \left(\dfrac{210 \text{ days}}{\text{season}} \times \dfrac{4 \text{ seasons}}{\text{yr}} \times \dfrac{}{365 \dfrac{\text{days}}{\text{yr}}}\right)^2}{}}$

$= 1.6 \times 10^8 \text{ mi}$ or $93{,}000{,}000 \times \sqrt[3]{\left(\dfrac{210 \times 4}{365}\right)^2}$

c. $\sqrt{\dfrac{(1 \text{ Earth yr})^2 \times (23{,}250{,}000 \text{ mi})^3}{(93{,}000{,}000 \text{ mi})^3}} = 0.13 \text{ Earth yr}$

or $1 \text{ Earth yr} \times \sqrt{\left(\dfrac{23{,}250{,}000 \text{ mi}}{93{,}000{,}000 \text{ mi}}\right)^3}$

13. a. The problem states that the more weight one carries in climbing a mountain the more one can climb. This is an obvious absurdity, but according to the conditions stated the solution is

$$\frac{4000 \text{ ft} \times (150 + 11) \text{ lb}}{(150 + 9) \text{ lb}} = 4050 \text{ ft} \quad (\text{not in significant figures})$$

If one assumed—and *so stated*—that an error had been made in the statement of the problem, a more reasonable solution would be

$$\frac{4000 \text{ ft} \times (150 + 9) \text{ lb}}{(150 + 11) \text{ lb}} = 3950 \text{ ft}$$

However, this solution would be incorrect if the stated assumption were incorrect.

b. If one accepts the problem as stated—that the more weight a climber carries, the greater the distance he travels—then one can say that the more weight he carries, the less time he takes to cover a distance.

$$\frac{2 \text{ hr} \times 5000 \text{ ft} \times (150 + 9) \text{ lb}}{4000 \text{ ft} \times [(150 - 20) + 5] \text{ lb}} = 3 \text{ hr}$$

c. Out of range of information

CHAPTER 3

1. 18.6 lb   **2.** 46 liters   **3.** $\dfrac{91 \text{ gr} \times 454 \text{ g}}{7000 \dfrac{\text{gr}}{\text{lb av}} \quad \text{lb av}} = 5.9 \text{ g}$

4. $\dfrac{50 \text{ g} \times 0.07143 \dfrac{\text{stone}}{\text{lb av}}}{454 \dfrac{\text{g}}{\text{lb av}}} = 8 \times 10^{-3} \text{ stone}$ **5.** 230 in.

6. 180 in.   **7.** 430 dry Br bbl   **8.** 6 Br gal

9. $\dfrac{91 \text{ pwt} \times 24 \dfrac{\text{gr}}{\text{pwt}} \times 454 \dfrac{\text{g}}{\text{lb av}}}{7000 \dfrac{\text{gr}}{\text{lb av}}} = 140 \text{ g}$ **10.** 2600 g

11. $\dfrac{99 \dfrac{\text{g}}{\text{lb av}} \times 7000 \dfrac{\text{gr}}{\text{lb av}}}{454 \dfrac{\text{g}}{\text{lb av}} \times 5760 \dfrac{\text{gr}}{\text{lb T}}} = 0.27 \text{ lb T}$

12. $\dfrac{71 \text{ Br bu} \times 0.1091 \text{ m}^3}{3 \dfrac{\text{Br bu}}{\text{Br bag}} \times 0.1637 \dfrac{\text{m}^3}{\text{dry Br bbl}}} = 16 \text{ dry Br bbl}$

13.   59 dry Br bbl   **14.** 0.01 pwt   **15.** 0.5 m³   **16.** 500 liters
16.   500 liters   **17.** 1.6×10^7 cm

18.

$$\frac{(100 - 14) \text{ ft} \quad \times 12 \text{ in.}}{\dfrac{\text{day} \qquad \text{ft} \quad \times 24 \text{ hr}}{\text{day}}} = 43 \text{ in./hr}$$

19.

$$\left[\frac{1 \text{ hp} - 1 \text{ met hp} \times 0.9863 \text{ hp}}{\text{met hp}} \right] \times \frac{745.2 \text{ w}}{\text{hp}} \times \frac{10^7 \text{ ergs}}{\text{sec w}}$$

$$= 1.021 \times 10^8 \text{ ergs/sec}$$

20.

$$\frac{0.983 \text{ g}}{\dfrac{\text{ml} \times 454 \text{ g}}{\text{lb av}}} \times \frac{155 \text{ U.S. gal} \times 4 \text{ qt}}{\dfrac{\text{gal} \times 1.06 \text{ qt}}{\text{liter}}} \times \frac{1000 \text{ ml}}{\text{liter}}$$

$$= 1270 \text{ lb av}$$

CHAPTER 4

1. a. Let x = number of spheres.

$$\frac{(40 - 5) \text{ lb}}{x} = \text{lb/sphere} \qquad Assumption: \text{ Spheres of uniform weight.}$$

Additional information needed: Number of spheres.

b. Let x = N's age, then $\dfrac{x}{3}$ = M's age.

Let y = R's age, then $\dfrac{y - 20}{3}$ = M's age.

Additional information needed: An age for one of these.

c. Let x = K's weight, then $7x$ = J's weight and $\dfrac{7x}{3}$ = L's weight.

Additional information needed: Weight for one of these.

d. Let x = T's rate of weight gain.

$3x$ = S's rate of weight gain   *Assumption:* Rate of weight gain
$0.7x$ = U's rate of weight gain   constant for each.

If y = the time, then y times x, $3x$, and $0.7x$, respectively, would give the weight gain.

Additional information needed: The rate for one of these and the time.

e. Let x = E's weight now.   *Assumption:* The phrase "Two years ago
$16x$ = D's weight now   D was half as heavy as E"

$\dfrac{x}{4}$ = E's weight 2 yr ago   has reference to both D's
                                and E's weights 2 years ago.

$\dfrac{x}{4 \times 2}$ = D's weight 2 yr ago

Additional information needed: Something's weight, either now or 2 years ago.

f. Let x = length of original rectangle and y = width of original rectangle. Let z = the amount by which the width was increased.

$4z$ = the amount by which the length was increased

New area = $(x + 4z)(y + z) = 800$

Old perimeter = $2x + 2y$

New perimeter = $2(x + 4z) + 2(y + z)$

Old area = xy

Additional information needed: Old area, old length or width; various combinations of information possible.

2. $\dfrac{30 - 20}{3} = 3.3 \qquad \dfrac{10}{3} = 3.3$

3. Here let R's age = $x + 20$.

$$x + \frac{x}{3} + (x + 20) = 50$$

$$3x + x + 3x + 60 = 150$$

$$x = 12.8$$

Check: $12.8 + \dfrac{12.8}{3} + (12.8 + 20) = 50$ (within significant figures)

4. Here let $x = (100 - 25)$ lb/yr = 75 lb/yr; $3x = 225$ lb/yr; $0.7x = 52.5$ lb/yr. For each, 1 yr $\times \dfrac{\text{lb}}{\text{yr}} = $ lb

5. $(25 + 3x) + (30 + x) + (35 + 0.7x) = 1030$ lb   *Assumption:* Weight gain

$\qquad\qquad\qquad\qquad 4.7x + 90 = 1030$ and rate of weight gain

$\qquad\qquad\qquad\qquad\qquad x = 200$ may be used interchange-

ably.

S, T, and U weigh $(25 + 600)$, $(30 + 200)$, and $(35 + 140)$ or 625, 230, and 175 lb, respectively.

6. a. D now is 16×100 or 1600 lb $(x = 100, 16x = 1600)$.

$\dfrac{x}{4} = \dfrac{100}{4} = 25$ lb (E's weight 2 yr ago)

$\dfrac{x}{8} = \dfrac{100}{8} = 12.5$ lb (D's weight 2 yr ago, not in significant figures)

b. Problem is vague as to whether absolute or relative increase in weight is wanted. Absolute increase in weight is $(1600 \text{ lb} - 12.5 \text{ lb})$. Relative increase in weight is $\dfrac{16x}{x} = \dfrac{16 \times 100}{\dfrac{100}{8}} = 128$-fold increase

$\qquad\qquad\qquad\qquad\qquad\qquad\quad \dfrac{}{8}$

7. Let x = side of original square.

$(3x)^2 = 50$ ft^2

$$x = \sqrt{\frac{50 \text{ ft}^2}{9}} = 2.36 \text{ ft (2 ft in significant figures)}$$

8.   Let x = amount of \$5.00/lb material.

$(100 - x)$ = amount of \$1.00/lb material

$x(5.00) + (100 - x)1.00 = 228$

$$x = 32$$

$$100 - x = 68$$

Therefore 32 lb of \$5.00 material and 68 lb of \$1.00 material will make 100 lb of a mixture worth \$228.

9.   Let x = increase in length; $8x$ = increase in width.

$(70 + x)(50 + 8x) = 4000$

$3500 + 610x + 8x^2 = 4000$

$8x^2 + 610x - 500 = 0$

$$x = \frac{-610 \pm \sqrt{(610)^2 - 4(8 \times -500)}}{2 \times 8}$$

$$= \frac{-610 \pm 623}{16}$$

Only reasonable choice is +623, so

$$x = \frac{-610 + 623}{16} = 0.81$$

$8x = 6.48$ (not in significant figures)

Rug must increase 0.81 ft in length and 6.48 ft in width.

10.   Let x = fraction of the weight of 1 liter of benzene to be used;

$1 - x$ = fraction of the weight of 1 liter of acetone to be used.

$x(879) + (1 - x)791 = 825$

$879x + 791 - 791x = 825$

$$88x = 34$$

$$x = 0.386$$

$$1 - x = 0.614$$

Weight of benzene = 0.386×879 g = 339 g

Weight of acetone = 0.614×791 g = 486 g

CHAPTER 5

1. a. 6.8×10^6 **b.** 7.2×10^3 **c.** 7.02×10^3 **d.** 7.002×10^3

    e. 7×10^3 **f.** 2.29×10^1 **g.** 1.6×10^1 **h.** 3.8×10^0

    i. 5×10^{-2} **j.** 5×10^{-3} **k.** 1.005×10^0 **l.** 8×10^{-3}

    m. 8.03×10^{-3} **n.** 6×10^0

2. a. 5000   **b.** 6200   **c.** 6020   **d.** 43

    e. 4.3   **f.** 0.0009   **g.** 0.0091

3. a. 7.5×10^4 **b.** 7.81×10^{11} **c.** 5×10^5 **d.** 8×10^1

    e. 5×10^1 **f.** 4.81×10^{-3} **g.** 6.9×10^{-6} **h.** 7×10^{-5}

    i. 9.2×10^{-11} **j.** 3.92×10^{-6} **k.** 4.81×10^0 **l.** 1.48×10^0

    m. 1.48×10^1 **n.** 1.995×10^{-1} **o.** 7.59×10^4 **p.** 8.21×10^0

CHAPTER 6

1.	21	**2.**	588	**3.**	344	**4.**	819
5.	1290	**6.**	2540	**7.**	5870	**8.**	9230
9.	4,913,000	**10.**	0.713	**11.**	5800	**12.**	716
13.	12	**14.**	9.42	**15.**	0.643	**16.**	3.70×10^{-5}
17.	275,000	**18.**	0.207	**19.**	16.8	**20.**	$\sqrt[3]{4.66} = 1.67$
21.	2.16	**22.**	0.126	**23.**	2010	**24.**	256
25.	64,000	**26.**	512	**27.**	24,400	**28. a.**	3
28. b.	7.98	**28. c.**	17.2	**28. d.**	82.5	**29. a.**	2.08
29. b.	3.99	**29. c.**	6.66	**29. d.**	19	**30.**	4060
31.	0.0231						

CHAPTER 7

1. a. $2 = \log_3 9$ **b.** $3 = \log_4 64$ **c.** $4 = \log_{10} 10,000$
   d. $2 = \log_{1/5} 1/25$ **e.** $\bar{3} = \log_2 1/8$ or $-3 = \log_2 1/8$
   f. $1/2 = \log_{25} 5$ **g.** $1/4 = \log_{81} 3$ **h.** $0 = \log_r 1$ **i.** $d = \log_c e$
   j. $3y = \log_8 z$ **k.** $1/2 = \log_{16} 4$ **l.** $3/2 = \log_2 2.2$
2. a. $5^2 = 25$ **b.** $4^4 = 256$ **c.** $2^6 = 64$ **d.** $10^{-5} = 0.00001$
   e. $25^{1/2} = 5$ **f.** $r^1 = r$ **g.** $r^0 = 1$ **h.** $10^{-2} = 0.01$
3. a. 3.6924   **b.** 0.4492   **c.** 1.2527   **4. a.** 590.1
4. b. 0.9034   **c.** 90.34   **d.** 1.005   **5. a.** $\bar{1}.5520$
5. b. 2.0857   **6. a.** $\bar{4}.7049$ is the log; 5.069×10^{-4} is the antilog.
6. b. 5.7049 is the log; 5.069×10^5 is the antilog.   **7. a.** 0.537
7. b. 7.177×10^{-5} **c.** 1.529×10^{-6} **d.** 45,960   **e.** 7.202×10^{23}
7. f. 2.694×10^{-10} **g.** 1.757×10^{17} **h.** 5.037

CHAPTER 8

1. (Refers to Problem 7, p. 99)   **a.** 3   **b.** 3   **c.** 3   **d.** 3   **e.** 3
   f. 1   **g.** 1   **h.** 2
2. a. 1 or infinite   **b.** 1 as stands; cannot tell, need more information.
   c. 2   **d.** 1   **e.** 4   **f.** 1   **3. a.** 2   **b.** 4   **c.** 3
4.   8.309, although on the basis of parts per thousand error one could argue for 8.31.

CHAPTER 9

1. a. 1.7 m   **b.** 4800 g   **c.** 4000 ml

1. d. $\dfrac{73 \text{ cm} \times 1000 \text{ mm}}{100 \text{ } \underline{\text{cm}} \quad \underline{\text{m}}} = 730 \text{ mm}$

e. $\dfrac{420 \text{ mm}}{1000 \text{ } \underline{\text{mm}} \times 1000 \text{ } \underline{\text{m}}}$ or $\dfrac{420 \text{ mm} \times 0.001 \text{ m} \times 0.001 \text{ km}}{\text{mm} \qquad \text{m}} = 4.2 \times 10^{-4} \text{ km}$

f. $7.9 \times 10^5 \text{ dg}$ **g.** $5.9 \times 10^{-4} \text{ kg}$

h. $\dfrac{17 \text{ cg} \times 10^6 \text{ } \mu\text{g}}{100 \text{ } \underline{\text{cg}} \quad \underline{\text{g}}} = 1.7 \times 10^5 \text{ } \mu\text{g}$ or $1.7 \times 10^5 \text{ } \gamma$ **i.** 31 mi

j. $\dfrac{5 \text{ km} \times 1000 \text{ m} \times 39.37 \text{ in.} \qquad\qquad\quad \times 60 \text{ sec} \times 60 \text{ min}}{\text{sec} \qquad \underline{\text{km}} \qquad\quad \underline{\text{m}} \times 12 \text{ } \underline{\text{in.}} \times 5280 \text{ } \underline{\text{ft}} \qquad \underline{\text{min}} \qquad \text{hr}}$
$$\phantom{\dfrac{5}{ft \quad mi}} = 1.1 \times 10^4 \text{ mi/hr}$$

k. $\dfrac{7 \text{ } \mu \times 10^3 \text{ mm}}{10^6 \text{ } \underline{\mu} \quad \underline{\text{m}}} = 7 \times 10^{-3} \text{ mm}$ **l.** $1.4 \times 10^4 \text{ m}\mu$ **m.** $4.5 \times 10^5 \text{ } \mu$

n. $\dfrac{11 \text{ m}\mu \qquad \times 10^3 \text{ mm}}{10^3 \text{ } \underline{\text{m}\mu} \times 10^6 \text{ } \underline{\mu} \quad \underline{\text{m}}} = 1.1 \times 10^{-5} \text{ mm}$

o. $\dfrac{45 \text{ cm} \times 10^9 \text{ nm}}{100 \text{ } \underline{\text{cm}} \quad \underline{\text{m}}} = 4.5 \times 10^8 \text{ nm}$

p. $\dfrac{14 \text{ } \mu \times 10^2 \text{ cm} \times 10^8 \text{ Å}}{10^6 \text{ } \underline{\mu} \quad \underline{\text{m}} \quad \underline{\text{cm}}} = 1.4 \times 10^5 \text{ Å}$

q. $\dfrac{41 \text{ pm}}{10^{12} \text{ } \underline{\text{pm}} \times 10^9 \text{ } \underline{\text{m}}}$ or $\dfrac{41 \text{ pm} \times 10^{-12} \text{ m} \times 10^{-9} \text{ Gm}}{\text{pm} \qquad \text{m}} = 4.1 \times 10^{-20} \text{ Gm}$

r. $9 \times 10^{18} \text{ } \mu$ **s.** $\dfrac{5 \text{ Å} \qquad\qquad \times 10^{12} \text{ pm}}{10^8 \text{ } \underline{\text{Å}} \times 100 \text{ } \underline{\text{cm}} \quad \underline{\text{m}}} = 5 \times 10^2 \text{ pm}$

t. $\dfrac{14 \text{ Tm} \times 10^{12} \text{ m} \quad \times 10^6 \text{ } \mu}{\text{mil} \qquad \underline{\text{Tm}} \qquad \underline{\text{m}} \times 1000 \text{ } \underline{\text{yr}} \times \text{"365" } \underline{\text{days}} \times 24 \text{ } \underline{\text{hr}} \times 3600 \text{ } \underline{\text{sec}} \times 10^3 \text{ msec}}$
$$ = 4.4 \times 10^8 \text{ } \mu/\text{msec}$$

u. $4.5 \times 10^7 \lambda$ **v.** $1.7 \times 10^2 \mu l$

2.
$$\frac{17\,\mu}{13\,\overset{\circ}{\text{A}}\;\underset{\text{par}}{}\times 10^{-8}\,\frac{\text{cm}}{\overset{\circ}{\text{A}}}\times 10^{-2}\,\frac{\text{m}}{\text{cm}}\times 10^6\,\frac{\mu}{\text{m}}} = 1 \times 10^6 \text{ par}$$

3. 2.2×10^7 ml   **4. a.** 125 cm^3 **b.** 179 $\overset{\circ}{\text{A}}^3$ **5. a.** 11.45 cm
5. b. 5.94×10^{-8} cm   **6.** 2 in. × 6 in. × 7 in. = 80 in.^{3};

$$2 \text{ in.} \times 6 \text{ in.} \times 7 \text{ in.} \times \left(2.54\,\frac{\text{cm}}{\text{in.}}\right)^3 = 1000 \text{ cm}^3$$

7.
$$\frac{108\,\text{m}\times155\,\text{m}\times35\,\text{m}\times\left(\dfrac{10^2\,\text{cm}}{\text{m}}\right)^3\times 1.06\,\text{qt}}{\times 1000\,\dfrac{\text{cm}^3}{\text{liter}}\quad \text{liter}\times 4\,\dfrac{\text{qt}}{\text{gal}}\times 525\,\dfrac{\text{gal}}{\text{min}}}$$
$$= 3.0 \times 10^5 \text{ min}$$

8. 10 m

9.
$$\frac{200\,\text{Br gal}\times\dfrac{1.201\,\text{U.S. gal}}{\text{Br gal}}\times\dfrac{4\,\text{qt}}{\text{U.S. gal}}\times\dfrac{1.06\,\text{qt}}{\text{liter}}}{}$$
$$\frac{\times 1000\,\dfrac{\text{cm}^3}{\text{liter}}}{\times\left(100\,\dfrac{\text{cm}}{\text{m}}\right)^3\times 3\,\text{m}\times 7\,\text{m}} = 0.04 \text{ m}$$

10.
$$\frac{200\,\text{Br gal}\times\dfrac{1.201\,\text{U.S. gal}}{\text{Br gal}}\times\dfrac{4\,\text{qt}}{\text{U.S. gal}}\times\dfrac{1.06\,\text{qt}}{\text{liter}}}{}$$
$$\frac{\times 1000\,\dfrac{\text{cm}^3}{\text{liter}}}{\times 3.14 \times (100\,\text{cm})^2} = 3 \times 10^4 \text{ cm}$$

11.
$$\frac{1\,\mu^3}{\left(10^6\,\dfrac{\mu}{\text{m}}\right)^3}\times\left(\frac{10^2\,\text{cm}}{\text{m}}\right)^3 = 1 \times 10^{-12}\text{ cm}^3$$

12.
$$\frac{1\,\mu^3}{\left(10^6\,\dfrac{\mu}{\text{m}}\right)^3}\times\left(\frac{10^2\,\text{cm}}{\text{m}}\right)^3\times\frac{10^6\,\lambda}{10^3\,\dfrac{\text{cm}^3}{\text{liter}}\;\text{liter}} = 1 \times 10^{-9}\,\lambda$$

13.
$$\frac{10\,\text{m}\mu\times 10\,\text{m}\mu\times 5\,\text{m}\mu}{\left(10^3\,\dfrac{\text{m}\mu}{\mu}\right)^3\times\left(10^6\,\dfrac{\mu}{\text{m}}\right)^3}\times\left(\frac{10^2\,\text{cm}}{\text{m}}\right)^3\times\frac{10^6\,\mu l}{10^3\,\dfrac{\text{cm}^3}{\text{liter}}\;\text{liter}}$$
$$= 5 \times 10^{-16}\,\mu l$$

14. $10^9\,\overset{\circ}{\text{A}}$

15. $\dfrac{1.33 \times 3.14 \times \dfrac{(8\,\mu)^3}{\left(\dfrac{10^6\,\mu}{m}\right)^3} \times \left(\dfrac{10^2\,cm}{m}\right)^3 \dfrac{\times 10^6\,\lambda}{liter}}{\times 10^3 \dfrac{cm^3}{liter}} = 2 \times 10^{-6}\,\lambda$

16. $\dfrac{\left(\dfrac{19\,\mu - 17\,\mu}{2}\right)^3 \times 1.33 \times 3.14 \times \left(\dfrac{10^2\,cm}{m}\right)^3 \dfrac{\times 10^6\,\mu l}{liter}}{\left(\dfrac{10^6\,\mu}{m}\right)^3 \times 10^3 \dfrac{cm^3}{liter}}$

$= 4.2 \times 10^{-9}\,\mu l$

17. 1.3×10^2 lt yr

18. $\dfrac{208 \text{ nau mi} \times 1.89 \times 10^{-4} \text{ mi}}{1.65 \times 10^{-4} \dfrac{\text{nau mi}}{\text{ft}} \qquad \text{ft} \times 9.29 \times 10^7 \dfrac{\text{mi}}{\text{ast unit}}}$

$\dfrac{\times 1.58 \times 10^{-5} \text{ lt yr}}{\text{ast unit}} = 4.05 \times 10^{-11} \text{ lt yr}$

19. $\dfrac{\left[\dfrac{1 \text{ nau mi}}{1.65 \times 10^{-4} \dfrac{\text{nau mi}}{\text{ft}}} - \dfrac{1 \text{ mi}}{1.89 \times 10^{-4} \dfrac{\text{mi}}{\text{ft}}}\right] \times 5280 \dfrac{\text{ft}}{\text{mi}} \times 9.29 \times 10^7 \dfrac{\text{mi}}{\text{ast unit}}}{}$

$= 2 \times 10^{-9} \text{ ast unit}$

CHAPTER 10

1. 2.2% **2.** 40 g **3.** 22 g **4.** 263 g **5.** 4 tons

6. $\dfrac{35 \text{ lb} \times 100}{85}$ or $\dfrac{35 \text{ lb}}{0.85} = 41 \text{ lb}$ **7.** 93%

8.

	1964 compared to 1900	*1900 compared to 1964*
under 40	$\dfrac{208 \times 100}{409} = 50.9\%$ inc	$\dfrac{208 \times 100}{617} = 33.7\%$ dec
21–40	$\dfrac{100 \times 100}{227} = 44.1\%$ dec	$\dfrac{100 \times 100}{127} = 78.7\%$ inc
under 6	$\dfrac{122 \times 100}{184} = 66.3\%$ dec	$\dfrac{122 \times 100}{62} = 197\%$ inc

Units omitted since only people involved:
21–40: in 1836, $227 + 0.787(227) = 406$; in 2028, $127 - 0.441(127) = 71$
under 6: in 1836, $184 + 1.97(184) = 546$; in 2028, $62 - 0.663\ (62) = 21$

9. $x - (0.038 + 0.027)x = 8500 \text{ gal};$ $x = \dfrac{8500 \text{ gal}}{0.935} = 9100 \text{ gal}$

10. 300 liters **11.** $1110 **12.** 580 g

13. $x - 0.10x = 10,000$ gal; $\quad x = \dfrac{10,000}{0.90} = 10,000$ gal*

14. $x + 2x = 55$ tons $\quad x = 55/3 = 18$ tons

15. a. $\dfrac{100 \text{ liters} \times 1000 \text{ cm}^3 \times 1 \times 10^{-5}}{\text{liter} \qquad 10^2} = 1 \times 10^{-2} \text{ cm}^3$

or $\quad 100 \times 1000 \times 1 \times 10^{-7} = 1 \times 10^{-2}$

b. $\dfrac{40 \text{ g} \times 10^2}{1 \times 10^{-4}} = 4 \times 10^7 \text{ g}$ **c.** $\dfrac{75 \text{ liters} \times 10^2}{1.8 \times 10^{-3}} = 4.2 \times 10^6 \text{ liters}$

d. $\dfrac{5000 \text{ liters} \times 0.7809 \times 28 \text{ g}}{0.2095 \qquad\qquad 22.4 \text{ liters}} = 20,000 \text{ liters}*$

CHAPTER 11

1. 0.9972 g/ml **2.** 1 g/cm³* **3.** $\dfrac{40.5 \text{ g}}{(48.9 - 23.8) \text{ ml}} = 1.61 \text{ g/ml}$

4. 8 g/cm³; $\dfrac{7700 \text{ g}}{\dfrac{454 \text{ g}}{\text{lb}} \times 2 \text{ in.} \times 3 \text{ in.} \times 10 \text{ in.} \left(\dfrac{12 \text{ in.}}{\text{ft}}\right)^3} = 490 \text{ lb/ft}^3$

5. 40 ml **6.** $14.3 \text{ ml} + \dfrac{150 \text{ g}}{19.3 \dfrac{\text{g}}{\text{ml}}} = 22.1 \text{ ml}$

7. $\dfrac{250 \text{ g} \times 100}{1.84 \dfrac{\text{g}}{\text{ml}} \times 96}$ or $\dfrac{250 \text{ g}}{1.84 \dfrac{\text{g}}{\text{ml}} \times 0.96} = 140 \text{ ml}$ **8.** 20 g **9.** 4×10^5 g

10. $\dfrac{9.3 \text{ g} \times 200 \text{ cm}^3}{\text{ml}} = 1860 \text{ g}$ (cm³ and ml can be used interchangeably)

11. $\dfrac{59.1 \text{ g}}{7.14 \dfrac{\text{g}}{\text{ml}} \times 10 \text{ in.} \times 7 \text{ in.} \times \left(2.54 \dfrac{\text{cm}}{\text{in.}}\right)^2} = 0.02 \text{ cm}$

$\dfrac{59.1 \text{ g}}{7.14 \dfrac{\text{g}}{\text{ml}} \times \left(2.54 \dfrac{\text{cm}}{\text{in.}}\right)^3 \times 10 \text{ in.} \times 7 \text{ in.}} = 7 \times 10^{-3} \text{ in.}$

---

*See Chapter 8 for discussion of significant figures in numbers such as 5000, 10,000, etc.

12. $\sqrt[3]{\dfrac{150\ g}{5.75\ \dfrac{g}{ml}}} = 3.0\ cm$

13. $\dfrac{40{,}000\ lb}{2\ ft \times 6\ ft \times 10\ ft \times 62.4\ \dfrac{lb}{ft^3}} = 5$

14. $400\ lb$ **15.** $21\ ft^3$ **16.** $1.98\ g/liter$

17. $\dfrac{14.183\ g - \left[14.019\ g - \left(\dfrac{1.29\ g}{liter} \times 0.100\ liter \right) \right]}{0.100\ liter} = 2.93\ g/liter$

18. $\dfrac{5\ g - \left[\dfrac{5\ g \times 1\ g}{19.3\ \dfrac{g}{ml}\ \ ml} \right]}{} = 4.74\ g$ (presuming 5 g is exactly 5 g; otherwise problem is unreasonable) (air buoyancy correction insignificant)

19. $\dfrac{50\ g - \left[\dfrac{50\ g \times 1\ g}{10.5\ \dfrac{g}{ml}\ \ ml} \right]}{} = 45\ g$ (presuming 50 g is exactly 50 g or problem is unreasonable)

$\dfrac{50\ g - \left[\dfrac{50\ g \times 1.84\ g}{10.5\ \dfrac{g}{ml}\ \ ml} \right]}{} = 41\ g$ (weightless in mercury; floats)

20. $\dfrac{(0.79 - 0.53)\ g}{ml} \times 10\ ft \times 10\ ft \times 100\ ft \times \left(\dfrac{12\ in.}{ft} \right)^3 \times \left(\dfrac{2.54\ cm}{in.} \right)^3$
$= 7 \times 10^7\ g$

21. $7 \times 10^6\ ml$

22. $\dfrac{7000\ m^3 \times \left(\dfrac{100\ cm}{m} \right)^3 \times (5.75 - 1.00)\ g/ml}{(1.00 - 0.53)\ g/ml} = 7 \times 10^{10}\ cm^3$

23. $\dfrac{5000\ kg \times 1000\ \dfrac{g}{kg} \times (10.5 - 1.0)\ g/ml \times 0.53\ \dfrac{g}{ml}}{10.5\ \dfrac{g}{ml}\ \ \ (1.00 - 0.53)\ g/ml} = 5 \times 10^6\ g$

24. $\dfrac{\left[300\ m^3 \times \left(\dfrac{100\ cm}{m} \right)^3 \times \dfrac{g}{ml} \right]}{}$

$+ \dfrac{\left[(5\ m \times 10\ m \times 10\ m) \times \left(\dfrac{100\ cm}{m} \right)^3 \times \dfrac{(1.00 - 0.53)\ g}{ml} \right]}{300\ m^3 \times \left(\dfrac{100\ cm}{m} \right)^3}$
$= 2\ g/cm^3$

25. $1 \times 10^4\ g;\ \ 1 \times 10^4\ ml;\ \ float;\ \ 175\ cm \times (1.00 - 0.77) = 40.3\ cm$

26. $\dfrac{3.14 \times (0.5\ ft)^2 \times 100\ ft \times (1.00 - 0.38) \times 62.4\ \dfrac{lb}{ft^3}}{} = 3 \times 10^3\ lb$

27. $\dfrac{\dfrac{1.05 - 1.00\ g}{ml} \times 10\ cm \times 10\ cm \times 3\ cm}{(1.00 - 0.77)\ \dfrac{g}{ml} \times 10\ cm \times 10\ cm} = 0.7\ cm$

28. $\dfrac{150 \text{ ft} \times 40 \text{ ft} \times 5 \text{ ft} \times 62.4 \text{ lb}}{\text{ft}^3} = 2 \times 10^6 \text{ lb}$

$\dfrac{150 \text{ ft} \times 40 \text{ ft} \times 3 \text{ ft} \qquad \times 62.4 \text{ lb/ft}^3}{10 \quad \times \quad 4 \text{ ft} \times 9 \text{ ft} \times 1 \text{ ft} \times 62.4 \text{ lb/ft}^3} = 50$

$\dfrac{150 \text{ ft} \times 40 \text{ ft} \times \qquad 5 \text{ ft} \times 62.4 \text{ lb/ft}^3}{150 \text{ ft} \times 40 \text{ ft} \times 4.995 \text{ ft} \times 62.4 \text{ lb/ft}^3} \quad \text{or} \quad \dfrac{5}{4.995} = 1.001$

29. $2000 \text{ tons} \qquad 1 \times 10^5 \text{ ft}^3$

$\dfrac{(3000 - 2000) \text{ tons} \times 2000 \text{ lb}}{\text{ton} \times 7.86 \times 62.4 \dfrac{\text{lb}}{\text{ft}^3}} = 4 \times 10^3 \text{ ft}^3$

30. % Fe = 35.58

31. 316 g (presuming the volume is exactly 1 in.^{3}); 300 g; weightless

32. $(25 \times 75 \text{ ft}^3 \times 62.4 \text{ lb/ft}^3) - (25 \times 100 \text{ lb}) = 100{,}000 \text{ lb}$

33. This can only be calculated if the object is totally submerged in the fluid. If so, 1 g/0.79 g ml^{-1} = 1.266 ml (not in significant figures).

34. $\dfrac{(105 - 89.5) \text{ g}}{1.00 \dfrac{\text{g}}{\text{ml}}} - \dfrac{105 \text{ g}}{8.93 \dfrac{\text{g}}{\text{ml}}} = 3.74 \text{ ml}$

CHAPTER 12

1. b. significant figures   **c.** approximately 0.992 ± 0.002 g/ml for both

2. b. 33.7 torr; 634 torr   **c.** 86°C; 13.1°C   **3. b.** 0.5 g; 30.3 g

3. c. 302 g   **4.** x/y against temperature or y/x against temperature

CHAPTER 13

1. $V\sqrt{MW} = k$ or $V_1\sqrt{MW_1} = V_2\sqrt{MW_2}$ **2.** $KE = \frac{1}{2}mv^2$

3. $E = km;$ $k = 9 \times 10^{20}$ ergs/g (from the data stated)

CHAPTER 14

1. a. 1.6×10^{11} ergs mole^{-1} **b.** 1.6×10^4 joules mole^{-1}

c. 3.8×10^3 cal mole^{-1}

2.
$$\sqrt{\dfrac{2 \times 1.6 \times 10^{11} \text{ ergs}}{\text{mole} \times \dfrac{222 \text{ g}}{\text{mole}}}} = 3.8 \times 10^4 \text{ cm sec}^{-1}$$

3.
$$\dfrac{2 \times 1.6 \times 10^{11} \text{ ergs}}{\text{mole} \times 3 \times 8.314 \times 10^7 \dfrac{\text{ergs}}{\text{mole-}^{\circ}\text{K}}} = 1.3 \times 10^3 \,^{\circ}\text{K}$$

4.
$$\dfrac{32 \text{ g}}{\text{mole}} \times \left(\dfrac{3 \times 100{,}000 \text{ cm}}{\text{sec}}\right)^2 \times 3 \times 8.314 \times 10^7 \dfrac{\text{ergs}}{\text{mole-}^{\circ}\text{K}} = 1 \times 10^4 \,^{\circ}\text{K}$$

5.
$$\sqrt{\dfrac{3 \times 8.314 \times 10^7 \dfrac{\text{ergs}}{\text{mole-}^{\circ}\text{K}} \times (273 + 2000)\,^{\circ}\text{K}}{\dfrac{4 \text{ g}}{\text{mole}}}} = 4 \times 10^5 \text{ cm sec}^{-1}$$

6.
$$\dfrac{14 \text{ g} \times \left(\dfrac{3 \times 10^{10} \text{ cm}}{\text{sec}}\right)^2 \times 10^{-7} \text{ joules} \times 0.001 \dfrac{\text{kcal}}{\text{cal}}}{\text{erg} \times 4.18 \dfrac{\text{joules}}{\text{cal}}}$$
$$= 3.1 \times 10^{11} \text{ kcal}$$

$$\dfrac{3.0 \times 10^{11} \text{ kcal}}{\dfrac{14 \text{ g}}{\dfrac{18.9 \text{ g}}{\text{ml}}}} = 4.1 \times 10^{11} \text{ kcal/cm}^3 \quad \text{(ml and cm}^3 \text{ can be used interchangeably)}$$

7. 23 g   **8.**
$$\dfrac{(150 - 10) \text{ mi}}{\text{hr} \times \dfrac{3 \text{ min}}{\dfrac{60 \text{ min}}{\text{hr}}}} = 2.8 \times 10^3 \text{ mi/hr}^2$$

9. 2600 mi/hr^2 **10.** 240 mi

11.
$$\dfrac{80 \text{ mi} \times 3 \text{ hr} + \left[\dfrac{1}{2} \times \dfrac{80 \text{ mi}}{\text{hr}^2} \times (3 \text{ hr})^2\right]}{\text{hr}} = 600 \text{ mi}$$

12.
$$\dfrac{2 \text{ ft}^2 \times 5 \text{ ft} \times 62.4 \dfrac{\text{lb}}{\text{ft}^3} \times 0.79}{2 \text{ ft}^2} = 246.5 \text{ lb/ft}^2 \text{ (not in significant figures)}$$

13. 3000 dynes   **14.**
$$\dfrac{1000 \text{ torr} \times 5000 \text{ liters}}{\dfrac{760 \text{ torr}}{\text{atm}}} = 7 \times 10^3 \text{ liter-atm}$$

15. 4×10^8 ft-lb   **16.** 9×10^8 ft-lb

17.
$$\dfrac{4 \text{ kg} \times 1000 \dfrac{\text{g}}{\text{kg}} \times 980 \dfrac{\text{dynes}}{\text{g (wt)}} \times \dfrac{1}{2} \times 7 \text{ m} \times 100 \dfrac{\text{cm}}{\text{m}} \times (5 \text{ sec})^2}{\text{sec}^2} = 3 \times 10^{10} \text{ ergs}$$

18. $$\dfrac{200 \text{ lb} \times 8 \text{ mi} \times 5280 \text{ ft}}{\text{mi} \times 1.5 \text{ hr} \times 60 \dfrac{\text{min}}{\text{hr}} \times 60 \dfrac{\text{sec}}{\text{min}} \times 550 \dfrac{\text{ft-lb}}{\text{sec-hp}}} = 3 \text{ hp}$$

19. $$\text{power} = \dfrac{2000 \text{ lb} \times 80 \text{ mi} \times 5280 \text{ ft}}{\text{mi} \times 80 \text{ min} \times 60 \dfrac{\text{sec}}{\text{min}}} \times \dfrac{1.356 \text{ w}}{\dfrac{\text{ft-lb}}{\text{sec}}}$$

$$= 2 \times 10^5 \text{ w}$$

power = 300 hp; work = 8×10^8 ft-lb

$$\text{work} = \dfrac{2 \times 10^5 \text{ w} \times 1 \dfrac{\text{joules}}{\text{sec-w}} \times 80 \text{ min} \times 60 \dfrac{\text{sec}}{\text{min}}}{} = 1 \times 10^9 \text{ joules}$$

20.
$$\left[\left(\dfrac{0 \text{ mi}}{\text{hr}} \right)^2 - \left(\dfrac{75 \text{ mi}}{\text{hr} \times 3600 \dfrac{\text{sec}}{\text{hr}}} \times \dfrac{5280 \text{ ft}}{\text{mi}} \right)^2 \right] \times 2 \times 120 \text{ ft}$$

$$= -50.42 \text{ ft sec}^{-2} \text{ (deceleration, not in significant figures)}$$

$$\dfrac{(0 - 75) \text{ mi} \times 5280 \dfrac{\text{ft}}{\text{mi}} \times 3600 \dfrac{\text{sec}}{\text{hr}}}{\text{hr} \times 50.42 \dfrac{\text{ft}}{\text{sec}^2}} = 2.182 \text{ sec}$$

$$\dfrac{4000 \text{ lb} \times 120 \text{ ft}}{2.182 \text{ sec} \times 550 \dfrac{\text{ft-lb}}{\text{sec-hp}}} = 400.0 \text{ hp} \quad \text{(not in significant figures)}$$

21. $$\dfrac{200 \text{ lb} \times 8 \text{ mi} \times 5280 \text{ ft}}{\text{mi} \times 10 \text{ min} \times 60 \dfrac{\text{sec}}{\text{min}}}$$

$$\times \dfrac{1.356 \text{ w}}{\dfrac{\text{ft-lb}}{\text{sec}}} \times \dfrac{0.001 \text{ kw}}{\text{w}} \times \dfrac{7 \text{ ¢}}{\text{kw-hr} \times 60 \dfrac{\text{min}}{\text{hr}}} = 20¢$$

CHAPTER 15

1. 22 liters **2.** 660°C **3.** 690 torr (other pressure units possible)

4. 3800 mm **5.** 690 liters; 1400% **6.** 880 torr **7.** 300°K

8. 3 atm **9.** $\dfrac{95 \text{ liters} \times (0 + 273)\,°K \times (748 - 17) \text{ mm}}{(19 + 273)\,°K \times 760 \text{ mm}} = 84 \text{ liters}$

10. $\dfrac{99 \text{ liters} \times 760 \text{ torr} \times (35 + 273) \,^\circ\text{K}}{(738 - 42) \text{ torr} \times (40 + 273) \,^\circ\text{K}} = 110 \text{ liters}$ *Assumption: Gas is dry at 40°C.*

11. 22 atm

12. $\dfrac{(-90 + 273) \,^\circ\text{K} \times 500 \text{ liters} \times 785 \text{ torr}}{150 \text{ liters} \times 29.9 \text{ in.} \times \dfrac{760 \text{ torr}}{29.9 \text{ torr}}} = 630 \,^\circ\text{K}$

13. 88.8°C   **14.** 122°F   **15.** 10°C

16. Since degrees F and degrees C will be numerically the same, let y represent both F and C.

$\dfrac{y - 32}{1.8} = 32 + 1.8y$

$y - 32 = (32 \times 1.8) + (1.8y \times 1.8)$

$y - 32 = 57.6 + 3.24y$

$-2.24y = 89.6$

$y = -40$

17. 14,000 atm; 280 lb/in.^{2} **18.** 40 in.

19. $\dfrac{710 \text{ mm} \times 13.65 \text{ g/ml}}{2.0 \text{ g/ml}} = 4800 \text{ mm}$

CHAPTER 16

1. 108.0104; 132.1388; 249.685   **2.** 8.3×10^{-20} mole

3. $\dfrac{49 \text{ g}}{174 \text{ g mole}^{-1}} \times \dfrac{2 \text{ moles K atoms}}{\text{mole K}_2\text{SO}_4} \times \dfrac{6.023 \times 10^{23} \text{ atoms}}{\text{mole}} = 3.4 \times 10^{23} \text{ atoms}$

4. 2000 liters   **5.** 2.74×10^{-19} mole   **6.** 1×10^{-2} mole

7. 2.108×10^{22} molecules   **8.** $\dfrac{25 \text{ liters} \times 42 \text{ g}}{22.4 \text{ liters} \quad \text{mole}} \bigg/ \dfrac{}{\text{mole}} = 47 \text{ g}$

9. $\dfrac{475 \text{ ml} \times 0.001 \text{ liter}}{\text{ml} \times \dfrac{22.4 \text{ liters}}{\text{mole}}} \times \dfrac{6.023 \times 10^{23} \text{ molecules}}{\text{mole}}$

$\times \dfrac{2 \text{ oxygen atoms}}{\text{molecule}} = 2.55 \times 10^{22} \text{ atoms}$

10. 4.0×10^{21} molecules

11. $\dfrac{10 \times 10^6 \text{ molecules} \times 197 \text{ g}}{6.023 \times 10^{23} \text{ molecules} \quad \text{mole}} \bigg/ \dfrac{}{\text{mole}} = 3.3 \times 10^{-15} \text{ g}$

12. 0.1311 g   **13.** 0.30 mole   **14.** 40.3 liters

15. $\dfrac{0.48 \text{ g}}{175 \text{ ml} \times 0.001 \text{ liter} \over \text{ml} \times 22.4 \frac{\text{liters}}{\text{mole}}} = 61$ g/mole or $\dfrac{0.48 \times 22.4}{175 \times 0.001}$

CHAPTER 17

1. 20.0 g mole^{-1}

2. $\dfrac{2.08 \text{ g}}{3.91 \text{ liters} \times 756 \text{ mm} \over 760 \text{ mm} \times 22.4 \frac{\text{liters}}{\text{mole}}} = 12.0$ g mole^{-1}

or $\dfrac{2.08 \times 760 \times 22.4}{3.91 \times 756}$

3. 5 liters   **4.** 3 liters   **5.** 6 liters

6. $\dfrac{22.4 \frac{\text{liters}}{\text{mole}} \times 4 \text{ g} \times 760 \text{ mm} \times (30 + 273)\,^{\circ}\text{K}}{17 \frac{\text{g}}{\text{mole}} \times 1500 \text{ mm} \times (0 + 273)\,^{\circ}\text{K}} = 3$ liters   **7.** 20 g

8. $\dfrac{10 \text{ liters} (743 - 55) \text{ torr} \times (0 + 273)\,^{\circ}\text{K} \times 44 \frac{\text{g}}{\text{mole}}}{760 \text{ torr} \times (273 + 40)\,^{\circ}\text{K} \times 22.4 \frac{\text{liters}}{\text{mole}}} = 20$ g

9. $\dfrac{350 \text{ ml} \times (0 + 273)\,^{\circ}\text{K} \times (756 - 17) \text{ torr} \times 0.001 \text{ liter}}{(19 + 273)\,^{\circ}\text{K} \times 760 \text{ torr} \times \text{ml} \times 22.4 \frac{\text{liters}}{\text{mole}}} \times 32 \frac{\text{g}}{\text{mole}} = 0.45$ g

10. 0.47 g   **11.** 7 liters

12. $\dfrac{22.4 \frac{\text{liters}}{\text{mole}} \times 10 \text{ g} \times (1500 + 273)\,^{\circ}\text{K} \times 760 \text{ torr}}{32 \frac{\text{g}}{\text{mole}} \times (0 + 273)\,^{\circ}\text{K} \times 1000 \text{ torr}} = 40$ liters

13. $\dfrac{22.4 \frac{\text{liters}}{\text{mole}} \times 0.38 \text{ g} \times (45 + 273)\,^{\circ}\text{K} \times 760 \text{ torr}}{32 \frac{\text{g}}{\text{mole}} \times (0 + 273)\,^{\circ}\text{K} \times (1800 - 72) \text{ torr}} = 0.14$ liter

14.

$$\dfrac{0.856 \text{ g}}{1.405 \text{ liters} \times \dfrac{(0 + 273)\,^\circ K \times 781 \text{ mm}}{(145 + 273)\,^\circ K \times 760 \text{ mm} \times 22.4 \dfrac{\text{liters}}{\text{mole}}}} = 20.3 \text{ g/mole}$$

or $\dfrac{0.856 \times (145 + 273) \times 760 \times 22.4}{1.405 \times (0 + 273) \times 781}$

15. $1160^\circ K$ or $887^\circ K$ (not in significant figures)

16. $1008^\circ K$ or $735^\circ C$ (not in significant figures)   **17.** 1.1 atm

CHAPTER 18

1. a. 0.15 mole liter^{-1} **b.** 0.20 *M*   **c.** 2.8 *M*

d. $\dfrac{6 \text{ moles} \times 50 \text{ liters}}{\text{liter} \times 100 \text{ liters}} = 3 \dfrac{\text{moles}}{\text{liter}}$ **e.** 2.5 *M*   **f.** 0.17 *M*

2. $\dfrac{5 \text{ g}}{160 \dfrac{\text{g}}{\text{mole}} \times 0.001 \dfrac{\text{mole}}{\text{liter}}} = 30 \text{ liters}$

3. $\left[\dfrac{175 \text{ ml N } 0.001 \text{ liter} \times 2 \text{ moles}}{\text{ml} \qquad \text{liter} \times 0.05 \dfrac{\text{mole}}{\text{liter}}}\right] - \dfrac{175 \text{ ml} \times 0.001 \text{ liter}}{\text{ml}}$

$= 7 \text{ liters}$

4.   8 g   **5.** 15 moles (assuming exactly 10 liters)

6. $\dfrac{0.008 \text{ mole} \times 100 \text{ ml} \times 0.001 \text{ liter} \times 6.023 \times 10^{23} \text{ molecules}}{\text{liter} \qquad \text{ml} \qquad \text{mole}}$

$= 5 \times 10^{20} \text{ molecules}$

7.   0.2 mole/liter   **8.** $\dfrac{0.01 \text{ mole} \times 3 \text{ liters} \times 46 \text{ g}}{\text{liter} \qquad \text{mole} \times 0.79 \dfrac{\text{g}}{\text{ml}}} = 2 \text{ ml}$

9.   5 g   **10.** $\left[\dfrac{15 \text{ moles} \times 6 \text{ liters} - 8 \text{ liters}}{\text{liter} \qquad 22.4 \dfrac{\text{liters}}{\text{mole}}} \times 6 \text{ liters}\right] = 0.6 \ M$

11.   0.6 *M*

CHAPTER 19

1. a. 0.54 molal   **b.** 0.24 molal   **2.** 11 g   **3.** 6600 g

CHAPTER 20

1. −0.388°C   **2.** 15 g mole^{-1}

3.
$$\frac{0.891 \text{ g} \times 1000 \text{ g}}{\dfrac{75 \text{ g} \times (100.092 - 100.000)°C}{\dfrac{0.512°C}{\text{mole}}}} \times \frac{2 \text{ moles of particles}}{1 \text{ mole of molecules}}$$

$$= 130 \text{ g mole}^{-1}$$

in easier to calculate form: $\dfrac{0.891 \times 1000 \times 0.512 \times 2}{75 \times (100.092 - 100.000) \times 1}$

4. 0.554 mole; 24.9 g

5.
$$\frac{(83.51 - 80.15)°C}{\dfrac{2.53°C}{\text{mole}}} \times \frac{136 \text{ g}}{\text{mole}} \times \frac{50 \text{ g}}{1000 \text{ g}} = 9 \text{ g}$$

6.
$$\frac{(8.21 - 5.31)°C}{\dfrac{0.852 \text{ g}}{\dfrac{136 \text{ g}}{\text{mole}}} \times \dfrac{1000 \text{ g}}{45.21 \text{ g}}} \quad \text{rearranged to} \quad \frac{(8.21 - 5.31) \times 136 \times 45.21}{0.852 \times 1000}$$

$$= 20.9°C \text{ mole}^{-1}$$

7. 75 g mole^{-1}
(Possible explanation: Each molecule breaks into two fragments.)

8.
$$\frac{80.15 + \left[\dfrac{2.53°C}{\text{mole}} \times \dfrac{0.99 \text{ g}}{128 \dfrac{\text{g}}{\text{mole}}} \times \dfrac{1000 \text{ g}}{80.0 \text{ ml} \times 0.88 \dfrac{\text{g}}{\text{ml}}}\right]}{} = 80°C \ (80 \pm 1°C)$$

CHAPTER 21

1. a. 80 g   **b.** 100 g

c. 70/40 is less than 70/36.5; since there is a 1:1 mole ratio, 70/40

governs: $\dfrac{70 \text{ g}}{40 \dfrac{\text{g}}{\text{mole}}} \times \dfrac{1 \times 58.4 \text{ g}}{1 \qquad \text{mole}} = 100 \text{ g}$

d. 70 g   **e.** 0.6 liter   **f.** 3 *M*   **g.** 0.15 *M*

h.
$$\frac{0.075 \text{ liter} \times 3.1 \text{ moles} \times 1 \times 40 \text{ g}}{\text{liter} \times 1 \times \text{mole} \times 10 \text{ g}} \times 100 = 90\%$$

2. a. 60 g   **b.** 100 g   **c.** $\dfrac{70 \text{ g}}{98 \dfrac{\text{g}}{\text{mole}}} \times \dfrac{1 \times 142 \text{ g}}{1 \qquad \text{mole}} = 100 \text{ g}$

2. d. 90 g   **e.** 0.3 liter   **f.** 2 M **g.** 0.30 M

  h. 90%   **3. a.** 0.527 g   **b.** 0.246 liter   **c.** 0.2 M

3. d. $\dfrac{0.350 \text{ liter} \times 6 \text{ moles} \times 2 \times 22.4 \text{ liters} \times 298°K \times \qquad 760 \text{ torr}}{\text{liter} \quad \times 8 \qquad\qquad \text{mole} \times 273°K \times (756 - 24) \text{ torr}}$

$$= 13 \text{ liters}$$

e. $\dfrac{80 \text{ liters NO} \times 3 \text{ moles Ag}_2\text{S} \times 2 \text{ moles Ag} \times 108 \text{ g}}{22.4 \dfrac{\text{liters}}{\text{mole}} \quad \times 2 \text{ moles NO} \times 1 \text{ mole Ag}_2\text{S} \quad \text{mole Ag}} = 1000 \text{ g}$

f. $\dfrac{5 \text{ liters} \times 3 \times 2 \times 108 \text{ g} \qquad\qquad \times 100}{22.4 \dfrac{\text{liters}}{\text{mole}} \times 2 \times 1 \qquad \text{mole} \times 100 \text{ g}} = 70\%$ **4. a.** 0.2 liter

4. b. $\dfrac{0.03250 \text{ liter} \times 1.80 \text{ moles} \times 1 \times 142 \text{ g} \qquad\qquad \times 100}{\text{liter} \quad \times 1 \qquad\qquad \text{mole} \times 11.3 \text{ g}} = 73.5\%$

  c. 1.28 M **5. a.** 72 liters*   **b.** 95 liters

5. c. $\dfrac{9 \text{ liters} \times \ (0 + 273)°K \times 756 \text{ torr} \times 8 \times (100 + 273)°K \times 760 \text{ mm}}{(40 + 273)°K \times 760 \text{ torr} \times 1 \times \quad (0 + 273)°K \times 785 \text{ mm}}$

$$= 83 \text{ liters}$$

  d. $\dfrac{9 \text{ liters} \times 8}{1 \times 0.20} = 360 \text{ liters}$ (strictly speaking not in
$\qquad\qquad\qquad\qquad\qquad$ significant figures)

  e. 600 liters   **f.** Assume air is at same conditions as the pentane; then

$\dfrac{50 \text{ g} \quad \times 8 \times 22.4 \text{ liters} \times (100 + 273)°K \times \quad 760 \text{ torr}}{72 \dfrac{\text{g}}{\text{mole}} \quad \times 1 \qquad \text{mole} \times \quad (0 + 273)°K \times 1000 \text{ torr}} = 100 \text{ liters}$

  g. $\dfrac{9 \text{ liters} \times 0.85 \times 8}{\times 1 \times 0.20} = 300 \text{ liters}$

6. a. $\dfrac{95 \text{ g} \quad \times 2 \times 36.5 \text{ g}}{97 \dfrac{\text{g}}{\text{mole}} \quad \times 1 \qquad \text{mole} \times 1.18 \dfrac{\text{g}}{\text{ml}} \times 0.37} = 160 \text{ ml}$

  b. $\dfrac{40 \text{ liters} \times 1 \times 97 \text{ g}}{22.4 \dfrac{\text{liters}}{\text{mole}} \times 1 \qquad \text{mole} \times 0.78} = 200 \text{ g}$

  c. $\dfrac{40 \text{ liters} \qquad\qquad \times 1 \times 97 \text{ g}}{0.95 \qquad \times 22.4 \dfrac{\text{liters}}{\text{mole}} \times 1 \qquad \text{mole} \times 0.78} = 200 \text{ g}$

---

*Strictly speaking, not correct in terms of significant figures, but one must use common sense with significant figures rather than slavishly follow arbitrary rules.

7. a. 1 liter   **b.** 74%   **c.** 6.78 g

8.   Let x = fraction associated with NaCl; $(1 - x)$ = fraction associated with NaBr.

$$x\left[\frac{1.00\ \text{g}}{\dfrac{58.44\ \text{g}}{\text{mole}}} \times 1 \times \frac{143.3\ \text{g}}{\text{mole}}\right] + (1 - x)\left[\frac{1.00\ \text{g}}{\dfrac{102.9\ \text{g}}{\text{mole}}} \times \frac{187.8\ \text{g}}{\text{mole}}\right]$$

$$= 2.39\ \text{g}$$

$$2.452x + (1 - x)1.825 = 2.39$$
$$0.627x = 0.56$$
$$x = 0.8931$$
$$1 - x = 0.1069$$

Therefore there is 89.3% NaCl and 10.7% NaBr.

9.   Let x = fraction associated with NaCl; $(1 - x)$ = fraction associated with NaBr.

$$x\left[\frac{1.00\ \text{g} \times 1}{\dfrac{58.44\ \text{g}}{\text{mole}} \times 1 \times \dfrac{0.100\ \text{mole}}{\text{liter}}}\right]$$

$$+ (1 - x)\left[\frac{1.00\ \text{g} \times 1}{\dfrac{102.9\ \text{g}}{\text{mole}} \times 1 \times \dfrac{0.100\ \text{mole}}{\text{liter}}}\right] = 131.4\ \frac{\text{ml}}{\text{liter}} \times 0.001\ \text{liter}$$

$$x = 0.4628$$
$$1 - x = 0.5372$$

Therefore there is 46.3% NaCl and 53.7% NaBr.

10.   Let x = fraction associated with NaCl; $(1 - x)$ = fraction associated with KCl.

$$x\left[\frac{1.00\ \text{g}}{\dfrac{58.44\ \text{g}}{\text{mole}} \times 1} \times 1 \times \frac{143.3\ \text{g}}{\text{mole}}\right]$$

$$+ (1 - x)\left[\frac{1.00\ \text{g}}{\dfrac{74.56\ \text{g}}{\text{mole}} \times 1} \times 1 \times \frac{143.3\ \text{g}}{\text{mole}}\right] = 2.08\ \text{g}$$

$$x = 0.2981$$
$$1 - x = 0.7019$$

Therefore there is 29.8% NaCl and 70.2% KCl.

CHAPTER 22

1. a. HgO **b.** $NiCl_2$ **c.** $NOBr_3$ **d.** Pd_2S

e. PtP_2O_7 **f.** Zn_3N_2 **2.** H_2F_2

3.   empirical formula: CH; molecular weight: 273; molecular formula: $C_{21}H_{21}$ **4.** ZnS   **5.** 0.05 mole of Pb; 0.10 mole of Cl_2, therefore $PbCl_4$ **6.** Volume corrected to STP is 47.72 liters; the problem is now the same as Problem 5.   **7.** empirical formula: C_2H_6O; molecular weight: 46; molecular formula: C_2H_6O

8.

$$\frac{56.1 \text{ liters} \times 273°K \times 745 \text{ torr}}{383°K \times 760 \text{ torr}} = 39.20 \text{ liters } \overline{CO_2} \text{ and } \overline{H_2O}$$

$$\frac{17.8 \text{ liters} \times 273°K \times 745 \text{ torr}}{283°K \times 760 \text{ torr}} = 16.83 \text{ liters } \overline{CO_2}$$

$$\frac{(39.20 - 16.83) \text{ liters}}{22.4 \dfrac{\text{liters}}{\text{mole}}} = 1.00 \text{ mole } \overline{H_2O}$$

$$\frac{16.83 \text{ liters}}{22.4 \dfrac{\text{liters}}{\text{mole}}} = 0.75 \text{ mole } \overline{CO_2}$$

$$\frac{1.00}{0.75} = 1.33; \qquad \frac{0.75}{0.75} = 1.00; \qquad 1.33 \times 3 = 4; \qquad 1.00 \times 3 = 3$$

4 moles of $\overline{H_2O}$ and 3 moles of $\overline{CO_2}$ were produced from 8 moles of H atoms and 3 moles of C atoms; therefore the formula is C_3H_8.

CHAPTER 23

1.   7900 cal   **2.** 9400 cal

3. $\left[\dfrac{1 \text{ cal}}{g\text{-}°C} \times 99 \text{ g} \times (79 - 0)°C\right] + \left[\dfrac{79.7 \text{ cal} \times 99 \text{ g}}{g}\right]$

$+ \left[\dfrac{0.46 \text{ cal}}{g\text{-}°C} \times 99 \text{ g} \times [0 - (-33)]°C\right] = (7821 \text{ cal} + 7890 \text{ cal} + 1503 \text{ cal})$
$= 17,000 \text{ cal}$

4.   53,000 cal   **5.** $(1503 + 9900 + 53,460) \text{ cal} = 65,000 \text{ cal}$

6. $(558 + 3965 + 2326) \text{ cal} = 7000 \text{ cal}$ **7.** 82 cal

8.   Equilibrium temperature of the nickel and the water must be the same. Let T_{eq} = the equilibrium temperature.

$$\frac{0.109 \text{ cal}}{g\text{-}°C} \times 75 \text{ g} \times (95°C - T_{eq}) = \frac{1 \text{ cal}}{g\text{-}°C} \times 100 \text{ g} \times (T_{eq} - 25°C)$$

$$(0.109 \times 75 \times 95) - (0.109 \times 75 \times T_{eq}) = (1 \times 100 \times T_{eq}) - (1 \times 100 \times 25)$$
$$T_{eq} = 30.29°C \text{ (not in significant figures)}$$

One cannot determine the number of significant figures in the answer here. The 100 g in the problem was deliberately stated improperly. It should have been stated as 1.00×10^2 g, 100 ± 1 g, etc., in order to indicate precision properly.

9. 54 cal

CHAPTER 24

1. less   **2.** liberated   **3.** 140 kcal; 9 kcal   **4.** 1 g

5. $$\frac{12 \text{ g}}{\text{mole} \times 94 \dfrac{\text{kcal}}{\text{mole}}} \times \frac{6000 \text{ gal}}{1000 \dfrac{\text{cal}}{\text{kcal}}} \times \frac{4 \text{ qt}}{\text{gal} \times 1.06 \dfrac{\text{qt}}{\text{liter}}} \times \frac{1000 \text{ ml}}{\text{liter}}$$

$$\times \frac{1 \text{ g}}{\text{ml}} \times \frac{1 \text{ cal}}{\text{g-}°C} \times (95-10)°C = 2 \times 10^5 \text{ g}$$

6. 3×10^9 cal   **7.** 3.8×10^5 g

8. $$\frac{3.8 \times 10^5 \text{ g}}{0.40 \times 454 \dfrac{\text{g}}{\text{lb}} \times 2000 \dfrac{\text{lb}}{\text{ton}}} = 1.0 \text{ ton}$$ **9.** +32 kcal

10. Energy is required to vaporize the mercury.   **11.** -91 kcal mole^{-1}

12. -111 kcal mole^{-1} **13.** 3.32×10^5 cal mole^{-1} **14.** -39.0 kcal

CHAPTER 25

1. 14 F   **2.** 14.95 g*   **3.** 23.88 g*

4. 16.71*   **5.** 59.22 g*   **6.** 4.724 F*

7. $$\frac{150 \text{ g}}{63.5 \dfrac{\text{g}}{\text{mole}}} \times \frac{2 \text{ F}}{\text{mole}} \times \frac{96,500 \text{ amp-sec}}{\text{F}} \times \frac{1}{2 \text{ amp}} = 2.280 \times 10^5 \text{ sec*}$$

CHAPTER 26

1. rate $\propto$ [F]; rate = k[F]

---

*Not in significant figures.

2.   rate $\propto [H]^2[J]$;   rate $= k[H]^2[J]$

$$k = \frac{rate}{[H]^2[J]} = \frac{3 \text{ ml}}{sec \times (1\ M)^2(1\ M)} = \frac{3 \text{ ml}}{sec\text{-}M^3}$$

$$rate = \frac{3 \text{ ml}}{sec\text{-}M^3} \frac{\times (2\ M)^2(2\ M)}{} = 24 \text{ ml/sec}$$

3. $k = 7$ ml/sec-M^2;   rate $= 35$ ml/sec

CHAPTER 27

1. a. $K = \dfrac{[D][E]}{[A][B][C]} = \dfrac{(0.5)(0.45)}{(0.2)(1.5)(1)} = 0.75$

b. Trial: $\dfrac{(1)(1)}{(1)(1)(1)} = 1$; this exceeds the constant.

The equilibrium in the equation as written must shift to the left, thereby increasing the denominator and decreasing the numerator in the equilibrium expression.

Let x = moles/liter of D that react with E to form more A, B, C
   x = moles/liter of E that react with D to form more A, B, C
   x = increased moles/liter for each of the reactants (A, B, C)

$$0.75 = \frac{(1-x)\,(1-x)}{(1+x)\,(1+x)\,(1+x)}$$

By approximation $x = 0.06$. At equilibrium A, B, and C are each 1.06 M; D and E are each 0.94 M.

c. $0.75 = \dfrac{(8-x)\,(7-x)}{(x)\,(x)\,(x)}$

By approximation x = about 3 (2.99 closer);   therefore A, B, and C are each 3 M (2.99); D is 5 M and E is 4 M.

2. a. $1 \times 10^{-9} = \dfrac{[H][I]^2}{[F]^2[G]} = \dfrac{(8/3 - x)\,(0.2/3 - 2x)^2}{(2x)^2\,(x)}$

b. Need less H and I, since K is so far under 1.

Let x = moles/liter of H that react with I to form F and G
   $2x$ = moles/liter of I that react with H to form F and G
   $2x$ = moles/liter of F formed
   x = moles/liter of G formed

$$1 \times 10^{-9} = \frac{(3-x)\,(4-2x)^2}{(1+2x)^2\,(2+x)}$$

3. $\quad 8 = \dfrac{(x)\,(2x)^2}{(13.3 - x)^3}$

By approximation $x = 7.4$; therefore A, B, C, and D and E are 5.9 atm, 5.9 atm, 5.9 atm, and 7.4 and 14.8 atm, respectively.

CHAPTER 28

1. $\quad 4.24 \times 10^{-3}\ M$ (not in significant figures)

2. $\quad 7.2 \times 10^{-5}\ M$ (not in significant figures)

3. $\quad 1.4 \times 10^{-10}\ M$ $\qquad\qquad$ **4.** $3.5 \times 10^{-12}\ M$ $\qquad\qquad$ **5.** $0.1\ M$

6. $\quad \dfrac{1.2 \times 10^{23} \times 0.1\ \text{mole} \times 97.43\ \text{g}}{\text{liter} \qquad\qquad \text{mole}} = 1.2 \times 10^{-20}\ \text{g/liter}$

INDEX